CONCEPTS OF BIOLOGY
a cultural perspective

PRENTICE-HALL SERIES IN BIOLOGICAL SCIENCE
Carl P. Swanson, Editor

NEAL D. BUFFALOE
J. B. THRONEBERRY

Professors of Biology
State College of Arkansas

CONCEPTS OF BIOLOGY

a cultural perspective

PRENTICE-HALL, INC., Englewood Cliffs, New Jersey

ISBN: 0-13-166256-2

Library of Congress Catalog Card No.: 72-9419

Printed in the United States of America

10 9 8 7 6 5 4 3 2

PRENTICE-HALL INTERNATIONAL, INC., *London*
PRENTICE-HALL OF AUSTRALIA, PTY. LTD., *Sydney*
PRENTICE-HALL OF CANADA LTD., *Toronto*
PRENTICE-HALL OF INDIA PRIVATE LTD., *New Delhi*
PRENTICE-HALL OF JAPAN, INC., *Tokyo*

CONTENTS

PREFACE

There is a kind of gentleman's agreement among university scholars that a specialist in one discipline will not trespass on the discipline of another specialist. The aim of this agreement is a laudable one: that of guarding against intellectual irresponsibility. When the specialist leaves his own specialty, he dares to walk where angels fear to tread, and his foolhardiness often brings no greater reward than a fair-sized portion of egg on his face.

In theory, this principle is sound. In practice, it is nearly impossible. For example, what are the metes and bounds of an academic discipline?

Is a cell biologist justified in speaking to the point of ecological principles? (He may *have* to if he teaches a class in introductory biology.) Is it legitimate for him to discuss organic chemistry? If so, how about psychology, political science, philosophy, or religion? Where does the specialist draw the line?

The rule of thumb observed by most teachers is one of relevance. It is one thing for a professor of biology to relate genetics and political philosophy in Russia (as we have done in this book) and quite another for him to lecture his class on communism and capitalism *within the framework of political science.*

Well and good. Most college professors have little difficulty making this distinction, and the American Association of University Professors gives it their complete blessing. But the system breaks down most often, not because a professor feels a sense of restraint, but because he feels inadequate and insecure when attempting to relate his field to some other. This is understandable and even commendable. Human knowledge is now so vast that a scholar feels inadequate even within his *own* field, to say nothing of other areas of specialization. (President Lowell of Harvard used to lampoon the conservatism of specialists by claiming that a graduate student in zoology meant to write his thesis on the last joint of the left hind leg of the Paleozoic cockroach, but because the professor who specialized in the last joint was on sabbatical, he was obliged to treat the whole leg.)

Scholarly integrity notwithstanding, the compartmentalization of knowledge that is so characteristic of most American and British institutions of higher education must stop somewhere. It creates an artificial atmosphere of learning for the student. He may receive a degree of integrated experience if he is fortunate enough to draw a good teacher in philosophy, possibly in English, but his chances are slim in the sciences.

This book is a calculated attempt to break this vicious cycle. It is primarily a textbook in biology for the "general education" student. However, for the biology major, we believe these viewpoints are even more valuable. We have tried to come to grips with biological science from historical, philosophical, and modern synthetic points of view. Thus, Part I, "Science and History," sets the stage. Part II, "Concepts of Biology," treats four important conceptual schemes of biology in sufficient depth, we feel, to render them meaningful. Part III, "The Fallout," relates biology to human affairs. This last section deserves some comment.

Most professional biologists feel a deep sense of urgency about the current ecological crisis and the looming problems of overpopulation, to mention only two biological issues that are highly relevant to human affairs. As we see it, two extreme approaches are being taken, and we consider both to be highly impractical: either withdrawal into the ivory tower of specialized biological knowledge, where the majority of us feel most secure, or a kind of frenzied condemnation of pollution and overpopulation without benefit of background, either historical, philosophical, or biological, on the part of the student. In this book, we have deliberately placed these issues in what we feel is a broad perspective, and we have tried to provide an adequate biological background for their understanding. Within the context of Part III, this background is more often implied than stated. We hope the student will have grasped the strategy and feel for biology as a science by the time he comes to grips with these practical issues.

We beg the indulgence of our colleagues and our students in this attempt to break new ground. We have doubtless made the kinds of mistakes that pioneers are condemned to make, and we will accept criticisms with gratitude. Since we make no claim to being professional historians, philosophers, political scientists, or theologians, we have tried to proceed with caution, and we have relied heavily upon the criticisms and suggestions of our colleagues in these areas.

Our debt to several of our colleagues on the faculty of State College of Arkansas is a great one. We have sought the counsel of many persons in several academic departments; chief among these are Professors Harold E. Cooper, Robert T. Kirkwood, William Foy Lisenby, N. Patrick Murray, and Mark B. Woodhouse. We cannot adequately express our appreciation for their advice and criticism, but we wish it clearly understood that the statements and implications in this work are our own. We wish to thank Inez Buffaloe and Marcia Lacy for their services in typing. Finally, we are deeply appreciative to Prentice-Hall, Inc. for their fine cooperation in producing this book, and most of all, for their willingness to publish a decidedly unorthodox, and quite possibly controversial, textbook of biology.

NEAL D. BUFFALOE
J.B. THRONEBERRY

Conway, Arkansas

CONCEPTS OF BIOLOGY
a cultural perspective

1

SCIENCE AND HISTORY

Every qualified teacher . . . is like a wealthy man who, in displaying his riches, brings forth out of his treasure things new and old.

—JESUS OF NAZARETH

Introduction

"A study of the past may so accumulate years to us," wrote the 17th-century scholar John Selden, "as if we had lived even from the beginning of time." It is in this sense that history and a sense of history are indispensable to an adequate understanding of every intellectual discipline, including science. To think otherwise is to create what might be called a cut-flower environment of knowledge: The blossoms of information may retain their beauty momentarily, and they may even assume the appearance of a

2

beautiful arrangement, but once severed from their roots, they are condemned to a temporary significance.

Even so, a worship of the past for its own sake is justifiable only in the case of the amateur historian; unless the events of history are used as floodlights, as it were, they are merely intellectual curiosities like any other relics. "The only use of a knowledge of the past," said philosopher Alfred North Whitehead, "is to equip us for the present." Preoccupation with the past and preoccupation with the present are the Scylla and Charybdis between which the student of a modern academic discipline must steer his course. Biological science is no exception to this rule. Of these two extremes, the tendency to ignore the past is by far the more frequent academic sin of the modern biologist, although a reluctance to accept the present is by no means unknown. But modern science is, by its very nature, an ongoing activity, and it is far easier to ignore the past than the present. However, it is not necessary to fall victim to either extreme. When we survey the mainstream of biological history, we are attempting to provide roots for the second and third parts of this work. In the spirit of John Selden, therefore, we dedicate this section of our book to the accumulation of years.

ONE

The Ancient World

It may justly be claimed that biology and biological science are two entirely different spheres of activity. Strictly speaking, and according to the roots from which the word is derived, *biology* (Greek *bios,* life $+$ *logos,* discourse) is the study of life. Admittedly, this definition is a broad and rather vague one that does not commit the practicing biologist to the scientific frame of reference. *Science* is the study of natural phenomena in a systematized manner to discover interconnected relationships that are useful both in explanation and in predictability. It is entirely possible, therefore, and almost certainly true, that men functioned as biologists long before they thought scientifically. In contrast, *biological science* (the scientific consideration of those phenomena associated with organisms) is a relatively new development.

It is impossible, of course, to determine when man first left off contemplating other living forms solely in terms of their food or sex value and began to think in terms of interconnected relationships in the abstract sense of biological science. From what we know of ancient man, the Cro-Magnon people were certainly capable of abstract thought, as indicated by their extraordinary cave-wall art. Neanderthal man buried his dead, and it can thus be reasonably inferred that he was capable of thinking abstractly about intangible values. Earlier humans and near-humans made tools, and it is reasonable to suppose that they may have indulged in an embryonic form of scientific thinking that, within our framework of definition, involved the formulation of interconnected relationships among natural phenomena and the abstract manipulation of these relationships in explaining the present and predicting the future.

From the scant evidence available to us, it seems apparent that primitive man developed an abstract sense of the natural and the supernatural almost simultaneously. Hence, in primitive societies, the most influential person was the medicine man, sorcerer, or witch doctor. Such a person was priest, physician, and philosopher, explainer *extraordinaire,* for whom the mysteries of nature were intimately related to the spirits of the universe. It was only in time that science and religion, both of which are traceable to primitive witchcraft, became separated into distinct spheres of activity. Whenever this separation occurred in a given society (and there are yet societies in which the division is not clearly discernible), it usually wrought a profound change. The priest gradually became restricted to those activities that related man to one or more deities; the physician turned more and more to nature for answers to his questions; and the philosopher developed methods for a rational inquiry into the nature of things.

Undoubtedly, this process of separation occurred to some extent in many ancient societies. It was at least partially accomplished by the ancient Babylonians, the Egyptians, the Hindus, and the Chinese. But it remained for the Greeks to make this distinction a sufficiently fine one that we can pick up a definite trail leading to the modern scientific tradition. In any reasonable and historically profitable sense, they were the founders of biological science and, indeed, of science as a whole.

Before entering into a discussion of ancient science, let us make an introductory observation. There are two broad categories of human thought as it can be applied to kinds of causal explanation—that is, the fundamental "how" or "why" of natural phenomena. These two approaches are termed the *empirical,* or *natural,* and the *supernatural.* By general agreement, science is operative only in the physical realm of being and has nothing to do with the supernatural. In other words, science is limited to the observable—that is, measurable—phenomena of a material universe. Science does not deny the possibility that other realities exist or that knowledge may legitimately be gained by means other than scientific ones. But the scientist is obliged to exclude supernatural considerations from his explanations and to *assume* that they play no part in his results. We might well call this the first principle of science: **It is obligatory that science postulate natural rather than supernatural explanations for natural phenomena, no matter how tentative these explanations may have to be.** For scientists to do otherwise has been largely fruitless, for then they make undependable predictions.

This scientific methodology was the contribution made by certain of the ancient Greeks to scientific thought. They never quite succeeded in directly stating the principle, but the germ of this idea was present in their methods.

1.1 THE GRECIAN WORLD

During the second millennium B.C., the Indo-European people whom we call Greeks came into possession of the region around the Aegean Sea (Fig. 1-1). They had invaded the region over a period of many centuries and had never become welded together politically as a nation, but they came gradually to share something of a common cultural tradition. By the sixth century B.C., a distinct civilization had emerged. Despite their loose political structure, an association of independent city-states, the Greeks had achieved a high degree of cultural stability. Success in trading had brought certain families a measure of wealth and, therefore, leisure. The travel involved in commercial pursuits brought in ideas from distant cultures, and a stimulus to thought was thus provided those men who had the time to think. By no means the least factor in the rise of Greek culture was the fortunate adoption of and improvement upon the Phoenician alphabet prior to the sixth century. These are a few of the many factors involved in the rise of the Greek civilization.

Over a period of some 400 years—roughly between 650 and 250 B.C. —Greece enjoyed a period of intellectual stimulation in which several *natural-philosophers* played a dominant role.[1] Perhaps the earliest of these, and by all accounts the spiritual father of the natural-philosophical movement, was Thales of Miletus (ca.640–ca.546 B.C.). The tradition was carried on through Socrates, Plato, and Aristotle, the grand trio of Greek philosophy. Although there were a few important philosophers of later

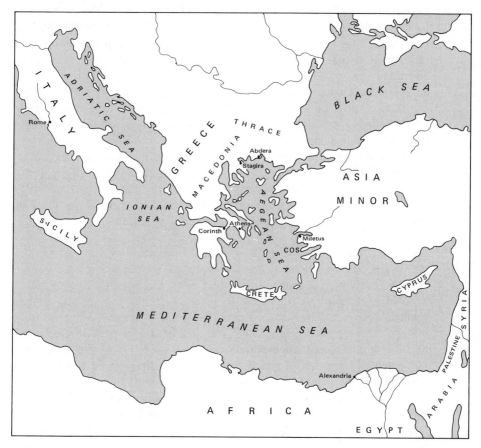

Figure 1.1. The Greco-Roman world of the eastern
Mediterranean region, highly generalized.

times, the movement had begun to decline severely by the time of Aristotle's
death in 322 B.C. Even though the ideas, interpretations, and speculations
of these Greek philosophers differed considerably, all the philosophers held
one common goal: They sought a coherent explanation of nature. The questions they asked were concerned with the causes of natural phenomena and
how these causes might be understood so as to relate these phenomena in
some meaningful way. Not infrequently, they fell back upon supernatural
explanations, but at the very least, it was in this cradle that science was born.

In order to establish the major contributions of Greek philosophy to
the development of science, we do not need to review the ideas of each
philosopher. The scientific tradition may be adequately traced through the
contributions of five men: Anaximander, Empedocles, Democritus,

Hippocrates, and Aristotle. Perhaps we should add a sixth, Thales, because he started the trend by posing a question: What is the fundamental physical substance of the universe? He concluded that it is water, probably because of its great abundance and its important role in the existence of both living and nonliving entities.

One of Thales' students, Anaximander (ca.611–ca.547 B.C.), carried the idea of physical causation further by proposing a fundamental substance called "the boundless," which he seemed to have conceived in physical, rather than nonphysical, terms. Using "the boundless" as a starting point, he developed a crude sort of evolutionary hypothesis for the entire universe, including organisms. Speculative as his ideas were, Anaximander stands as one of the great founders of scientific thought because of his development of a broad conceptual scheme based on natural rather than supernatural explanations. In this respect, he represents the spirit of scientific endeavor to a far greater degree than his predecessor, Thales, who apparently failed to develop a working conceptual scheme around his notion that water is the fundamental substance of the universe.

Not only was Anaximander the first of the Greek natural-philosophers (excluding Thales) to emphasize in a meaningful way that natural phenomena require natural explanations, but he also followed what we may call the second principle of science: **The goal of science is to develop comprehensive conceptual schemes** (natural explanations on a large scale) **that are potentially capable of giving rise to theories that can be tested.** Thus, speculation and imaginative thinking play an important role in scientific endeavor, because they lead to organized thought-systems within which observation and experimentation become meaningful. Anaximander's "boundless" has long since been superseded by more fruitful conceptual schemes, but it appears that he may well have been the first human being to formulate an actual scientific—that is, naturalistic—framework of thought to account for the existence of and activity within the material universe. For this reason, he is frequently called the Father of Science. At the very least, he is highly deserving of a place in history.

Empedocles (ca.495–ca.435 B.C.) was a native of Sicily, which was at that time under the domination of Greek culture. As was true of Thales and Anaximander, his thought was a tangle of metaphysical speculation and natural observation. But he did make two contributions of interest to us, namely, the *doctrine of elements* and the *notion of causality*. Neither idea originated with him, but he developed each to a point of usefulness.

Empedocles suggested that the material world consists of four basic elements: fire, air, water, and earth. Everything else that exists is either a combination of two or more of these elements, or is a result of their interaction. As far as man and the higher animals are concerned, their bodies are regulated by four fluids, or humors, that are the counterparts of these elements: blood, phlegm, yellow bile, and black bile. Interestingly, physical science rejected the Empedoclean concept of the nature of matter long ago, but the humoral theory of human disease was generally accepted through most of the 19th century, and vestiges of it remain in medical practice even today.

Although Empedocles ascribed many natural phenomena to mystical and supernatural causes, he believed very strongly that such phenomena can be explained at least partially on a physical basis. Thus, he was among the first to espouse the doctrine of causality, which was only implied, for the most part, in the conceptual scheme of Anaximander. Nowadays, we almost intuitively view a natural event as being the result of a natural cause. But, as we shall see, this way of looking at nature has undergone a long and painful evolution. Empedocles saw the principle dimly, to be sure, but at least he saw it.

The doctrine of the four elements with its subsidiary humoral theory has long since been replaced by more fruitful concepts. In common terminology, we might say that this general notion is false; yet, we said earlier that Empedocles developed it to a "point of usefulness." How can something that has been proven false be called useful? Now this question is very important for science, because scientists are continually sharpening concepts, replacing theories with better ones, and in general, building new ideas on the shoulders of old ones. *But strictly speaking, the language of science does not include the words "true" and "false."* A concept or a theory is held to be correct as long as it is the best explanation available for a set of natural phenomena; whether it is the best concept or theory that might conceivably be offered, or whether it is "true," is quite beside the point. Empedocles' doctrine of the four elements was at least an explanation (and indeed, for certain phenomena, a very useful one in the absence of a more sophisticated explanation) based on the principle of causality. Since antiquity never produced a science of chemistry, his conceptual scheme served until a more fruitful theory replaced it. This is the way science works. It builds a framework of hypotheses (tentative explanations), theories (hypotheses that have developed usefulness in explanation and predictability), and concepts (broad ideas). To base one's acceptance of a scientific generalization (hypothesis, theory, or concept) on the criterion of whether it is "false" or "true" is to misunderstand the nature of science.*

The fourth natural-philosopher who figures in our story was

---

* We do not suggest that the concepts of "true" and "false" have no meaning in science. But "truth" is a multilevelled word. When it is applied to hypotheses, theories, or conceptual schemes, it implies a dogmatism that is contrary to the spirit of scientific endeavor.

Democritus (ca.460–ca.370 B.C.), a contemporary of Empedocles. He was a native of Abdera in Thrace. Although he carried out a number of biological investigations, he is best remembered for his elaboration of a particulate theory of matter. To Democritus, the entire world and its various phenomena were to be explained in terms of minute, invisible particles in constant motion and whose presence, absence, or interaction in a given situation produced the results of perceptual experience. Thus, in a speculative sense, he proposed a kind of primitive atomic theory and anticipated modern physical science by more than two millennia. Unfortunately, antiquity lacked the materials and methods whereby this conceptual scheme could be extended, so it was not immediately fruitful.

Striking as the atomic theory of Democritus was, it was not his most significant contribution to the development of science. On the whole, it was a lucky speculation, no more defensible philosophically than a thousand other ancient notions, including a number of fantastic ideas held by Democritus himself. Of far greater importance was his materialistic explanation for matter and everything that stems from matter. In this respect, he went much further than Empedocles or any of his predecessors.

At this point, let us return to what we have called the first principle of science. To a very great extent, we owe this basic postulate to Democritus, although he was by no means entirely free of metaphysical speculations regarding nature. But of the several Greek natural-philosophers who contributed to this view of nature, Democritus is by far the clearest and most consistent in his explanation of matter and existence. His particulate concept of matter, although untestable at the time, has long since proved fruitful; and despite its speculative nature, it enabled him to explain the material universe within the bounds of material concepts.

It would be stretching a point to call our next figure a philosopher, although he did study philosophy in Athens as a young man. This person is Hippocrates (ca.460–ca.377 B.C.), a native of the island of Cos, which lies just off the western coast of Asia Minor. He was educated within the framework of a medical tradition that had long existed on Cos. Because of his extensive writings, he is the best-known physician of antiquity. He interests us because he exemplifies the influence of scientific theory upon practical affairs.

Hippocrates represents a concept of medical practice that developed concurrently with Greek natural-philosophy. Its starting point was the premise, first set in motion by Anaximander and developed much further by his successors, that natural effects are best explained by natural causes. Hence, the rational school of medicine, exemplified by Hippocrates, largely rejected the supernatural factors of demons, spirits, and the like as causative forces in human disease. They accepted the Empedoclean doctrine of the four humors, with certain modifications, but they also employed herbs and other medicinal sources in their practice. Hippocrates himself viewed medical practice as an art based on science, and it would appear that he understood quite clearly the implications of scientific thought for medicine. He emphasized in his writings that it does no good to explain a disease by saying that it has a divine cause, since this kind of "explanation" is self-defeating; in fact, Hippocrates contended that such a view does neither medicine nor the gods any real service. Instead, he urged the physician to seek preceding physical causes for pathological conditions.

Since Hippocrates and his colleagues were enormously successful in medical practice, at least by comparison with their less rational competitors, they added an empirical dimension to Greek philosophy that we would do well to note. Great conceptual schemes in science have a way of serving as fertile soil within which the practical and applied arts strike root. Undoubtedly, there were people in ancient Greece who derided men like Anaximander, Empedocles, and Democritus as hopeless visionaries. Even many who may have benefited from the healing arts developed by the Hippocratic school probably failed to see the connection between natural philosophy and medical science. But in Hippocrates we see a classic example of the influence of a conceptual scheme upon practical affairs.

Unfortunately, medical practice was the only area in which the thought-systems of natural philosophy could be tested in ancient Greece. Speculation and the formulation of conceptual schemes are absolutely essential to science, but it cannot live upon speculation alone. It is understandable, therefore, why the spirit of scientific inquiry almost died with the ancient Greeks. Anaximander, Empedocles, and Democritus had established a firm base for scientific endeavor, but there were neither materials nor workmen for any logical extension of their conceptual schemes into the "real" world of observable phenomena. Philosophically speaking, perhaps it can be said that they were premature by many centuries.

However, there was another philosophical reason why the scientific spirit as expressed by these men (and others) eventually ran into difficulties. They were all essentially *materialists;* that is, they held that ultimate reality is to be found in matter. This starting point enabled them to provide a partially coherent explanation of nature, but it became apparent that it left no place for values when drawn to its logical conclusion. Consequently, by around 400 B.C., many thinkers were disillusioned, because they witnessed in their society a deterioration of traditional moral and ethical values. Although a number of social and political events contributed to this deterioration, it was well known that the "scientific" (materialistic) spirit played an important part also. For Socrates and Plato, therefore, the problem was to build a philosophically defensible system of ethics. As a consequence, these two philosophers turned from a search for a coherent explanation of nature to what they regarded as a more fundamental question: What is reality as it applies to man's well-being? Since the pursuit of this question led ultimately to the thought-system of Aristotle, in which we are greatly interested as it influenced the subsequent development of science, let us examine it in some detail.

Socrates, late in the fifth century B.C., was the first philosopher to turn from the world of nature as a whole to a study of man himself. In Athens, he gradually attracted a crowd of students with whom he pursued two great questions: the nature of virtue and the ideal state of existence for man. It was a time when the traditional Greek polytheism, on the one hand, and the extreme materialism, on the other hand, had left the more penetrating minds in despair; and so Socrates had little difficulty in arousing the interest of young Athenians. In essence, he argued for the reality of goodness and wisdom, maintaining that if a man will only open his mind to an honest inquiry after that which is high and noble, he can attain it. This line of thought might seem to be far removed from the history of science in general and of biology in particular, but let us see how it influenced Plato, and through him, Aristotle.

As it turned out, Socrates was put to death for his views. Apparently, this example of loyalty to principle made such a deep impression upon Plato, who was Socrates' pupil, that he devoted the rest of his life to building a system of thought that he hoped would answer the basic question about the nature of ultimate reality, especially in the realm of ethics. Several years after his master's death (and after the furor surrounding Socrates had largely subsided), he founded a school in Athens known as the Academy. Here, he developed a doctrine of idealism, whose central theme was the existence of certain eternal, rationally conceived, perfect states of being, which he called "forms" or "ideals." These forms represent ultimate reality, Plato said, and knowledge of them is accessible to man only through the process of abstract thought. Essentially, therefore, his teaching might be summarized as follows: He believed that perceived objects (stones, horses, trees) are only "less real" images of their ideal "forms," which are more real. The "most real" of all forms are the ethical ones (for example, goodness, truth, and wisdom). Thus, he carried Socrates' disenchantment with nature to a point of virtually denying its importance.

It was from the totality of this world-view that Aristotle's own philosophy was distilled. Born at Stagira, a city of Macedonia that lay about 200 miles north of Athens, Aristotle belonged to a family of physicians. He was thoroughly initiated into the medical traditions of his region as a youth, and at the age of 18 he was sent to Athens to receive training in philosophy as a part of his medical education. Enrolling in Plato's school, he was gradually drawn from medicine into philosophy. In fact, he almost made the student life a permanent career; some historians say he studied with Plato for 20 years, until the latter's death in 347. He left Athens after Plato's death and settled in Asia Minor, from whence he returned to Macedonia in 338. The emperor, Philip, soon appointed him tutor to his son, Alexander, who was to become conqueror and ruler of most of the civilized world. Under the sponsorship of Alexander, Aristotle prospered sufficiently so that he was able to move back to Athens in 334, where he founded a school known as the Lyceum. For 12 years, he was undisputed master of philosophy in Athens, but his enviable position lasted only until Alexander's death in 323. At that point, Athens overthrew the Macedonian yoke; Aristotle fled the city and died the next year in exile.

Aristotle's conceptual framework was one of Platonic idealism, but he gave it his own interpretation. To Plato, a given object is only an imperfect copy or "representation" of its form, which is the true reality. To Aristotle, the ideal form is always found expressed in particular objects. He conceived of matter as a potentiality, not an actuality. For example, the metal of a sword is only a potentiality, and not until it becomes a sword (or variously, a spear, an axe, a farming implement) does it truly exist as a form. This is not to say that Aristotle forsook all abstract and metaphysical notions of reality; in essence, he merely denied that Plato's "forms" were the only real things in existence. Perhaps it could be said that Aristotle's watchword was "becoming"—that is, nature shows a gradation of patterns culminating in the higher organisms—whereas Plato's major theme was "being." Within the framework of ancient thought, the difference is that Aristotle's concept of nature was dynamic; Plato's, static. Hence, Aristotle considered biology to be the model science, because development ("becoming") is such a major process in biology.

Since Aristotle believed in the importance of material entities as vehicles of the ideal order, it is no accident that he, rather than Socrates or Plato, became the first great biologist. Philosophically, Socrates *could* have been a biologist or any other sort of naturalist, but he considered that there were more important things with which to concern himself. In contrast, it is inconceivable that Plato could ever have been a naturalist, primarily because he did not believe that nature could afford stable knowledge. But with a modification of Platonic idealism as his base of operation, Aristotle probably explored more of the biological world than has any other single person who ever lived. Of course, he was considered the expert in a new field, and through the patronage of Alexander, he had almost unlimited funds at his disposal. Thus, the Athenian Lyceum became virtually one big school of biology, and apparently Aristotle had dozens, if not hundreds, of assistants. The knowledge that resulted from this vast amount of activity was distilled into well over a hundred books, most of which are no longer extant. However, enough of Aristotle's writings remain to give us some idea of his overall contributions to biological knowledge. Much of it is erroneous and almost all of it is descriptive, but it was a start.

Aristotle's major contributions were in the areas of taxonomy (classification) and morphology (form and structure). He worked out a crude system of categories for such animals as came to his attention (some 500 species), and he laid the groundwork for a similar endeavor with plants on the part of his pupil and eventual successor at the Lyceum, Theophrastus. Aristotle was particularly interested in marine animals; he made a number of keen observations on the morphology and natural history of certain fish, mollusks, arthropods, and echinoderms in particular. In short, he was a great morphologist, and we owe to him the tradition of astuteness in observation that is so essential to a study of biological materials. Furthermore, he proved adept at making generalizations about such topics as circulation and reproduction, thus anticipating a clarification of the inductive method in science by many centuries.

There is no question that Aristotle was a great biologist. However, it is now obvious that his thought-system lost something by having developed through the Socratic-Platonic tradition rather than from the pre-Socratic materialists. Certainly, he fails to represent the tradition of Anaximander, Empedocles, and Democritus, whose actual work with natural materials was minimal, but whose philosophic base of operation was much nearer the modern scientific tradition. Aristotle was essentially an observer, not an experimenter. Although both observation and experimentation are essential to scientific endeavor, it is doubtful that observation alone qualifies as science unless it leads to some type of experimentation or, finally, to theories and conceptual schemes. It is significant that Aristotle arrived at very few generalizations regarding the world of life. His writings consist mainly of isolated descriptions, and even his system of animal classification is not set forth as a formal scheme but has to be pieced together from scattered references. Nevertheless, it was Aristotle who was followed in the endeavor that passed for science during some eighteen centuries following his time.

As we shall see, certain social and religious factors later rendered Aristotle's total thought-system acceptable to the people of medieval times. This thought-system consists of two major features, at least as it affected the later development of science, and it is these two features in combination that we shall refer to subsequently as Aristotelianism.

First of all, Aristotle's concept of material reality led inevitably to an extremely limited and finite view of nature and the universe. Since ultimate reality in his system is the actuality of objects, one has merely to examine and describe all existing natural entities in order to capture empirical knowledge in its totality. Hence, Aristotle's concept of knowledge was finite, as though the world of material reality were a closed sphere within which man could investigate until he had finished the task completely (Fig. 1-2). To Aristotle's credit, he seems to have conceived of this

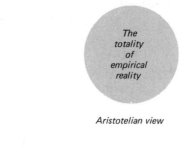

Aristotelian view

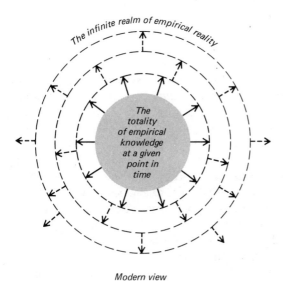

Modern view

Figure 1.2. Diagrammatic representation of the Aristotelian and modern views of the nature of empirical reality.

task as immensely greater than did his admirers of later centuries, many of whom apparently imagined that Aristotle himself knew everything about the material universe. But it seems fair to say that it was not until the myth of the closed universe was widely rejected that science took on the dynamic, ongoing cast that it has assumed in modern times. In other words, the figure has been completely reversed: Present knowledge is a sphere that increases in diameter constantly and whose boundaries have no theoretical limits. To extend the figure, knowledge begets knowledge in a kind of volumetric progression by extending hypotheses from the known into the unknown (Fig. 1–2). Thus, the more surface exposure knowledge has with the void of ignorance, the more rapidly it advances.

The second feature of Aristotle's view of nature that influenced the further development of science was his teleological view of nature. *Teleology* (sometimes called *finalism*) is the viewpoint that all life processes, whether in an organ, an organism, or a species, have purposes and goals. This idea developed from Aristotle's theory of "becoming," and it flavored the whole of his science. To illustrate, an acorn was Aristotle's "matter," the oak tree his "form." In teleological terms, the purpose of the acorn is to grow into an oak. In a manner of speaking, this view is consistent with modern scientific thought. It is readily conceded that an acorn is *potentially* an oak, because it is composed of atoms and molecules organized in such a way that it has a material basis for growth to maturity. But Aristotle was the product of a tradition that had rejected materialism; to him, an acorn has a built-in, nonmaterial power (which he called an *entelechy*) that drives it toward perfection of form.

The Aristotelian outlook was adequate for the science of Aristotle's day, but a later age crystallized it into a dogmatic system that served the cause of science poorly at that time. By *dogmatism,* we mean a framework of thought that *rules out in advance* the possibility of discovering or accepting empirical evidence that might weigh against the belief in question. For this reason, Aristotelianism eventually constituted a barrier to the further development of the scientific outlook. Dogmatism and science are natural enemies and cannot coexist successfully; where either flourishes, the other is bound to wither. As we shall see, dogmatism became clearly dominant to the scientific viewpoint many centuries after Aristotle, and it is somewhat ironic that the Father of Biology should also be remembered as the author of a great deal of scientific confusion.

It has long been fashionable in some philosophical and scientific circles to hold Aristotle responsible for several centuries of "bad" science.[2] It seems more realistic to view him as a pioneer who, quite understandably, made a pioneer's mistakes. It would be as justifiable to blame Freud or Darwin for their incomplete thought-systems, developed more than two millennia later, as to maintain that Aristotle was a "bad" philosopher and scientist. Actually, his contributions were significant in both areas. It was only because his primitive cosmic views became useful in later centuries to the dominant socio-theological systems that a large degree of confusion resulted. In the larger sense, therefore, it was not Aristotle who was to blame, but the social framework of these later times that embraced Aristotelianism with all its inadequacies. In fact, it is difficult to believe that the open-minded, intellectually curious Aristotle would have endorsed the dogmatism with which his name was later associated, any more than Jesus would have endorsed many of the acts that have been performed in the name of Christianity. Thus, strange though it may seem, "Aristotelianism" is not equivalent to "Aristotle's thought and attitude."

Actually, Aristotle provided biology with a much-needed factual base, and he *did* generalize scientifically to a certain degree. A biologist who lived more than 2,000 years after Aristotle, Carolus Linnaeus, once said that "the first step of science is to know one thing from another." In this respect, Aristotle was a great scientist. Certainly he produced a tremendous body of factual knowledge that the visionary pre-Socratic natural-philosophers never succeeded in producing; and even if factual knowledge is not the essence of science, it nevertheless constitutes a foundation that is necessary before science can proceed to other things.

Although Aristotle's school actually lasted for more than eight centuries after his death, it soon lost its identification with biological investigations. With one or two exceptions, his successors did not really influence the course of scientific history. In fact, the entire cultural influence of Greece had declined by the latter part of the fourth century B.C. Its most noble philosophers and the men who had some insight into the nature of science had already lived and died. Alexander's death in 323 removed the unifying power from the Greek city-states, and the ensuing political chaos was unfavorable to cultural progress. It was to be many centuries before the world would see anything comparable to ancient Greece at its best. In the meantime, forces developed that influenced profoundly the subsequent history of Western civilization.

1.2 THE ROMAN WORLD

While the Greek civilization was undergoing its development, an entirely different sort of culture evolved on the Italian peninsula. The city of Rome itself was founded about 800 B.C., and in time, the Romans brought the entire peninsula into subjugation. By about the middle of the second century B.C., they were undisputed masters of the western Mediterranean area. Turning their attention to the eastern regions, they quickly overran the small, disunited Greek states that had arisen from Alexander's divided empire. By the middle of the first century B.C., the Romans ruled virtually the entire Mediterranean region as well as certain areas beyond it.

Rome had to develop an administrative system to govern its expanding empire. Although Roman history was marked by a certain degree of internal revolution and change in administrative structure, the empire succeeded, on the whole, in maintaining a stable system of law and government for several centuries. Whereas the Greek city-states had never developed any great degree of civil unity and the better Greek minds had been occupied with cultural problems, most of Rome's talents were channeled into legal, administrative, and military pursuits. Also, by tradition, the inhabitants of the Italian peninsula were strongly oriented toward agriculture and the practical arts. As a consequence, such talent as might have been expended on scientific matters was largely devoted to military, agricultural, and industrial technology.

Even before the conquest of the eastern Mediterranean by Rome during the second century B.C., Greek culture had made itself felt on the Italian peninsula and in Sicily through the migration of certain peoples from the east. By the end of the second century, both the city of Rome itself and the entire peninsula was heavily populated with Greek physicians, teachers, and artisans. In addition, a great many Greek slaves were in the service of wealthy Romans; and, as a general rule, these slaves were more highly cultured and better educated than their masters. Furthermore, Roman soldiers, merchants, and administrators carried the influence of Greek culture back to Italy. By the end of the first century B.C., the Roman poet Horace was able to say with a considerable degree of justification, "Captive Greece has captured her rude conqueror."

Although Rome adopted Greek cultural standards, she did not take over the spirit of scientific inquiry. Apparently, this attitude reflected the greater appreciation of the Roman mind for *things* rather than for *ideas*. Greek sculpture became something of a status symbol in the homes of the wealthier Romans, but in some contrast, there seems to have been little demand for the writings of Plato. In the scientific realm itself, the Romans adapted only those principles of Greek science that had a practical application to medicine or technology. As a consequence, even these areas eventually stagnated, because they were bereft of further theoretical support that comes only from creative thought.

Actually, just two Romans figure prominently in the history of science, and their distinction is due not so much to their actual contributions as to their eventual influence. The first of these is Pliny the Elder (23–79 A.D.), a native of northern Italy. He studied in Rome as a youth, and eventually followed a public career, serving in various roles in both civil and military affairs. All the while, he maintained an active interest in nature, and his travels brought him into contact with persons whose real or fictitious experiences with natural phenomena were of great interest to his impressionable mind. With a considerable lack of discrimination, Pliny wrote one account after another, eventually composing a 37-volume encyclopedia to which he gave the simple title *Natural History*. It dealt with virtually all aspects of nature that could be explored at that time; despite the fantastic stories it contains, this work is one of the really significant contributions of antiquity. Pliny carried out few investigations himself; rather, he was a compiler, and his work is a reflection of descriptive natural science as it was studied in ancient times. Despite the general untrustworthiness of many inclusions, Pliny's *Natural History* served as a major source of information for a great many centuries.

powerfully, although indirectly, and any attempt to trace the development of modern science must take this influence into account.

Because of the Bible, we have a much clearer picture of the Hebrew civilization than that of any other ancient people. Tracing their ancestry to the patriarch Abraham (ca.1900 B.C.), they became welded into a nation under the leadership of Moses (ca.1300 B.C.). The Mosaic Law, or Code, sets forth a high standard of ethical conduct and emphasizes the primacy of Yahweh (Jehovah) as the one true God. The Hebrews (also called Israelites, and later on Jews), were unique among the ancient peoples in their monotheism. Their political fortunes were highest around 1000 B.C. when David, the first king of a unified Israel, established a strong monarchy. However, this kingdom began to disintegrate shortly after his death; and by the sixth century B.C., the Israelites had all but lost their national identity through military defeat and exile into foreign lands. However, a number of Jews were allowed to return to their native Palestine from Persian captivity in 537 B.C., and they rebuilt the city of Jerusalem. Although they never again attained the stature of David's kingdom, they managed to remain a distinct people up to the time of Christ, and indeed, they have done so to the present day.

The Christian religion was an outgrowth of Judaism. In contrast to the provincial character of its parent religion, however, Christianity aspired to permeate the entire world. Its founder, Jesus Christ, extended the Mosaic Code and the insights of the Hebrew prophets into a religion of love for God and one's fellow men. He bade his followers to carry this message to "the whole creation." Beginning at Jerusalem about 29 A.D., they proceeded to accomplish their task with a zeal and a devotion generally unmatched in all of human history. Before the end of the century, they had carried the Christian gospel into a large part of the civilized world, and their influence was such that it could be said by certain of their enemies that they had "turned the world upside down."

At this time, of course, Rome was in firm control of the civilized world. It was the general policy of the Romans not to interfere with the religious affairs of their subjects, and at first, Rome largely ignored the Christian movement. From time to time, emperors and in some cases lesser officials launched extensive persecutions against the Christians, which seemed only to strengthen the cause of Christianity. The empire alternately tolerated and persecuted the Christian religion until 313 A.D., when its adherents were granted freedom of worship by the emperor, Constantine the Great. Shortly afterward, Constantine himself embraced Christianity and elevated it to the position of a state religion. Later on in the fourth century, it then became the only religion tolerated by the state. Thus, within a relatively short time, Christianity rose from rags to riches. It was soon to become apparent that this was not an unmixed blessing.

The scientific tradition had virtually ceased to exist by the fourth century A.D. Its disappearance was due in large part, apparently, to the earlier decline of Greek civilization and the failure of the Romans to carry this particular tradition forward. Because the decline in science was accompanied by the rise of Christianity, a cause-and-effect relationship has sometimes been inferred by students of history. This inference is unwarranted. It is true that the Judeo-Christian outlook did nothing to promote science. Judaism made its greatest contribution in the realm of ethics and morality, and early Christianity was much too preoccupied with other-worldly values to be greatly concerned with any sort of emphasis upon the material universe. Moreover, the Greek culture, which had nurtured the scientific spirit, had begun to decline long before the advent of Christianity. But even if the rise of Christianity had exactly paralleled the decline of science, it would be difficult to substantiate a cause-and-effect relationship. For three centuries after its establishment as a religion distinct from Judaism, Christianity's impact on Roman society was a limited one. It was not until later centuries that the Christian religion became an important factor in science; and by that time, it had assumed a dogmatic cast that was largely absent from its earlier form. Strictly speaking, it was not Christianity but dogmatism that eventually came into conflict with science.[3]

In many ways, the Roman Empire's endorsement of Christianity was fatal. Throughout the first three centuries of its existence, Christianity had managed to keep its ranks relatively free of individuals whose motives were questionable. Periodic and frequent persecutions by Roman authorities constituted a selective factor that tended to discourage all but the most committed from membership. This situation changed during the fourth century, and large numbers of individuals nominally embraced Christianity out of political or social expediency. The Church flourished numerically but only at the sacrifice of its high standards. The moral decline of Rome had already begun, continuing until the city was invaded in the fifth century A.D. It was to this decadent Rome that the Church tied its fortunes. Administratively, the Church completed the task (already begun centuries earlier) of modeling its structure after that of the empire. This organization was a strengthening factor, but it also paved the way for the authoritarian and dogmatic attitudes that were to dominate Christianity all through the Middle Ages. For science, this atmosphere was barren; many centuries passed before science could make even a feeble comeback.[4]

Meanwhile, Rome continued its downward plunge toward complete dissolution. The possible explanations for the decline and fall of the Roman Empire are numerous and doubtless hold a great many lessons for modern students of political science. Suffice it to say that Western Europe was thrown into political, cultural, and economic chaos. Rome had scarcely kept the spirit of science alive, but science fared even worse under the German barbarians who conquered Rome. In the East, the Byzantine, or

East Roman, Empire was established in 395 A.D. Its headquarters were at Constantinople, founded by Constantine in 330. The traditional culture was maintained here for some centuries longer, with varying fortunes, and Constantinople itself was not captured by enemy forces until 1204 A.D. In Western Europe, however, the old order had largely passed away by the early part of the fifth century, and an almost total darkness lay over the earth. It was many centuries before the cultural hibernation was ended; because science is a cultural phenomenon, it likewise slept for a long period.

QUESTIONS FOR REVIEW AND DISCUSSION

1. Suppose a gardener discovers that two of his tomato plants have wilted and appear to be dying. Can you formulate at least three *naturalistic* hypotheses (tentative explanations) that might occur to the gardener in his attempts to account for the demise of his plants? Can you think of a hypothesis that would be completely inconsistent with the first principle of science?

2. The second principle of science speaks of "conceptual schemes that are potentially capable of giving rise to theories that can be tested." Chapter 4 of this book discusses a conceptual scheme, *biogenesis.* Before reading further, consult the glossary for a brief definition of this term and try to formulate at least one theory that is capable of being tested. Distinguish among the terms *hypothesis, conceptual scheme,* and *theory.*

3. List each person mentioned in this chapter and describe his significance to the theme of the chapter.

4. In what ways might the word "truth" differ in meaning to a historian, a philosopher, a theologian, and a scientist?

5. How did Socrates, Plato, and Aristotle differ, as a group, from most of the natural-philosophers who preceded them? What effect did this difference have on the development of science?

6. Why do the authors maintain that "Aristotelianism" is not equivalent to "what Aristotle thought"?

7. For what reasons do you think the Romans failed to develop a scientific tradition? What is the difference between science and technology?

8. What is teleology, and how is it exemplified by both Pliny and Galen? Why are teleological explanations of biological phenomena viewed with suspicion by most modern biologists?

9. Since the Judeo-Christian culture contributed only minimally to the development of science, why do you suppose the authors devote attention to it?

10. How did the Roman Empire influence the development of the Christian Church during the fourth and fifth centuries A.D.? What does this influence have to do with science?

REFERENCES

Jones, W. T. *A History of Western Philosophy: The Classical Mind* (2nd ed.). New York: Harcourt, Brace and World, Inc., 1969. This is the first of a four-volume set; the other volumes will be annotated at the ends of appropriate succeeding chapters. A very lucid, yet scholarly, history of philosophy.

Nordenskiold, Erik. *The History of Biology.* New York: Tudor Publishing Co., 1928. Probably the most exhaustive and comprehensive history of biology yet compiled.

Singer, Charles. *A History of Biology.* New York: Henry Schuman, 1950. A very penetrating history, less encyclopedic than that of Nordenskiold.

Whitehead, A. N. *Science and the Modern World.* New York: The Macmillan Company, 1925. This volume by an outstanding philosopher is "must" reading for all who would understand modern science in historical perspective. The first chapter, "The Origins of Modern Science," is particularly appropriate to our consideration of the ancient world.

TWO

The Long Sleep

With the fall of the Roman Empire, society in Western Europe was thrown into a state of complete chaos. The barbarian tribes that filtered into the region from the north and east were ill-prepared to govern. Throughout most of the region where Rome had provided a high degree of political stability, one government followed another in rapid succession. As a result, poverty and brutality became widespread, and most people were so concerned with sheer survival that little attention could be devoted to cultural developments, including science. Furthermore, almost all the ancient writings became lost due to the social turmoil and to the widespread neglect of learning. Many centuries passed before this cultural paralysis was overcome.

Thus, Western Europe entered into the long period of intellectual stagnation, extending roughly from the 5th through the 12th centuries, known to history as the Middle Ages.* As a period, it was not devoid of social stability; in fact, it came to be quite stable indeed. However, the first centuries of the Middle Ages were marked by widespread unrest, and that part of the period, extending roughly from the fifth through the ninth centuries, is known as the Dark Ages.

And dark they were—from every standpoint. Culture, including science, had fared badly enough under the Romans; it came dangerously near to dying out altogether at the hands of their crude successors. Fortunately, Western Europe was not the whole civilized world. The eastern portion of the old Roman empire, centered around Constantinople, fared somewhat better. But it was the rising Arab culture, built upon the unifying power of Islam, that did more than anything else to nurture the spirit of science during the Dark Ages. Building on the foundation of Greek science, the Arabs made great progress in mathematics, astronomy, and chemistry. However, they labored under a severe handicap: The Koran was held to contain all the knowledge needed by man, and such progress as the Arabs made was largely accomplished during periods when the Koran was interpreted rather loosely by those in positions of authority. Eventually, Arabian science had considerable influence on Western European thought.

Since it was in Western Europe that a cultural revival ultimately led to the modern scientific tradition, we shall center our attention upon the affairs of that region. But it should be kept in mind that cultures such as the Arab one played an important role in the eventual rise of modern science and thus deserve a place in its history.

2.1 THE MEDIEVAL WORLD

Certain regions of Western Europe enjoyed a degree of social and political stability during the Dark Ages. Notable among these was the kingdom of the Franks, in what later became France, and a portion of the British Isles. But on the whole, such order as prevailed was due to the in-

---

* Scholars vary in defining the length of this period. It is probably more meaningful to regard the Middle Ages as extending through the 14th century. However, the 13th and 14th centuries witnessed a great ferment of intellectual activity, which led to the Renaissance, a period that usually includes the 15th and 16th centuries.

fluence of the Roman Catholic Church. As we have noted, the Church had modeled its organization after that of the Roman Empire, and by the time that government fell, the Church possessed a hierarchical framework that enabled it to serve Western Europe as a kind of substitute empire. In the early part of the Dark Ages, the Church was able to weather the barbarian invasions successfully. Later on, it became sufficiently powerful in a political sense to dictate terms to the nations themselves. Thus, Rome continued to be the center of authority; the change was merely from a civil to an ecclesiastical form of government.

To a large degree, this development was fortunate. Despite the fact that the Church often abused its authority, and its officials frequently resembled Caesar's descendants more than Christ's, it at least provided some social stability and a place where men could turn for comfort and inspiration. Moreover, only through the Church were works of art and literature preserved. Many of the writings of antiquity, notably the books of the Bible, were laboriously translated and reproduced by Catholic monks. During the later Middle Ages, the writings of Aristotle, Pliny, and Galen, and certain other ancients, also became highly regarded. Consequently, not only was some ancient literature saved and carried forward but the arts of writing and translation were also developed.

Perhaps the major reason for the almost complete absence of a medieval science, at least in Western Europe, was the temperament of a society that had been nurtured into existence by the Church. The major theme of life was eternal salvation, not how to get along in the present world. As a consequence, the overall outlook was other-worldly rather than this-worldly. Whatever may be said for this outlook in terms of its intrinsic value or its capacity to stabilize society, it drew attention away from nature and, indeed, from the whole of culture and learning. It was not until this society outgrew its satisfaction with the merely pious life that it began to search for knowledge and understanding.[1] Of course, throughout the Middle Ages, there were isolated instances of dissatisfaction with the totally religious outlook. As a generalization, however, it seems fair to say that society did not begin to stir until around the 11th century. Even then, a renewed interest in culture and learning grew very slowly.

2.2 THE SLEEPWALKING: SCHOLASTICISM

The eventual outcome of a general revival of learning, restricted at first to the clergy, was the rise of universities during the 12th century. These institutions grew out of the cathedral schools, where one or a few monks gave instruction to lay persons in reading, writing, theology, and music. There was no common pattern to the development of universities, since they arose independently in different countries, but in general, organization was rather loose until an increase in numbers of students necessitated some form of internal government. Within the recognized ecclesiastical framework of church authority, students had considerable voice in the university operation. They dictated the specific curriculum, as well as the terms of a given course, and held almost unlimited powers over the professors. In some cases, payment was made directly to the professor for the right to participate in his course; if he proved unpopular, he was literally starved out of the system. As the universities became organized into faculties with deans and other administrative officials, the students generally had a strong voice in their election. Of course, the rules varied from place to place. In general, the universities of Italy (following the lead of Bologna), France, and Spain were as described above; while those of England, Germany, and the Scandinavian region (following the lead of the University of Paris, an exception to the other French universities) were controlled by the faculty from the start. As a social institution, the university was totally without historical precedent. Whereas Plato's Academy and Aristotle's Lyceum attracted limited numbers of students, enrollment in a medieval university sometimes reached the tens of thousands. Thus, mass education almost became a reality; and despite the generally low quality of instruction, it was inevitable that the bonds of ignorance, superstition, and dogmatism would be broken in a few minds. Through universities, medieval men took small but firm steps toward emancipation from ignorance. We can say that, intellectually, Western Europe was walking in her sleep, but at least she was walking.

Even though the medieval universities displayed individual differences, they followed a remarkably uniform basic curriculum. Beginning work was a form of the liberal arts and corresponded roughly to the modern undergraduate curriculum. It included seven subjects, divided into two separate groups: the *trivium,* which consisted of grammar, logic, and rhetoric; and the *quadrivium,* which covered arithmetic, astronomy, geometry, and music. In addition to the liberal arts program, most universities maintained specialized schools of law, medicine, and theology. The pursuit of work in these advanced areas corresponded to present-day postgraduate study.

Since the term "university" connotes to the modern mind a place of free inquiry, it should be emphasized that this was far from the case in these medieval institutions. The word is derived from the Latin *universitas,* meaning "community." Originally, it was used as a collective noun to describe virtually any sort of aggregation. The reason it came to be applied to institutions of learning was not because the word described any kind of intellectual framework, but because the schools, with their numbers of students and teachers, constituted a community. If a modern university student could be transported in time back to the 12th or 13th century in Bologna, or Oxford, or Paris, he would undoubtedly receive a great shock. It is taken for granted nowadays that intellectual freedom is a way of life for the university student; but had a medieval student come to such an institution for the purpose of real inquiry, he would have been sorely disappointed, if not persecuted. These were schools of *indoctrination,* not of *education,* and there is a vast difference. Even the teaching methods were attuned to this philosophy; instruction was by formal lecture from a pulpit and resembled nothing more than the ecclesiastical sermon. The entire conceptual framework of medieval education as represented by the universities is now called *Scholasticism.* Let us examine this viewpoint in more detail.

Every aspect of medieval life, including education, was directly connected to the attitudes of the Roman Catholic Church. In order to survive the hazardous experiences of the Dark Ages, the Church became ultraconservative; and by the 12th century, no departure was tolerated from the tenets that it endorsed officially. At first, church doctrine included only the teachings of the Bible (as interpreted by the Church) and a select number of church traditions. Gradually, however, recognition was given to certain of the ancient writings other than the Bible. Of particular interest to us is the fact that these works eventually included the writings of Aristotle, Pliny, and Galen, whose teleological views coincided rather well with Church doctrine. Indeed, Pliny and Galen were considered near-Christians; and in fact, it was actually claimed in some quarters that they were Christians, probably to lend the greater weight to their writings. Aristotle, on the other hand, was a heathen by Church standards. But during a time when Church authorities were seeking ways to maintain a hold on their subjects by the use of safe written materials, they came to recognize that Aristotle was potentially a strong ally. His metaphysical notions of causality and his closed universe fitted ideally into the dogmatic framework that the Church sought to maintain. Moreover, these ideas were hallowed by the simple virtue of their being old. By this time, the Church had committed itself to a worship of the past, and its authorities found a strong ally in Aristotle. Of course, this latter-day Aristotelianism did not accurately reflect Aristotle himself, whose thirst for new empirical knowledge would have made him a poor Scholastic indeed. Paradoxical as it might seem, medieval Aristotelianism consisted of basic metaphysical assumptions that Aristotle might well have rejected had he lived in the Middle Ages.

In any case, the monks of the later Middle Ages were set to work gathering and translating the works of Aristotle (a project already carried forward by the Arabs). Eventually, his influence far outran that of Pliny and Galen. The extant writings of Pliny were devoted exclusively to natural history, a subject of little interest to the medieval mind; and those of Galen were of value mainly to practitioners of medicine. In contrast, Aristotle had written on a wide variety of subjects, all within much the same philosophical framework; and he was set forth as the authority *par excellence* for every secular discipline worth studying. Thus it came to be that the recognized authorities were the Church in spiritual affairs and Aristotle in the secular realm, including science.

The assimilation of Aristotle's ideas, however, was a slow process. By the 13th century, it had become apparent to men of thought that church and society faced something of a dilemma. The medieval religious orientation, with its emphasis on salvation, still dominated the Western mind, but that same mind had become interested in new knowledge. It must be remembered, of course, that Aristotle and the other thinkers of antiquity represented "new knowledge" to medieval society and that their ideas were not always reconcilable with the traditional thought-patterns. In fact, Aristotle's writings were banned in a number of universities well into the 14th century.

It was to this problem of how to reconcile Christian and classical viewpoints of man and the universe that the Italian scholar, Thomas Aquinas (1225–1274), addressed himself.[2] Thomas was a highly intelligent theologian and philosopher, a member of the Dominican Order. In time, his writings completely revolutionized Roman Catholic doctrine. However, he is important to the history of science because he played a significant role in altering attitudes toward new knowledge. It is true that he was a Scholastic in outlook and that his framework of thought was strongly Aristotelian. Nevertheless, he did much to encourage the spirit of impartial inquiry. Of course, he was a theologian, and his inquiry was into the arguments of theologians. But the very fact that he was willing to use philosophical arguments in theological debates constituted a very definite step toward the attitudes that would eventually make possible the advent of scientific inquiry.

In effect, Thomas distinguished between theology and philosophy, and by so doing, he wrought something of an epistemological revolution for his time. Theology, he argued, is based on faith; philosophy depends upon reason. It should be pointed out that in medieval thought prior to Thomas, reason was looked upon with considerable suspicion by many churchmen; they believed it contradicted faith. Not so, Thomas declared; faith (based on revelation and tradition) is illuminated, or perfected, through reason. He pointed out that Aristotle, for example, had disclosed many valuable insights about man and the natural world; therefore, if one wanted to know anything about these subjects, one should consult

Aristotle and then allow Christian revelation to illuminate Aristotle's views.

Although this might seem to be a halting step forward, it was a most important one. In essence, Thomas believed that there is legitimate and valuable knowledge that cannot be gained through faith. It need not detain us here that he was more interested in what reason could do for faith than in what reason could do for science. Nevertheless, he addressed himself to the major problem of his society (the faith-reason conflict), and his proposal for a solution to that problem became widely accepted within a relatively short time.

Yet, the scientific attitude of impartial inquiry was a long way off, because even after the classical thinkers were accepted, they were generally viewed as authorities in the spirit of Scholasticism. The honor in which the classical authors came to be held in the medieval world is well illustrated by an anecdote that has survived the intervening centuries:

> In the year of our Lord 1432, there arose a grievous quarrel among the brethren over the number of teeth in the mouth of a horse. For 13 days the disputation raged without ceasing. All the ancient books and chronicles were fetched out, and wonderful and ponderous erudition, such as was never before heard of in this region, was made manifest. At the beginning of the fourteenth day, a youthful friar of goodly bearing asked his learned superiors for permission to add a word, and straightway, to the wonderment of the disputants,′ whose deep wisdom he sore vexed, he beseeched them to unbend in a manner coarse and unheard of, and to look in the open mouth of a horse and find answer to their questionings. At this, their dignity being grievously hurt, they waxed exceedingly wroth; and, joining in a mighty uproar, they flew upon him and smote him hip and thigh, and cast him out forthwith. For, said they, surely Satan hath tempted this bold neophyte to declare unholy and unheard-of ways of finding truth contrary to all the teachings of the fathers. After many days more of grievous strife the dove of peace sat on the assembly, and they as one man, declaring the problem to be an everlasting mystery because of a grievous dearth of historical and theological evidence thereof, so ordered the same writ down.[3]

The story may well be apocryphal, but such arguments undoubtedly occurred very commonly. It illustrates the essence of Scholasticism: a worship of the past, a distrust of new information, a preference for words as opposed to insights, and an insistence by many Scholastics that God had revealed his entire will, including such knowledge of nature as He deemed important, to the holy men of old.[4]

Since the medieval universities were committed to a Scholastic outlook, it is hardly surprising that the cause of science fared badly among them. In fact, no work of any importance in the biological sciences originated in Western Europe during the Middle Ages. Except for some progress in technology, this was true for the physical sciences. It was absolutely impossible for anything resembling modern science to flourish within the framework of Scholasticism.

The case of Roger Bacon (ca.1214–ca.1294) well represents this point. An Englishman who received his education at the universities of Oxford and Paris, Bacon was a Franciscan monk. Bacon developed a liking for scientific experimentation as a pastime. He merely sought to satisfy his curiosity about nature by using a few chemicals and some crude physical apparatus—no more than that. But he wrote numerous treatises and so gained widespread distrust as a heretic. Accused of witchcraft and certain related evils, he was committed to prison, where he remained for several years.

Roger Bacon is of more than passing interest to the history of science. For all his misfortunes (and for that matter, his limited scientific outlook), he managed to get two major points across to his contemporaries: **Scholasticism is an unworthy framework for education; nature can be understood only in terms of observation and experimentation, not through a blind devotion to the past.** It was a long time—centuries, in fact—before Scholasticism died out; but by the 13th century, a lonely voice was being lifted here and there in protest of dogmatism. The scientific spirit had died, for all practical purposes, in antiquity. It was revived, however dimly, when such men as Roger Bacon began to advocate a study of nature through observation and experimentation rather than through revelation and tradition.

2.3 TWO ROADS TO TRUTH: WILLIAM OF OCKHAM

Although the 13th century witnessed a considerable change in outlook among the churchmen of Western Europe, and a few people such as Roger Bacon began to cry out for reform, Scholastic attitudes remained dominant. Even the reforms brought about by Thomas Aquinas, whose major objective was to reconcile the areas of faith and reason, failed to liberate society as a whole from the bonds of dogmatism and authoritarianism. During the late 13th and early 14th centuries, a number of churchmen began to attack Thomas's synthesis of faith and reason on the grounds that these two areas of human thought must be kept separate and free from each other if each is to flourish in its rightful way. The arguments of these thinkers are essentially theological ones and need not detain us here. For our purposes, let us examine the reaction of William of Ockham (ca.1300–

ca.1349), an English philosopher, who was one of the most influential of the churchmen who took serious issue with the Thomistic synthesis.[5]

Although Ockham agreed with a great deal that Thomas had said, he disagreed completely on the question of faith versus reason. According to Ockham, faith does not supplement reason; the two areas may even be contradictory. Recognition of this principle does not reject theology, which is essentially dependent on faith and is not concerned with reason. But it does free philosophy, since philosophy is dependent on reason and since faith is largely irrelevant to the interests and methods of philosophy. Thus, Ockham would separate faith from reason, that is, theology from philosophy (which included what we would presently call science, according to Ockham's thought-system). By implication, therefore, Ockham held that there are two roads to truth, and that science can travel only one of them.

Of the several aspects of Ockham's philosophy that have stood the test of time, one is particularly valuable to science. It is known as *Ockham's razor,* because he used it to cut away verbosity in the realm of ideas. Stated concisely, this rule says: **Do not invoke unnecessary explanations for a given phenomenon.** Thus, Ockham would trim away, with his "razor," an entire realm of such unobservable universals as "spirits" and "ideals" in explanation of natural phenomena.

It would be difficult to overestimate the value of Ockham's thought to the development of science or, for that matter, to the whole of philosophy. He laid the groundwork for a naturalistic, as opposed to a supernatural, foundation for science, and what we have called the first principle of science might well be termed Ockham's principle. There was nothing completely new, of course, about Ockham's insistence that theological systems of thought are not adaptable to a fruitful study of nature; essentially the same point had been made by certain of the pre-Socratic Greeks. But it must be remembered that many centuries and a great deal of theological and philosophical confusion separated these Greeks and Ockham. He deserves great credit for his attempt to clarify this principle within the framework of a society that was dominated by Scholastic viewpoints. It took no little courage to challenge this thought-system. Indeed, had his contemporaries realized the full implications of his teachings, Ockham would undoubtedly have fared much worse than he did. As it was, he encountered serious difficulty throughout his career.

In summary, Western Europe began its cultural slumber long before the actual fall of the Roman Empire but became totally somnolent during the fifth century. Gradually, society stabilized around the Church; thus, attitudes became strongly oriented toward the pious life with an aim toward eternal salvation. By at least the 11th century, however, there was widespread dissatisfaction with the merely pious life. As a result, numbers of individuals sought to increase their knowledge of the present world. The medieval universities arose as one expression of this change in outlook, with Scholasticism as the central educational philosophy. Meanwhile, the Church began to search for a theological and philosophical base that would satisfy the quest for knowledge without sacrificing the traditional faith-system. In the 13th century, Thomas Aquinas effected a synthesis between faith and reason that eventually became the official posture of the Church. However, this synthesis was far from satisfactory to many churchmen of the time; they insisted that theology and philosophy must seek their different kinds of truth by separate means. Probably the most important of these churchmen was William of Ockham, whose influence during the early 14th century was such that he helped to pave the way for the development of modern science.

The Middle Ages, therefore, might be viewed as having three periods of development. From the 5th through the 10th centuries, society was culturally asleep. It underwent a kind of sleepwalking stage (Scholasticism) during the 11th and 12th centuries. Then during the 13th and 14th centuries, medieval society began to awaken. Of course, this analogy is an oversimplification; some ten centuries of Western civilization can hardly be described accurately by a brief summarization. But for our purposes, it seems fair to say that modern scientific attitudes did not develop until well after the Middle Ages—that is, until the Renaissance. We have merely attempted to provide some background for understanding how that development occurred.

QUESTIONS FOR REVIEW AND DISCUSSION

1.   There was almost no truly scientific activity in Western Europe during the Middle Ages. How do you account for this deficiency?

2.   What was Scholasticism? Do you think that Scholastic attitudes are completely dead in modern colleges and universities?

3.   Contrast the medieval university with the modern university in terms of intellectual outlook.

4.   What was Thomas Aquinas' major contribution to Western thought? How did this contribution affect the development of science in Western Europe?

5.   What was William of Ockham's major contribution to Western thought and how did it affect the development of science in Western Europe?

6.   What distinguishes the Dark Ages from the Later Middle Ages? How might we subdivide this latter period from a cultural perspective?

REFERENCES

Copleston, F. *Medieval Philosophy.* New York: Harper and Row, 1952. A comprehensive treatment of medieval philosophy by an outstanding student of the period.

Gilson, E. *The Spirit of Medieval Philosophy.* New York: Charles Scribner's Sons, 1936. An excellent introduction to medieval philosophy.

Jones, W. T. *A History of Western Philosophy: The Medieval Mind* (2nd ed.). New York: Harcourt, Brace and World, Inc., 1969. The second volume of the four-volume work described at the end of Chapter 1.

Strayer, J. and D. Munro. *The Middle Ages: 395–1500* (5th ed.). New York: Appleton-Century-Crofts, 1970. A comprehensive history of the medieval period.

THREE

The Great Awakening

The gestation period of an intellectual movement, like that of a complex animal, may take a long time. Men such as Roger Bacon and William of Ockham were distant forerunners of modern scientific thought. Their voices were not heard by their contemporaries who remained in the wilderness of Scholasticism, restricted by the traditional medieval attitudes. Even Bacon and Ockham—although they provided valuable insights—were in many ways typical of this era. Society would have to change considerably before modern science could evolve.

As we have seen, all aspects of medieval society revolved around religion. In medieval science—such as it was—the universe was considered to be a vast memorial to the glory of God, and any pursuit of empirical knowledge was generally conducted in something of a worshipful attitude. Thus, medieval science either dealt with practical matters, such as agriculture and mechanics; or it was mystical and teleological. Consequently, even when Aristotle was "Christianized," it was more for the sake of his teleology than for the sake of his science.

Although it is difficult to identify an exact end to the Middle Ages and a beginning of the Renaissance, it seems fair to say that the one ended and the other began when this whole attitude was changed on a wide scale. The process actually was set in motion when Thomas Aquinas made the study of Aristotle and other classical figures respectable. Their outlook had been secular, and so it was inevitable that secularism would make serious inroads into the medieval religious viewpoint. In fact, the history of culture (including science) since Thomas Aquinas shows a steady trend toward secularization, with the result that the modern mind has returned to the secular viewpoint of the Greeks and now shares little of the essentially religious viewpoint of medieval times. It was the conflict between these two viewpoints that caused the stresses of the late medieval period (the 13th and 14th centuries). This conflict also extended into the Renaissance (the 15th and 16th centuries). It was in the wake of this conflict that modern science was born.

3.1　THE RENAISSANCE

The word "renaissance" means "revival." Essentially, it was a time when widespread interest was manifested in the literature, the art, and the science of the classical world. Thus, the attitudes were backward-looking, but the emphasis was mainly secular rather than religious. Insofar as science is concerned, we must emphasize that it was not the *cause* of the Renaissance; science developed merely as one aspect of a general cultural phenomenon. If one searches for underlying causes, one must consider a number of factors: the widespread dissatisfaction with the totally religious outlook; renewed communication with other cultures through an increase in trade; an increasing interest in travel; the invention of printing in the 15th century; a widespread emphasis upon education, which—inadequate though the system was—went a long way toward emancipating minds. These and numerous other factors ushered in the Renaissance.

The first significant indications of a general cultural awakening occurred in Italy during the 14th and 15th centuries when a number of writers and artists adopted the secular viewpoint in creative works. Foremost among these pioneers were Petrarch, Boccaccio and, somewhat later, Leonardo da Vinci and Michelangelo. Each of these men was an enthusiastic student of the ancient Greek culture, and each worked tirelessly to uncover hidden treasures of the past. A very important factor in the Italian Renaissance was the fortunate political situation that existed in certain areas of that region during the 14th and 15th centuries. The Italian peninsula was divided into a number of city-states, similar to those in ancient Greece. Some of them (for example, Florence, Milan, and Venice) were ruled during part of this time by families who encouraged liberal education. Furthermore, these families supported the work of artists and writers with grants of money. Gradually, the joy of discovery and the spirit of creative endeavor became so much a way of life to those engaged in artistic and literary pursuits that this attitude spread eventually to all areas of learning. Thus, it is no mere accident of history that the scientific tradition traces its rebirth not to the medieval artisans and alchemists, who shared the materials but not the attitudes of science, but rather to the men who brought about the Italian Renaissance in art and literature.[1] Truly creative work in any area demands, among other ingredients, an attitude that we have called *impartial inquiry*. This attitude was not characteristic of the medieval technologists. It became, however, the first principle of the Renaissance artists and writers and, later on, of the Renaissance scientists.

However, it is very easy to oversimplify the Renaissance; it should not be thought that all developments were "good" as contrasted with the "bad" attitudes of the preceding Middle Ages. Let us remember that the prevailing philosophy was still backward-looking; and in some ways, Renaissance art, literature, and even science were less creative than their medieval counterparts. The Renaissance, like the 13th and 14th centuries, was a time of great stress and no small amount of confusion. If it was an age of discovery and emancipation, it was nevertheless an age that saw a considerable amount of dogmatism and authoritarianism. But it does seem fair to say that enough secularization and impartial inquiry—barely enough—came about during this period to give birth to modern science.

While rulers of the Italian city-states encouraged a rebirth of impartial inquiry in the arts and the humanities, life came back to the natural sciences much more slowly. The medieval conception of nature was a formidable barrier to overcome, probably accounting therefore for the relative lateness of any significant scientific work. Although a renaissance in the arts was a heroic achievement, it actually did not involve the difficulties that existed with the natural sciences. Artistic and literary expressions were at least existent during the Middle Ages; the same can hardly be said for science. In retrospect, it seems evident that medieval attitudes toward nature were more difficult to overcome than those held in art and literature.

Nevertheless, accomplishments in the arts led inevitably to a renewed interest in the human body as a subject. There is no doubt that the late Renaissance anatomists such as Andreas Vesalius (1514–1564) became interested in their subject through the work of such artists as Leonardo da Vinci (1452–1519). This purely descriptive work in anatomy led ultimately to experimental research, such as that of William Harvey (1578–1657) on the circulation of blood. Eventually, therefore, great conceptual schemes were made possible in biology.

As travel and exploration brought new plants, animals, and other natural objects to the attention of Western Europeans, a renewed interest in nature developed. Due to wholesale neglect, even the natural history of Europe itself was ripe for study, but by the year 1600 a considerable amount of purely descriptive work had been accomplished. Furthermore, the invention of several instruments (for example, the telescope and the compound microscope) enabled students of nature to focus their attention upon new worlds, so to speak. The invention of printing about 1454 greatly facilitated the spread of information. Subsequently, the development of engravings and woodcuts allowed the printing of illustrations, which then stimulated the study of natural history and undoubtedly played a major role in shaping new attitudes toward nature.

But as important as descriptive natural history and technology are to science, they do not constitute its essence. Remember the second principle of science: **The goal of science is to develop comprehensive conceptual schemes that are potentially capable of giving rise to theories that can be tested.** Accordingly, the birth of modern science can properly be said to have occurred when, and only when, observation and experimentation were sufficiently practiced that conceptual schemes of far-reaching importance began to emerge.

3.2 THE SCIENTIFIC REVOLUTION

Science as we know it had a fairly definite beginning in a burst of activity that occurred during the late 16th and early 17th centuries. At that time, it was generally known in the intellectual community as *experimental philosophy*. J. B. Conant, a 20th-century scientist and educator, maintains that this burst of activity, which ushered in the modern scientific age, was the result of three streams of thought and action: *speculative thinking, deductive reasoning,* and *"cut-and-try"* experimentation.[2] He traces the first two of these streams of thought back to the medieval scholars, and the third to the medieval artisans and technicians. Thus, according to his view, it was the amalgamation of these three streams, occurring as it did in the wake of Renaissance attitudes toward learning, that started the scientific revolution. Let us examine each within a scientific framework of thought by considering the development of astronomy, which played a major role in ushering in the scientific age.

3.2A The Birth of Modern Science: Copernicus to Galileo

During the second century A.D., Claudius Ptolemy, an Alexandrian mathematician and astronomer, set forth a model of the universe. It was based upon the assumption that the earth is stationary and that all planetary motion relates to the earth as a fixed point. On the basis of this assumption, Ptolemy performed some excellent work regarding relative distances between observable bodies in the universe. In this respect, his map of the heavens is reasonably accurate even by modern standards. Although his geocentric model was based to some extent upon observations and measurements made by other individuals, his role in its development was such that it has been called the *Ptolemaic* system ever since his time. By the later Middle Ages, this system had acquired the dogmatic stamp of approval so characteristic of medieval society, and it was widely regarded as the absolute and final truth about the universe. Two reasons for this attitude seem evident. In the first place, it was consistent with common-sense observations; and as a conceptual scheme, it worked. In the second place, it conformed to the theological notion that God must surely have placed man at the center of His creation; and even in the Bible there was proof of a geocentric universe—otherwise, why would Joshua have commanded the sun to stand still (Joshua 10:13)?

It was within this framework of thought that Nicolaus Copernicus (1473–1543), a Polish astronomer, offered an alternative conceptual scheme, one in which the sun became the center of the universe. However, Copernicus offered his theory very tentatively, for understandable reasons. In fact, his theory was not published until the year of his death, following decades of careful observation and measurement on his part. By the time all the implications of his scheme were realized, Copernicus was safely dead. Using the Copernican model as a starting point, later astronomers carefully refined its details, developed a host of theories from the parent conceptual scheme, and consistently ran into trouble with the Church. Notable among these successors of Copernicus were Tycho Brahe (1546–1601), Johannes Kepler (1571–1630), Galileo Galilei (1564–1642), and Isaac Newton (1642–1727).

What led Copernicus to challenge the Ptolemaic system? Certainly, he was no revolutionary. He dedicated the book setting forth his conceptual scheme to Pope Paul III; and from the very first, he sought to avoid any conflict with the church. Had he proved the Ptolemaic model wrong? No. It was more satisfactory in some respects (say, to common-sense experience) than his own model. Most of the objections of Copernicus to the Ptolemaic system came from his detailed observations and are rather technical, but they can be summarized as follows. Certain predictions based on the assumption of a geocentric universe were not borne out by observation; and the longer one worked with the Ptolemaic model mathematically, the more one was obliged to disregard certain observable phenomena. Copernicus was not able to explain all the apparent inconsistencies in his alternate model, since it lacked many refinements; essentially, it was the Ptolemaic system with the earth and the sun merely reversed in position. It seemed to him, however, that a heliocentric universe presented fewer difficulties than a geocentric one.

It is very important that we note the strategy of Copernicus. *He proceeded mostly on intuition;* that is, he applied what Conant has termed *speculative thinking.* Furthermore, he declined to meet Ptolemaic dogmatism with Copernican dogmatism; he merely said, in effect, "I would like to offer an alternative system for consideration." This attitude, plus the fact that he was a loyal and exceedingly prudent canon of the Church, is probably what saved his conceptual scheme from utter disgrace. As a matter of fact, the strongest immediate opposition to his model came not from Roman Catholic quarters but from the Lutherans and Calvinists.* It was not until 1616, by which time the theological implications had become more fully apparent, that his book was placed on the Papal Index of Forbidden Books, remaining there until 1835. In any case, it should be noted that great conceptual schemes are often constructed in just this tentative fashion. Thus, science does not differ essentially from any other type of creative endeavor. Intuition and speculative thought are just as important to the scientist as they are to the artist.

Suppose Copernicus had been wrong in his conjecture that the universe is sun-centered, not earth-centered? It still would have been a valuable conceptual scheme because it stimulated a vast amount of research and caused men to reexamine their basic assumptions and mathematical formulas in order to see if they were actually valid. At the risk of citing a fundamental aspect of science to the point of tiresomeness, let us note once

---

* This point is worthy of consideration for those who seek to establish a causal relationship between the rise of Protestantism and the rise of modern science. If anything, early Protestants were more dogmatic than Roman Catholics of the same period, especially since Protestantism emphasized the authority of the Bible to a greater extent, or at least in a different manner, than did the Roman Catholic Church.

more that **whether a conceptual scheme is "true" or "false" is not the crucial point—its value to science is measured by the degree to which it stimulates further scientific activity.**

A succession of astronomers elaborated upon the conceptual scheme of Copernicus after his death. Galileo, in particular, worked from the theoretical mathematics of Copernicus, Brahe, and Kepler to formulate highly valuable scientific theories. Since we are interested at this point in clarifying what is meant by deductive reasoning and cut-and-try experimentation (Conant's second and third points, mentioned previously), we shall examine one small part of Galileo's work. But first, let us explain what is meant by deductive reasoning and cut-and-try experimentation.

Deduction is a thought-process that starts with a certain generalization —that is, a hypothesis, theory, or law—and states what that generalization has to say about any particular future event. It is sometimes called "if . . . then" reasoning. Cut-and-try experimentation is virtually self-explanatory; the expression simply means the establishment of such conditions that will either validate or invalidate the generalization or, in the absence of any theoretical component, will reveal what will happen under any particular set of conditions.

One implication of Galileo's total thought-system as he developed it mathematically from the Copernican conceptual scheme was a theory of motion concerning two free-falling bodies. If both are dropped simultaneously from a certain height, both will strike the ground at precisely the same moment regardless of any differences in weight. This theory directly contradicted Aristotelian physics. Aristotle had taught that the rate of fall is directly proportional to the weight of an object. Galileo's thought-process in this instance could have run as follows: "If my theory of motion is correct, then a cannonball weighing 100 pounds and a musket ball weighing four ounces, if dropped simultaneously from a great height, should strike the ground simultaneously. If Aristotle's theory of motion is correct, then the cannonball should strike the ground far ahead of the bullet. It should be a simple matter to test this theory. I shall simply obtain the two weights, find a suitable location, procure the assistance of an observer, and perform the experiment." Although there is no evidence that Galileo performed this experiment at the leaning tower of Pisa, as tradition has it, there is abundant testimony in his writings that he did carry it out at some location and satisfied himself that his theory was right; Aristotle's was wrong.

There are several implications to this work that are worthy of note at this point:

1. Galileo built his work upon that of his immediate predecessors in the new "experimental philosophy," thus taking advantage of accumulated knowledge. He did not regard these predecessors as authority figures whose statements were above question;

rather, he checked out their work carefully by every means available to him before proceeding with his own work. In this way his inquiry was impartial.

2. He took advantage of technological developments in his pursuit of scientific problems. Chief among these developments was the invention of the telescope about 1608. Galileo first trained his telescope upon the heavens in 1610. With the aid of this new instrument, he was able to carry out to great lengths procedures of verification and prediction in astronomy. Technology as such is not science (in terms of Conant's three essential ingredients, can you explain why it is not?), but it is an indispensable aid to science.

3. He successfully bridged the gap between theoretical mathematics and empirical procedure—that is, observation and experimentation. In this respect, he stands as the great pioneer of quantitative methodology in science. It is no marvel, therefore, that he defined the goal of science as being "to measure what can be measured and to make measurable what cannot [presently] be measured."

4. He successfully challenged Aristotelian physics and thus defied centuries of tradition. Although we have not traced the main stream of Galileo's work, it eventually brought him into conflict with authorities of the Church, and he was forced to deny the validity of his work in physics and astronomy. However, from the purely historical viewpoint, the storm of controversy that spanned nearly a century from Copernicus to Galileo provided something of a definitional basis for such clashes as might occur in the future between science and theology. It was dogmatism versus impartial inquiry; more than any other single development in science to that point, the stir that arose over the Copernican hypothesis (including Galileo's work) clarified the battle lines.

5. Finally, Galileo carried out fully and brilliantly the three activities that we have emphasized as being essential to scientific procedure: speculative thinking, deductive reasoning, and cut-and-try experimentation. He followed this procedure so effectively and so fruitfully that many historians regard him as the father of modern science.

3.2B The Advent of Biological Science

In general, biological science lagged somewhat behind physical science during the Renaissance and post-Renaissance period. Apparently, one outstanding reason for this slow development was that a great deal of observational work had to be done in biology before it could become truly scientific We do not minimize the importance of this descriptive work, of course; we called attention earlier to the valuable research in anatomy that was accomplished during the early 16th century by Andreas Vesalius, and the invention of the microscope late in the same century led to a spectacular burst of activity in the 17th century.

One of the earliest achievements of experimental biology was the clarification of the circulation of human blood by William Harvey, whose book on the subject was published in 1628. Harvey was an English physician who had taken his medical degree at the University of Padua, in northern Italy. Despite the fact that Padua was traditionally a stronghold of Aristotelianism, it had also been a leading center of impartial inquiry during the 16th century. Not only were Vesalius and (much later) Galileo members of the faculty at Padua, but a host of independent-minded researchers between the times of these two giants had contributed significantly to the development of a scientific revolution. Herbert Butterfield, in his classic *The Origins of Modern Science,* maintains that the greatness of Padua as a research center lay in the fact that its crowning glory was its medical school, which emphasized the "secular" as opposed to the "Christianized" Aristotle.[3] In any event, Harvey, as a student, was privileged to participate in a great tradition that was just developing into the modern scientific revolution.

The study of anatomy and physiology—such as it was—during the late 16th and early 17th centuries was based on the Galenic idea that blood does not actually circulate but rather ebbs and flows along the blood vessels. Galen also had suggested that food is converted to blood in the liver and that this blood is carried outward to nourish the body. Vesalius and several of his successors had pondered the difficulties of this theory; and by the time of Harvey, it was widely suspected that Galen had been wrong. Although Harvey's predecessors certainly did him great service by recognizing many of the difficulties in Galen's theories, it was Harvey who performed the brilliant experiments that largely cleared up the mystery.

Harvey seems to have been set to thinking on the problem by considering the valves of the veins. These valves had been described by an earlier Paduan anatomist, who missed their significance. Harvey saw very quickly, once he was able to free himself of the Galenic viewpoint, that blood could not flow through the veins *away* from the heart, because the valves all turned *toward* the heart. At the same time, he considered the problem of the pulmonary (lung) circulation and other related difficulties. Finally, he measured (note that he resorted to experimentation) the quantity of blood expelled from the heart at a single beat; and by calculation, he saw immediately that the quantity of blood involved was simply impossible to account for by the Galenic theory. Apparently by a process of elimination, Harvey concluded that only one conceptual scheme could possibly account for the data: The blood must circulate continuously throughout the body.

Let us note that Harvey's work contains, at one point or another, all the ingredients of scientific procedure that we have identified: speculative thinking, deductive reasoning, and cut-and-try experimentation. Although his work is not the first example of biological experimentation in the modern period, it may fairly be said that Harvey ushered in a new way of proceeding in the pursuit of biological problems. He, therefore, is often called the father of experimental biology.

Despite the great value of Harvey's discovery and, perhaps more significantly, the implications of his work for biology, Harvey is almost an isolated case for his time. On the whole, it was to be many decades before experimentation based on deductive reasoning made a place for itself in biology. In contrast, it was firmly established in the physical sciences well before the time of Harvey.

There is at least one major reason why biological experimentation lagged: the inherent difficulty of working experimentally with living organisms. As is well known now, but was not fully appreciated until fairly recent times, even the simplest living system is far more complex than anything found in the nonliving world. As a result, the experimenter is faced with numerous *variables* that may be extremely difficult, if not impossible, to control. For this reason, biology depends heavily upon the *controlled experiment,* wherein an effort is made to keep every variable constant except the one under immediate consideration.[4] Thus, the controlled experiment is a procedure that is aimed at the elimination of all variables except one. It is accomplished by performing two (or more, as the case demands) experiments under identical conditions in every respect except for a single variable, in order that any observed differences may be attributed to the particular variable selected for testing. Because experimental work in biology is so frequently plagued by variables, due to the complexities of living systems, the controlled experiment is essentially a way of life for those who test conceptual schemes in biology. In contrast, physical science is not nearly so dependent upon this method of experimentation.

About the middle of the 17th century, when physical science was making tremendous gains, a cultural phenomenon of far-reaching importance occurred in Italy. This development was the establishment of a scientific society, the Accademia del Cimento, which was founded in Florence mainly to carry on the work of Galileo and his pupils. However, one of its members became interested in problems other than those concerned with physical science. This person was Francesco Redi (1626?–1698?). A poet and physician, Redi was somehow led to consider the problem of spontaneous generation. According to the Aristotelian concept of nature (based on the principle of development, or "becoming"), organisms arise spontaneously from animal carcasses and slime. This was a popular notion even in the 17th century; it even was confirmed by common-sense observation. Just how Redi came to formulate the conceptual scheme that life comes only from life is not entirely clear. As in the case of Copernicus, the alternate and accepted conceptual scheme did not agree with his intuition, so he proposed a new explanation: The carcasses, slime, or other decaying matter serve only as a medium wherein certain organisms grow; and these organisms "are all generated by insemination," as he put it.

In order to test this conceptual scheme, Redi developed an amazingly simple, yet singularly effective, experiment, which he carried out in the year 1668. Previous observation had convinced him that the maggots found in putrefying matter were the offspring of flies, which seemed always to be present and depositing eggs. When he devised his experiment, therefore, his deductive reasoning went something like this: "If the maggots originate from the eggs of flies, then meat kept from contact with flies should fail to produce maggots. By the same token (as I already know quite well), meat exposed to flies will develop maggots." Accordingly, Redi selected eight identical jars. He placed a dead snake in each of the first two, some fish in the second two, some eels in the third pair, and a slice of veal in each of the fourth pair. He covered one jar of each pair with a loose-meshed paper, and he left one jar of each pair open. It was mid-July, and the activity of flies was evident. Before very long, maggots appeared in all four of the control jars; but even after many weeks, none had appeared in the experimental jars. Redi did observe that flies were attracted to the paper covers and occasionally deposited eggs upon them. Not content with this initial experiment, he repeated it many times with a variety of materials and under a variety of conditions. He even included dead flies in one set of experimental jars. But in no single instance did he ever procure maggots unless living flies were allowed to come into contact with the meat.

The far-reaching importance of Redi's conceptual scheme will become apparent as we pursue the topic of *biogenesis* (the concept that life comes only from life) in the next chapter. But for the time being, let us note the singular beauty of his experiment. Not only is it a classic example of variable control; of equal importance is the fact that he varied his conditions and verified his results until he felt that he could do no more to confirm the validity of his conceptual scheme. But did he *prove* that life comes only from life? No. Great conceptual schemes, as we have noted, are not "proven" by a single experimental approach. As a matter of fact, only the most simple verbalisms are subject to ultimate and final proof in science, and the terms "prove" and "proof" are used very hesitantly by scientists. Actually, as we shall see, the whole question of spontaneous generation was reopened at a different level shortly after Redi's death in

1698. Despite the several grave theological implications of his conceptual scheme, however, the validity of biogenesis for the world of organisms that are visible to the unaided eye was never subjected to serious question after 1668. Certainly, there was still room for argument. Nevertheless, the elegance of Redi's experiments and the completeness of his entire course of action were sufficient to persuade at least the intellectual community that spontaneous generation of such organisms as flies does not occur. If there was a single effective counterargument against Redi during the 17th century, history does not record it.

Redi's work would have been meaningless without controls. Their essentiality to his experiments is so obvious that we are inclined to wonder why he is paid honor for including them. But experimental methodology was not clear during the 17th century. Scholastic thought-patterns still dominated science as a whole, and even most of those scholars who possessed a scientific curiosity preferred speculation to experimentation. In contrast, such men as Galileo, Harvey, and Redi were a new breed. Because of their influence, it would be difficult to overemphasize the importance of the 17th century to the history of science. It was the century of experimentation, and these men were foremost among those who set the pace for succeeding generations.

3.3 THE QUEST FOR CERTAINTY

"No one," wrote Immanuel Kant in 1781, "will attempt to construct a science, unless he has some idea to rest on as a proper basis. . . . it will often be found that the originator of a science and even his latest successors remain attached to an erroneous idea, which they cannot render clear to themselves, and that they thus fail in determining the true content, the articulation or systematic unity, and the limits of their science." [5]

In the course of its development following the Middle Ages, science necessarily became subjected to the evaluation and criticism of philosophy. As a matter of fact, the interaction between philosophy and science (defining both in modern terms) during this formative period was mutually constructive. We have already seen that Thomas Aquinas and William of Ockham, who were philosophers, had an important influence upon the development of science. It was inevitable, of course, that philosophy would become profoundly affected by the new way of acquiring knowledge.

It would take us entirely too far from our subject to attempt even a summary review of the history of Renaissance and post-Renaissance philosophy. Nevertheless, the foundations of modern science were built to a great extent upon philosophical concepts that emerged during this era, and some of these concepts are essential to our framework of thought. At this point, let us approach the subject of scientific philosophy by a somewhat indirect route.

It would appear that one of mankind's neverending quests is for some kind of certainty, or absolute reliability. You will recall that, in this search, the Greek philosophers of antiquity asked the question, "What is real?" For the pre-Socratic "scientists," a materialistic view of nature provided them with their answer. For Plato, ultimate reality resided in "forms." To Aristotle, the actuality of objects constituted their reality. It may be argued that these philosophers did not always equate reality with certainty, but there is good reason to believe that an underlying urge to identify certainty led them to formulate the questions that they asked. In the Middle Ages, the quest for certainty centered around the Church and its teachings; most people were content with the assurance of eternal salvation. The widespread contentment generated by this assurance began to deteriorate in the later Middle Ages as men sought enlightenment in the secular realm. But as they turned to human reason for their certainty, it soon became evident that one man's thought-processes differed from another's. It began to appear that no certainty could be found in the area of reason. Then, when the intellectual world was beginning to wonder what area of human thought *could* be trusted, the scientific revolution burst upon the scene.

With the advent of science and scientific methodology, it seemed to many people that mankind had finally come to an area where certainty was available. The Renaissance and post-Renaissance period was a time when the quest for certainty reached almost fever-pitch, because the old verities had been largely swept away and nothing new had appeared to replace them. Therefore, it is not surprising that the most influential philosophers of that period became preoccupied with scientific methodology as a means for attaining certainty in the empirical realm. For our purposes, we shall examine the views of two 17th-century philosophers, Francis Bacon and René Descartes, and an 18th-century figure, Immanuel Kant.

3.3A The Methods of Science: Francis Bacon

By the end of the 16th century, it was apparent to thoughtful scholars that the new "experimental philosophy" was exerting a profound effect upon the thought of Western Europe. Scholastic and Renaissance attitudes of devotion to the past were being challenged, and the developing scientific revolution was a major factor in the changes that were occurring. It was in this intellectual climate that Francis Bacon (1561–1626), English statesman and philosopher, made his impact upon scientific thought.[6]

Impatient with both the science and the philosophy of his day, Bacon sought to cut the last ties with scholastic modes of thought, and he succeeded remarkably well. Feeling that science needed a unique and distinctive method for pursuing knowledge, he aimed to provide such a method. Bacon accepted observation and experimentation as the proper channels for accomplishing scientific work, but it appeared to him that most of those thinkers who studied nature did not go about their tasks in an orderly fashion. He advocated, instead, that the *inductive method* be used as the key to empirical knowledge.

Induction is defined as a process of reasoning whereby generalizations are derived from particular instances of various phenomena. For example, if one were totally unfamiliar with birds and proceeded to examine as many different specimens as he could find, one would eventually come to say, "All birds have feathers." Notice the process of going from particular events to a generalization—that is, a theory, principle, or law. Having formulated his generalization, one may then proceed with the companion process of deduction, by means of which the generalization, in conjunction with other relevant data, may be used to explain certain present events or to predict the occurrence of certain future events. Thus, if one sees a bird flying at a distance, he is willing to hazard the prediction that, if caught, the creature would be seen to have feathers. Neither induction nor deduction is infallible, of course. The entire process is something like trying to learn the wagering rules (induction) and then using them to place a bet (deduction). The more often one wins his bet, the more scientific is his entire operation.

Without question, Bacon provided science with tremendous insight through his elaboration of induction. But he failed to emphasize the role of deduction as well, particularly in deriving testable consequences from hypotheses. Furthermore, he did not seem to sense clearly the overall strategy of science; that is, he possessed no adequate concept of the means by which hypotheses (tentative explanations) are formulated. To Bacon, one merely began collecting particular facts; and, in time, an adequate hypothesis would automatically come into being. Apparently, he was unaware that in most cases of scientific investigation, a hypothesis precedes the gathering of factual knowledge, not the other way around. In short, Bacon was not a "working" scientist and really indulged only in some sophisticated puttering. His writings indicate that he would not have known how to proceed with such experimentation as that we have described earlier in connection with Galileo, Harvey, and Redi. Nevertheless, his detachment from actual scientific work gave him an objective advantage, and his contribution to the formulation of a fruitful methodology for science was considerable.

It would be unfair to Bacon's viewpoint to imply that he was obsessed with the quest for certainty. Actually, his overall goal was a "total reconstruction of the sciences, arts and all human knowledge," as he put it. Nevertheless, even his statement of such an ambitious undertaking (at which he was markedly unsuccessful) betrays his anxiety over the state of uncertainty that existed in the intellectual world of his time. In any event, he was a part of an intellectual community that was deeply concerned with the problem of making science and philosophy consistent with each other. In this regard, he achieved considerable success through his contributions to a meaningful scientific methodology.

3.3B Science and Mechanism: René Descartes

Like Francis Bacon, the French mathematician and philosopher René Descartes (1596–1650) felt that science needed a more clear-cut method for pursuing its objectives.[7] Also like Bacon, he was not primarily a practicing scientist (although he worked in optics and mathematics to some extent). His writings show some of the same artificiality and lack of feeling for the strategy of science that characterized Bacon. Nevertheless, Descartes profoundly influenced the subsequent development of science through his revolutionary influence upon philosophy. Breaking with the past entirely, he aimed to separate philosophy from theology and to give it a valid method. In addition, he was intent upon discovering some method whereby indubitable knowledge could be gained empirically. The quest for certainty, therefore, was very real for him.

Descartes was impressed by the success of mathematics and science in the pursuit of empirical knowledge, and he hoped to provide philosophy with something like the certainty of mathematics. In pursuit of this goal, he founded a totally new school of philosophical thought called *rationalism,** which contrasted so sharply with predominating attitudes up to his time that Descartes is often called the father of modern philosophy.

Although impressed by the development of the new methodology in science, Descartes also recognized some of the philosophical problems

---

* The term "rationalism" had been used before Descartes' time to describe the concept that man possesses the capacity to grasp certain eternal truths without resorting to sense experience, as in Plato's thought-system. Paradoxically, it came to mean almost the opposite; namely, that man can arrive at a true knowledge of the universe through observation, experimentation, and reasoning *without* the assistance of divinely revealed truths or "ideals." As Descartes and his followers used the expression, rationalism describes a particular method of pursuing knowledge, that of employing deductive reasoning based upon presumably self-evident principles. Mathematics, for example, is almost purely rationalistic in this sense, and it is for this reason that Descartes and his school of thought emphasized mathematics as a model of how to proceed in gaining knowledge.

raised by this development. It had become apparent to both scientists and philosophers that a mechanical view of the universe swept away the traditional ways of thinking about God. In fact, a contemporary of Descartes, Thomas Hobbes (1588–1679), had already pointed out that this "new" way of looking at science logically swept away everything except matter and its behavior according to mechanical laws—the concept of a God who is active in the affairs of men, the notion of values—everything except matter and motion. Consistent with this, Hobbes was a thoroughgoing mechanist who held that there is no reality other than physical reality. The major problem of Hobbes's contemporaries, including Descartes, was that they felt driven to accept the scientific way of looking at the world, but they shrank from accepting its implications for the nature of man and the concept of God. In other words, medieval philosophy had emphasized metaphysical reality to the absolute exclusion of scientific reality. Hobbes reversed this idea completely in his system by emphasizing scientific reality to the absolute exclusion of metaphysical reality. It was Descartes who proposed a solution to the resulting dilemma. The fact that his system is loaded with difficulties need not detain us just now; the important thing to note is that it wrought a major change in philosophy and it profoundly influenced the further development of science.

To review the whole of Descartes' philosophy (called *Cartesianism,* because he used the name Cartesius in his Latin writings) would be largely fruitless within our present context. Essentially, it was the proposal that there are two kinds of substance in the universe: mind (including the mind of God) and matter. Each type of substance occupies its own sphere of activity. Thus, the physical universe is to be studied according to mechanistic principles, and the scientist is free to *act as if* there is no other reality. Science and theology are not in conflict, because each operates within its own sphere. This complete separation of mind and matter, together with its implications and difficulties, is known as *Cartesian dualism.*

Once he had effected (to his satisfaction and to that of many of his contemporaries) a compromise between science and theology, Descartes proposed a thoroughly mechanistic view of the universe and even of man, excluding his soul and mind. Let us be careful to note that Descartes did not *invent* the mechanistic viewpoint. This concept goes back to the pre-Socratic Greeks, and then Hobbes developed it to a fine point. Perhaps it is fair to say that Descartes popularized the concept and gave it respectability in the eyes of his contemporaries. At any rate, he reduced every organized natural system, including living forms and the human body itself, to the level of a machine. He concluded that only if the scientist regards an organism as a machine, finally explicable by physical concepts, can it be studied with profit. Impressed by the precision of mathematics, Descartes recommended the extension of its methods of analysis to the entire natural world. Just as the number 125 is the sum of 25 fives or 125 ones, so the whole of an organism can be regarded merely as the sum of its parts. Called *reductionism,* this viewpoint had and continues to have extremely important ramifications especially for biological science. It was part of a thoroughly mechanistic view of life and the universe that was made popular by Descartes and the 17th-century rationalistic school of philosophy.

Another point of Cartesian philosophy that has had profound implications for science is the rejection of teleology in the realm of physical reality. This attitude constituted a sharp break with Aristotelian thought. Consistent with the whole of Descartes' outlook, it was a major challenge to Scholasticism. Although Descartes believed in God, he maintained that it is useless to seek a purpose for the physical universe or anything in it, since the mind of God is unsearchable. Thus, Descartes extended Ockham's dualistic approach to knowledge into the realm of purpose, where he completely ruled out any possibility for dealing profitably with teleological concepts in the world of empirical knowledge. In fact, he doubted the value of doing so even in metaphysical thought. The practice of explaining objects, organisms, or physical phenomena by their results, so common in Scholastic thought, was held by Descartes to be totally worthless, and indeed harmful, as a method in science.

Thus, Descartes led the final major attack on Scholasticism. As a result, both science and philosophy effectively parted company with Scholasticism during the 17th century, even though Scholasticism did linger in some of the European universities for a long time.

Despite its effectiveness in helping to discredit Scholasticism and in clarifying some of the major problems faced by science and philosophy, Cartesianism is subject to numerous criticisms. Perhaps the most serious for biology is the problem of interaction between mind and body. Obviously, there is interaction, but Descartes evaded this difficulty. Although a great many attempts have been made since his time to resolve this paradox, it remains the basic enigma for those thinkers who would embrace any form of Cartesian dualism. In fact, this problem has been deepened immeasurably by modern physiological and psychological research. Dualism was not a completely satisfactory compromise even in the 17th century; but it was widely accepted, because it appeared to be a lesser evil than its apparent alternatives, Aristotelian teleology and Hobbesian mechanism. For biological science, there are some further difficulties. The study of living systems cannot be accommodated fully by Cartesian reductionism, and some form of teleology is a necessary assumption at certain levels of biological study. (We shall further discuss these subjects in a later chapter.) Furthermore, if carried to its logical consequences, Cartesian dualism would render impossible any scientific investigation of human or animal minds.

Perhaps the most serious fallacy of Descartes' thought-system, at least as it affected his scientific philosophy, was his supposition that he had indeed found an answer to the quest for intellectual certainty. To the extent that scientists were influenced by Descartes, his faith in the rational-istic method gave them a false confidence that has lingered in science to the present day. To state the matter somewhat differently, scientific methodology has come to be so spectacularly successful in pursuing em-pirical knowledge that it is quite easy for the scientist to assume that he is dealing with certainty. This assumption has grave implications for both science and philosophy.

Nevertheless, Descartes was singularly effective in his contributions to scientific thought. His emphasis upon a mechanistic viewpoint helped to promote a workable methodology for science. His dualism was some-what accepted in theological circles, so that scientists became considerably less persecuted by religious bias and dogmatism. Since the Cartesian view so profoundly influenced both science and philosophy during the 17th and 18th centuries, any attempt to understand modern science must take it into account.

3.3C The Nature of Reality: Immanuel Kant

Through the latter half of the 17th and a large part of the 18th cen-tury, Western Europe was involved in a great turmoil in philosophy. The *rationalists,* following the lead of Descartes, sought indubitable knowledge (the quest for certainty) through deductive reasoning. The *empiricists,* who had reacted against the idea that indubitable knowledge is available through reasoning, held that sense perception was the sole source of reliable knowl-edge. The empiricists were not quite as concerned with the problem of certainty as were the rationalists, but they held that, to the extent that cer-tainty is available to the minds of men, it must come from the actual world of "things," not from the mental world of ideas. During this time, the scientists themselves continued to explore the world of nature, remaining generally oblivious to the arguments of the philosophers.[8]

During this period, the Scottish philosopher David Hume (1711–1776) attacked both the rationalist and the empiricist positions regarding reality. Reason, he declared, can only relate ideas; it cannot yield in-dubitable knowledge about anything, certainly not about the world of sense perception. On the other hand, he attacked both empiricism and science for assuming the validity of causal relationships between events, as well as for relying upon inductive inference. Essentially, then, Hume's philosophy denied the existence of scientific knowledge. Thus, since Hume's arguments were not challenged successfully during the mid-18th century, philosophy as a whole was reduced to a state of confusion wherein many philosophers doubted that stable knowledge of any kind could exist.

It was to this state of confusion that the German mathematician, physicist, and philosopher Immanuel Kant (1724–1804) addressed himself, and in doing so, he revolutionized philosophy perhaps even more thoroughly than Descartes had done in his day.[9] At a relatively advanced age (he was in his fifties), Kant came to realize that some kind of order had to be made out of the chaos that existed in philosophy following Hume's criticisms of rationalism, empiricism, and science. Furthermore, Kant feared that if science were not shown to have certain limitations, its continued successes within a mechanistic framework of thought would soon leave no place for values. His apprehension is reminiscent of the reaction by Socrates and his contemporaries to the materialism of the Greek "scientists" (see Chapter 1).

Kant conceded that Hume's criticism, especially of rationalism, had a great deal of validity. What disturbed Kant was that, logically, Hume's argument effectively destroyed both rationalistic methods and scientific methods as legitimate avenues for pursuing knowledge. It was Kant's aim, therefore, to find a satisfactory compromise that would give both philosophy and science a respectable base of operation. He proposed that it is fallacious to regard knowledge as an "either-or" issue—that is, that knowledge must derive either from the mind or from sense perception. According to Kant, it derives from both. Furthermore, Kant declared, both the rationalists and the empiricists had been wrong about the nature of sense perception. The common assumption seems to have been that a "real" object makes a certain definite impression on the mind and that, to the empiricist at least, this impression was "reality." Kant challenged this idea, and proposed that instead of the mind conforming to objects, objects conform to the operation of the mind. Thus, the mind is not so much blank paper that merely records experience as though it were a ledger sheet; it is a complex organ that "conditions" sensory data according to various rational categories. Hence, knowledge is an interaction of reason and experience.

It would remove us too far from our subject to explore the implications of Kant's theory of knowledge for rationalism, empiricism, and the whole of philosophy. What are its implications for science?

There is always a tendency in science to identify ultimate reality with sense experience. This viewpoint has its roots in Aristotle's thought-system. It is supremely ironic that in spite of the efforts made during the 17th and 18th centuries to reject Aristotelian thought, the science of Kant's time had fallen into the habit of assuming that it was dealing with ultimate reality. Not so, Kant declared. The world as it appears to us is not necessarily equivalent to reality. He distinguished between the world of ultimate reality (a kind of ideal state for any given object, which may be termed a "thing-in-itself" and which is totally unknowable) and the world of sense experience (which is *not* necessarily the ultimate reality, because our knowledge of any given object is conditioned by our minds).

To modernize this concept somewhat, let us consider a desk that happens to be sitting in a room. There is no way for us to determine what the desk "really" is—that is, the "desk-in-itself" as it exists apart from sense experience. And even at the perceptive level, reality is elusive. A seller of furniture gives his impression of its reality: "As you can all see, it is a piece of furniture with certain dimensions that can be expressed mathematically, and that is all one needs to say about it." A carpenter objects: "No, you are missing a great deal. This is an organized piece of oak, having a certain value on an accepted scale of hardness." Next, a botanist claims: "Both of you have missed the point. This desk is *really* a dead plant tissue called xylem, as you would see if you were to examine one of its splinters microscopically." An objection is forthcoming from a chemist: "Well, if you want to know what this desk *really* is, it is an aggregation of organic molecules." An engineer with some training in physics tries to settle the whole problem: "If you want to get down to ultimate reality, this desk is merely a vast collection of organized neutrons and protons." At this point, a theoretical physicist corrects him: "Do you really believe ultimate reality is simply a matter of neutrons and protons? We are not at all certain about this; and the search continues for the fundamental units of matter, if they indeed exist."

Perhaps this example is stretching Kant's intent to a degree, but it partially illustrates the problem with which he attempted to deal. It is never possible, he insisted, to arrive at ultimate reality, the thing-in-itself, because sense experiences are subjectively conditioned, and we cannot step outside our own minds. Now if this seems to be utter nonsense, it should be remembered that the science of Kant's time was generally confident that it was actually dealing with ultimate reality, and the whole trend was toward a dogmatism that threatened to choke off the hard-won spirit of impartial inquiry that had emerged from the Renaissance. Even today, scientists must occasionally remind themselves to be tolerant of each other's viewpoints or levels of interest.

There is another extension of Kantian philosophy that is extremely important, especially for biological science, and this is Kant's view of teleology, or purposiveness. He made it entirely clear that he did not hold with teleology as a world view. Although he attempted to justify belief in God on moral grounds, he demolished the teleological argument for the whole of metaphysics. Furthermore, he maintained that science must proceed on a mechanistic basis and that the scientist is obliged to "pursue natural mechanism, in respect to the explanation of natural products, so far as it can be done with probability." But there are levels of organization in the living world, Kant argued, the phenomena of which cannot be accounted for on purely mechanical grounds. Thus, breaking sharply with Descartes, he insisted that a whole is not always the mere sum of its parts. This view is the basis for recognition of a phenomenon called *emergence,* with which we shall deal at some length in a later chapter.

To summarize, the late 16th and early 17th centuries in Western Europe were characterized by a feverish quest for certainty. Many philosophers and scientists pursued this quest in the empirical world of sense experience, feeling that all knowledge came from scientific methodology. In one way or another, the thought-systems of Bacon, Hobbes, and Descartes contributed to this feeling. Science made spectacular gains during the 17th and 18th centuries; by the time of Kant, the scientific community generally assumed that it had discovered the key to indubitable knowledge. Both Hume and Kant, however, challenged this idea, and Kant developed an elaborate system of thought that has had a profound influence upon scientific philosophy. In fact, his influence has been so great in all of philosophy that in a real sense, philosophy since his time has been largely an attempt to deal with the ramifications of his thought.

In terms of the quest for certainty, Kant's thought-system went far toward dissolving the entire issue in the intellectual world. In effect, he maintained that certainty is not available to human minds; so the best that we can do is to proceed with that premise as a starting point. A host of philosophers since his time have enlarged this concept in a variety of directions. As a result, it may fairly be said that a modern scholar is one who has learned to live with uncertainty. This is especially true in science. In fact, we might formulate a third principle of science, as follows: **Science does not deal with certainties, but with probabilities.** We shall elaborate upon this principle later.

In the larger view, science has been relatively unaffected since the 17th century by philosophic thought. The average "working" scientist has usually been content to act as if the world of perceptual experience is ultimate reality, at least in an operational sense, because he can achieve his objectives entirely within that framework.[10] However, this attitude has serious implications even for science, and we shall return to this subject in a later chapter.

3.4 POST-RENAISSANCE BIOLOGY

Since the 17th century, two streams of thought have been evident in biology. One of these, which we might call *experimental biology,* is in the scientific tradition of Bacon, Descartes, Galileo, Harvey, and Redi. It has relied heavily upon speculative thinking, deductive reasoning, and cut-and-try experimentation as procedural activities. In the next section of this book, we trace this stream of thought by using a historical approach to the conceptual schemes of biogenesis, the cell theory, Mendelian genetics, and Darwinian evolution. It is enough to say at this point that experimental biology has taken its place alongside the physical sciences in the scientific revolution that began in the late Renaissance and post-Renaissance period. In this role, it has not only made its rightful impact in the realm of ideas; it has also contributed immeasurably to an improved standard of living among the civilized peoples of the world.

The second stream of biological thought is one that might be called *natural history*. It traces its origin in modern times to the Renaissance explorers and the Renaissance observers of animal and plant diversity. The pursuit of natural history has also contributed much to the realm of ideas and to the improvement of the quality of human life. Furthermore, it boasts an illustrious history of its own and continues to be a very active and important part of biology.

Since we have already exemplified the experimental approach to living systems, and since this is largely our emphasis throughout the next section of this book, let us concentrate momentarily on the tradition of natural history as it is exemplified by an outstanding, and relatively early, biologist. This person was Carolus Linnaeus (1707–1778), a Swedish botanist who probably did more to put natural history in a scientific framework than anyone else in the history of biology.

As long as relatively few species of organisms were known to man, it was not difficult for students of natural history to communicate with each other regarding their findings and researches. However, with the great burst of interest in nature that occurred during the Renaissance and post-Renaissance era and with the explorations to distant lands that brought in more and more new specimens, a critical need for systems of naming and classification arose. For example, Aristotle had described only some 500 kinds (species) of animals; and his pupil, Theophrastus, had described about the same number of plant species. These numbers, representing recognized species, did not change greatly until well into the Renaissance; in fact, some of the more extreme Aristotelians believed that no other species existed. However, it has been estimated that, by the year 1700, almost 10,000 species of plants were known and probably twice that many animal species. Clearly, some sort of classification system was needed.

A number of naturalists up to the time of Linnaeus had suggested methods of classifying organisms. However, it remained for Linnaeus to extract the best from the work of his predecessors and to build a system of naming and classification that still serves biology to the present day. Essentially, the Linnaean system is based on two major premises, namely, the use of Latin or latinized names and the classification of living forms according to a hierarchy of categories ranging from the most specific groups that ordinarily need to be recognized taxonomically (species) to the most general groups (kingdoms). The selection of Latin as the language of taxonomy has proved to be most fortunate, since it is no longer a vernacular language and, therefore, is not subject to basic grammatical changes. Furthermore, it has been employed for centuries as the language of scholarship and thus has found ready acceptance among civilized peoples. Although the original categories erected by Linnaeus (kingdom, class, order, genus, and species) have been expanded to accommodate an improved knowledge of organisms, the fact that the system itself remains highly workable is a tribute to its founder. At the present time, some 400,000 plant species and well over a million animal species are recognized. Despite a changed outlook with regard to species (based largely on genetic and evolutionary insights that have developed since the time of Linnaeus), the system is sufficiently flexible to accommodate these large numbers.

As for Linnaeus, he was a man for his time. He has often been misrepresented as a dull plodder who lacked the brilliance for a career in experimental biology, but this picture is a distortion of facts. Actually, a careful review of his work reveals that he indulged in speculative thinking, deductive reasoning, and cut-and-try experimentation—although experimentation in natural history differs from that in what we have termed experimental biology. In any event, Linnaeus accomplished what was most needed for his time: He established a system that was necessary to biological science before it could move on to other pursuits.

Nothing could be more fruitless than to attempt a comparison of experimental biology and natural history with an aim toward determining which is more "scientific" or which is of more value to science as a whole. In a sense, of course, natural history often lacks some of the elements of science as we have defined it; but ultimately, it involves some form of speculative thinking, deductive reasoning, and cut-and-try experimentation. On the other hand, "experimental" biology is not always fully scientific in this respect, since it often borders on the merely technological. Furthermore, there is often no fine dividing line between the two areas. It is not at all unusual for a given biologist to be involved in both activities simultaneously. There is, nevertheless, a fundamental difference in outlook and method, and we would do well to identify this difference. Natural history is essentially an observational science; experimental biology (as the name implies) is essentially experimental. Many natural historians have tended to be much the same in temperament as other scholarly observers, such as literary figures; in contrast, experimental biologists have tended to be more like the analyzers and measurers of physical science.[11] Both streams of thought, separately and together, have produced the tremendously broad field that we presently call "biological science."

In conclusion, we have attempted to show something of the historical roots that support modern biological science by introducing relevant material from history, philosophy, physical science, and from biological science itself. With this background, let us now go on to a number of important concepts that have arisen out of this framework.

QUESTIONS FOR REVIEW AND DISCUSSION

1. At what point in the Renaissance did modern science begin, according to the authors? What are the chief factors that led to the development of modern science?

2. What three processes or activities are essential to science, according to J. B. Conant? What does each of his expressions mean?

3. Why is it reasonable that Nicholaus Copernicus might be regarded as the father of modern science?

4. Was the Renaissance a time of complete emancipation from the dogmatism and authoritarianism that marked the Middle Ages? Explain.

5. Review the five points listed by the authors regarding the work of Galileo and write a summary of Galileo's scientific methodology.

6. How may we account for the fact that modern biological science developed much more slowly than did modern physical science?

7. Why is William Harvey often called the father of experimental biology?

8. Review the contribution of Carolus Linnaeus to the development of biological science. In what important way or ways does natural history differ from experimental biology?

9. What is a controlled experiment? Cite an example of such an experiment that was performed during the 17th century. Why is the controlled experiment of special importance to biology?

10. Summarize the thought and contribution to science of these three men: Francis Bacon, René Descartes, and Immanuel Kant.

11. In what sense was Cartesianism a reaction to the philosophy of Thomas Hobbes? How did 18th-century rationalism, empiricism, scientism, and the philosophy of David Hume all converge in providing a stimulus for Immanuel Kant to develop his philosophy?

12. After having read Chapter 3, do you see why scientists use such terms as "fact," "truth," and "proof" very sparingly? What connection do you see between their reluctance to use these terms and the discussion in this chapter on certainty?

REFERENCES

Butterfield, H. *The Origins of Modern Science.* New York: The Macmillan Company, 1952. This extraordinary book by a distinguished historian covers the period 1300 to 1800.

Conant, J. B. *Science and Common Sense.* New Haven: Yale University Press, 1951. A classic study in the nature of science.

Durant, W. *The Story of Philosophy.* New York: Pocket Books, Inc., 1954. A layman's history of philosophy, very readable, and generally reliable.

Jones, W. T. *A History of Western Philosophy: Hobbes to Hume* (2nd ed.); *Kant to Wittgenstein and Sartre* (2nd ed.). New York: Harcourt, Brace and World, Inc., 1969. The third and fourth volumes of the four-volume work described at the end of Chapter 1.

2

CONCEPTS OF BIOLOGY

Introduction

Since the time of Aristotle, biologists have been gathering and assimilating data. As a result, the factual base of modern biological science is now so vast that scarcely any biologist, no matter how thorough his training, would dare call himself a *general* biologist. How, therefore, is the modern student to go about understanding this tremendously large field to even a minimal degree, particularly if his time in the subject is limited? Indeed, by what authority can any teacher of biology say of the data at his disposal, "This piece of information is essential to a general understanding, but that other is not?"

If science were merely organized knowledge of the material universe, as some have been tempted to define science, this problem would be insurmountable. At the very least, there would be as many solutions as there are teachers of science. Fortunately, however, there is an alternative, that of selecting for detailed study a few of the great conceptual schemes of the particular science under consideration. This is the approach we have chosen in this book.

We have selected four conceptual schemes: Biogenesis, the cell theory, Mendelian genetics, and Darwinian evolution. Certainly, a great deal of material that is important to biological science lies outside the direct influence of these four topics, and some of this material will be introduced in the last part of this book. Nevertheless, historically speaking, it appears that biological science has received its greatest stimulus from these four conceptual schemes. Furthermore, each scheme has served as a stimulus to the others, chiefly (we believe) in the order in which we shall consider them.

In any event, it should be possible to gain some understanding of how biological scientists proceed to grapple with their problems; to impart this understanding is one of our major aims in writing this book.

FOUR

Life

The question, "What is life?" has plagued biologists for many centuries. The chief reason is that the term "life" represents a host of characteristics that cannot be gathered into a neat definitional package. It is axiomatic in formulating definitions that one must describe a concept or an idea in terms that are simpler than and basic to the concept itself, and herein lies the problem. *The concept of life is fundamental to many of the terms we need to use in defining it.* To a degree, the chemist has the same problem in defining "matter"; the physicist experiences similar difficulty with the term "energy"; and the artist finds it almost impossible to explain what "beauty" is.[1]

It is rather obvious that "living systems" are, at least fundamentally, physical objects possessing mass and occupying space; that is, they have a material existence. Consequently, the basic question can be stated as follows: What is the difference between "nonliving" and "living" aggregates of matter or between a living body and its corpse? In the light of our study in Part I, perhaps it is evident that, historically, students of this question have approached it from two different viewpoints. The problem of life can be relegated to the supernatural realm, or it can be included within the physical (natural) realm. Many of the ancients conceived of the essence of life as a "life principle," "psyche," or some other vague entity. For Aristotle, it was an "entelechy." For Democritus, who formulated a conceptual scheme around ultimate particles that he called atoms, there were special "soul" atoms that he considered to be of a finer and more noble texture than "material" atoms. Thus, he relied ultimately upon a nonmaterial explanation of the nature of life. Even Descartes, who popularized the mechanistic viewpoint in science, made an exception of the human organism. He conceived of the world as consisting of both material and nonmaterial entities; examples of the latter category are such processes as reasoning, thinking, and feeling. Descartes proposed that most living phenomena or functions in human beings have a material basis but that a "rational soul" acts directly upon the material body at some point.

Actually, vitalism (the viewpoint that life must ultimately be explained in nonmaterial terms) is by no means a dead issue even at the present time; it emerges occasionally in current biological thought. However, as we pointed out earlier, the biological scientist is obliged to assume that any differences existent between the "living" and the "nonliving" must have a physical rather than a nonmaterial basis; any other approach cannot be expected to further our scientific knowledge. In other words, vitalism is in serious conflict with the first principle of science.

In restricting ourselves to physical or natural explanations, we have not, by any means, simplified the problem of discovering what life is.[2] There still remains an apparent antithesis, or conflict, between the concepts of "living" and "nonliving." Biology, to a far greater degree than any other science, is rooted in apparent antitheses. Some phenomena can be approached unequivocally on an either-or basis. However, particularly the life-phenomenon, because of its great complexity, can be approached more profitably by visualizing a continuum with extremes at each end that blend into one another in the middle of the continuum. In other cases, the principle of complementarity is quite helpful. This viewpoint assumes that a phenomenon may be approached from different operational standpoints, with the result that different statements, all equally valid, can be made about the phenomenon.[3] In the remainder of this section, we shall illustrate these three methods of explanation.

The unequivocal (either-or) explanation may be completely valid in some cases. For example, an electric light switch is either on or off, John is either in the room or he is not, and so on. The type of explanation based upon points along a continuum can be illustrated by a seemingly hot-cold antithesis. One object may be hotter or colder than another, whereas a light switch cannot be "more" on or "more" off. In describing complementarity, one might say that this book has a certain number of chapters, a certain number of paragraphs, and a certain number of pages. The figures are different, but equally correct, and equally valid in describing the book.

For the sake of simplicity, one might easily wish that the life-phenomenon could be approached on an either-or basis and neatly defined. However, such is not the case. In viewing a "living system" strictly as a physical entity representing a complex of matter and energy, the scientist is faced with the problem of determining at what point in a continuum of the organization of matter and energy the life-phenomenon arises or emerges (Fig. 4-1). In other words, he is obliged to decide what properties must exist or emerge, and to what degree, before the entire complex may legitimately be considered "living." One can go far toward understanding life by studying its perceptible characteristics, such as metabolism and self-perpetuation. Within this framework, the phenomenon we call life *can* be approached by means of hypotheses, conceptual schemes, and theories.

As exemplified by Aristotle (in much of his work) and by the host of descriptive biologists who have been active since the early Renaissance, it is not necessary to labor under any conceptual scheme at all in studying the phenomenon of life. Armed with nothing more than an active curiosity, one may become expert in his knowledge of beetles, mammals, ferns, or flowering plants. Nevertheless, before biology could become biological science, it was necessary that conceptual schemes be developed that could lead ultimately to the formulation and use of theories. Basic to all such conceptual schemes, and certainly the most fruitful in its overall influence, is that of *biogenesis,* which holds that life comes only from life in an unbroken chain, at least under conditions now prevailing on earth. We have seen how Francesco Redi dealt with this conceptual scheme on an experimental basis; let us now trace its development to modern times.

4.1 THE BIOGENESIS-ABIOGENESIS CONTROVERSY [4]

In 1676, eight years after Francesco Redi's classic work was reported, the Dutchman Anton van Leeuwenhoek (1632–1723) discovered the

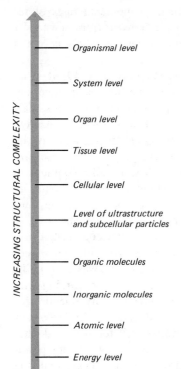

INCREASING STRUCTURAL COMPLEXITY

— Organismal level

— System level

— Organ level

— Tissue level

— Cellular level

— Level of ultrastructure
and subcellular particles

— Organic molecules

— Inorganic molecules

— Atomic level

— Energy level

Figure 4.1. Diagrammatic representation
of the continuum described by increasing
levels of complexity in the natural realm
of existence.

world of microorganisms. Using a microscope that he had constructed himself, Leeuwenhoek observed species after species of protozoa, micro-
crustacea, and even bacteria. Fortunately, he communicated his findings
to the Royal Society of London, then a leading organization of men who
were dedicated to scientific pursuits, and before the close of the 17th century it was widely known that such organisms existed.

By their very nature, microorganisms differ from macroorganisms in
several important respects. For one thing, their rates of reproduction are
usually quite phenomenal—for example, some bacteria may double their
populations every 20 minutes under ideal conditions. Hence, from the very
beginning, microorganisms were considered fundamentally different from
the animals and plants of common experience, a view that we no longer
consider justified in its entirety. There are differences, yes—but subsequent developments, especially those within the past two or three decades,
indicate that at the biochemical and biophysical levels, all life is one.

Although Redi's work had dealt with the supposed spontaneous generation for the higher organisms, this concept was still maintained for the
microbial world. It should be remembered that the tiny organisms in the
microbial world were generally considered to be almost as simple as ob-

jects in the nonliving world. Furthermore, their phenomenal rates of reproduction made it appear as though they arose *de novo* ("from newness") in pond water or nutrient materials, so it came to be commonly accepted that they arose spontaneously.

This notion gained a high degree of respectability in 1749 when an English priest, John Needham (1713–1781), reported the results of certain experiments he had performed. Needham filled a number of glass vials with mutton gravy, stoppered them tightly, and heated them "violently" in hot ashes for an undisclosed period of time. Quite understandably, he assumed that he had destroyed any life that might possibly be present in the gravy. Upon removing the vials from the ashes, he allowed them to stand at room temperature for a week or so. Within a few days, each vial was found to be teeming with microorganisms. To Needham, the conclusion was simple: He had proved that microorganisms arise *de novo*.

Despite the fact that Needham's experiments were accomplished in a completely haphazard manner without any sort of controls, his views were rather widely accepted. Of course, experimental biology was still in its infancy, and there were few men who possessed the feel for working with microorganisms. Consequently, it is easy to understand why scientists of that period might accept Needham's conceptual scheme (*abiogenesis*) uncritically. After all, it seemed to account rather well for observed phenomena in the microbial world, and there was no overwhelming philosophical reason for rejecting the notion that life could arise from nonliving antecedents.

But at least one scientist was not convinced. This was an Italian, Lazarro Spallanzani (1729–1799), a fellow-priest with Needham. Like Redi before him, Spallanzani intuitively suspected that abiogenesis was an oversimplification of natural principles. His intuition was not merely an unsupported hunch. Spallanzani had already accomplished some notable work in biology, and he perceived weaknesses in Needham's procedures from the time he first learned of them. Consequently, he painstakingly repeated Needham's experiments and uncovered two fundamental weaknesses. Cork stoppers do not prevent the entrance of microorganisms into glass vessels, and heating gravy in ashes does not destroy all the microorganisms. It merely destroys so many that the few remaining ones are hard to find. When the gravy cools, these few multiply rapidly and are soon quite evident. In his own mind, Spallanzani formulated an alternate conceptual scheme to abiogenesis, namely, *biogenesis*. All life comes from life, Spallanzani postulated, regardless of whether organisms are as large as Redi's maggots or as small as Leeuwenhoek's bacteria.

But Spallanzani was not content merely to play the devil's advocate with Needham. After exposing the weaknesses of Needham's experiments, Spallanzani proceeded to devise experiments of his own. Using a nutrient soup much like Needham's gravy, Spallanzani arranged a series of flasks in such a manner that the contents of one were boiled for a certain length of time, the next a little longer, and so on. In each case, he melted the neck of the flask immediately after heating it and thereby sealed it hermetically. From these and similar experiments, Spallanzani was able to establish several important principles. First of all, it takes quite a long time to kill microorganisms by boiling the medium in which they are situated. Secondly, it is incredibly easy to reinfect a sterile medium; all that is necessary is to allow nonsterile air to reach it. Spallanzani reasoned, quite correctly, that ordinary air is usually supplied with microorganisms or with some form of life that can give rise to microorganisms. After exhaustive repetition and verification of his experiments and results, Spallanzani published the summation of his work in 1769.

In all probability, Spallanzani's work would have settled the issue at the microbial level had he been dealing with scientists whose insights were as keen as his own. As it was, he merely succeeded in dividing the scientific community into two opposing camps, each with its own entrenched prejudices. Furthermore, a development in chemistry during the 1770's encouraged the champions of abiogenesis. This was the discovery of oxygen, which was shown to be essential to living systems.* The disciples of Needham were quick to point out that Spallanzani had "tortured" the vital force (considered to be oxygen by that time) and had then excluded fresh oxygen by his hermetical sealing methods. All that is required to generate new life from lifeless broth, they maintained, is to bring it into contact with oxygen.

The controversy raged on for very nearly another 100 years with a minimum of experimentation and a maximum of heated speculation. By and large, such experiments as were performed came from the proponents of biogenesis, and these experiments were designed to show that a combination of sterile oxygen and sterile broth would *not* produce living forms. Representative of these experiments was the approach of the German biologist Theodor Schwann (1810–1882), who reported his work in 1838. Schwann boiled a meat broth to the point of sterility and then passed heated air into it (Fig. 4-2). He reasoned that if Spallanzani were right in his hypothesis that ordinary air contains microorganisms or their "seeds," then heating the air should destroy them before they had an opportunity to reach the broth. Of course, his opponents were able to maintain that he had altered the oxygen of this incoming air in some critical way. Despite the fact that Schwann demonstrated by chemical analysis that the heated

---

* As it happens, there are many microorganisms, called *anaerobes,* that do not utilize gaseous oxygen in their life processes, but these organisms were completely unknown and unsuspected at that time.

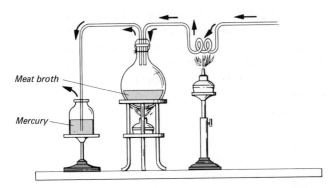

Figure 4.2. Schwann's apparatus for passing heated air into a flask of sterile meat broth. Air was blown through the series of tubes, as indicated by arrows, and finally escaped to the atmosphere through a mercury bath.

air *still* contained virtually all of its original oxygen, they remained un-moved.

Perhaps Schwann's work would have left no doubt about biogenesis had it not been for two factors. Shortly after Schwann published his results, the German chemist Justus von Liebig (1802–1873) came out in favor of spontaneous generation. He had no evidence for it, and his lengthy treatise told of no experimentation, but the sheer weight of his considerable pres-tige was enough to draw attention away from Schwann's careful work. Secondly, when Schwann's meat-broth experiments were repeated using milk as the nutrient medium, the results were confusing. We know now that milk is a great deal harder to sterilize than meat broth; but at that time, it was taken for granted that a long period of boiling would kill any living thing regardless of the medium.

Various investigators attempted to resolve the problem over the next two decades. Although some excellent work was performed, the scientific community as a whole remained divided on the issue of spontaneous gen-eration. Finally, in 1860, the French Academy of Science offered a prize to the person who could demonstrate in a valid manner whether or not spontaneous generation did indeed occur. At about this time, the French chemist and biologist Louis Pasteur (1822–1895) became interested in the problem. His interest arose partly from his arguments with Justus von Liebig over the nature of biochemical reactions associated with yeast cells and partly from his conviction that spontaneous generation was a myth. He began a series of experiments that culminated in a demonstration so utterly simple in design and so completely convincing that the scientific community as a whole considered the issue resolved (Fig. 4-3).

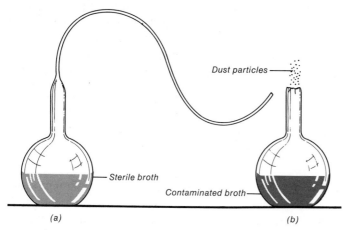

Figure 4.3. (a) The type of flask used by Pasteur in his studies on spontaneous generation. Because of the curvature of the neck, dust particles could not enter the flask of sterile nutrient broth, but air could. (b) Appearance of flask 24 hours after the neck had been broken. Deeper color of broth represents microbial growth. This experiment culminated several years of intensive work by Pasteur and showed conclusively that germ-free air does not interact with a sterile nutrient medium to produce microorganisms.

Actually, a number of difficulties still remained, and it was not until the mid-1870's that the problems of complete sterilization of media were finally solved. By that time, it was realized that the reproductive bodies of some microorganisms are so difficult to kill by heat that they can withstand hours of boiling. But long before the turn of the century, the major philosophical justification for believing in spontaneous generation, the notion of simplicity, was beginning to fade. Evidence from microbial physiology and biochemistry had been accumulating since Pasteur's time; as a result, it became increasingly apparent that even the simplest organism is infinitely more complex than anything in the nonliving world. Once it was accepted that a great gap does indeed exist between the living and the nonliving, such notions as spontaneous generation seemed akin to magic. Thus, while it has never been disproven in the strict sense (and after all, only the most simple verbalisms are subject to final proof in science), biologists' disenchantment with abiogenesis became almost total within a few years after Pasteur's famous demonstration.

However, the extent to which a gap exists between the "living" and the "nonliving" depends upon the operational viewpoint that one uses in making a distinction between the two. In 19th-century terms, the gap is large indeed. In modern terms, and viewed in the mechanistic concept of a continuum, a sharp distinction becomes difficult. It must also be pointed out that the concept of biogenesis, as formulated in the 19th century, does nothing to illuminate the origin of life. We shall reexamine these problems a little further on, but first, let us attempt to gain some insight into the nature of life from a mechanistic point of view.

4.2 THE NATURE OF LIFE: A MECHANISTIC APPROACH [5]

The identification of life as a phenomenon that appears along a continuum of the organization of energy and matter is a vague concept. It describes, but it does not explain. What is energy, and what is matter? How do they interact? Unless *some* kind of answer can be given to these and related questions, we cannot hope to answer the larger question, "What is life?" or even approach it very meaningfully. Therefore, let us digress at this point and consider these fundamental concepts of physical science.

4.2A The Nature of Matter and Energy

Physical scientists find it useful, for their purposes, to define matter and energy in rather technical terms since the two are, to a great degree, interconvertible. As a result, a physicist or a chemist would have great difficulty in making a sharp distinction between matter and energy. However, biologists find it much more useful to conceive of matter and energy as being separate and distinct things, because, in living systems, one does not encounter their interconversion to any great extent. In other words, biological scientists and physical scientists usually maintain different conceptual schemes for matter and energy; whether the two are "really" different is operationally beside the point. It is sufficient for our purposes that we consider them so.

MATTER

Anything possessing mass and occupying space is called *matter*. In common experience, the term includes objects, substances, or indeed any *thing* that is detectible to our senses or to instruments that can, in turn, interpret data for our senses. In terms of form, matter may exist in any one of three states: a *solid*, a *liquid,* or a *gas*. With rare exceptions, any substance can be converted from one of these states to another by the addition or subtraction of heat. For example, water (a liquid) can be changed to ice (a solid) by the subtraction of heat, or to steam (a gas) by the addition of heat. Let us be careful to note that such *physical* changes do not alter the fundamental nature of water; all that is required to effect a further physical change is to add or subtract more heat, as the case may require. For a really fundamental, or *chemical,* change to occur, it would be necessary either to combine water with something else in the formation of a new substance or to separate it into its component parts (hydrogen and oxygen).

By studying chemical changes and other phenomena, physical scientists have concluded that matter consists of fundamental particles called *atoms.* For our purposes, an atom may be considered the smallest unit of matter that can enter into chemical changes. Exact methods of computation indicate that atoms are incredibly small; it has been estimated that 100 million atoms arranged in a row would measure only an inch. Compared with the number of possible existing substances, there are relatively few kinds of atoms. To be exact, physical scientists recognize the existence of only 92 naturally occurring kinds, although others have been produced artificially.

Let us suppose that we can obtain a substance made up of only one kind of atom. This would be an elementary substance—or, as it is generally termed, an *element,* of which only 92 kinds exist in nature. Hence, an element is a substance composed of similar atoms. All these elements have been given names, some of which existed long before the particulate nature of the elements they represent was known. For purposes of brevity, there are symbols that represent each name. Generally, a symbol represents the first letter or the first and second letters of the English or Latin name of the element. For example, the symbol of the element hydrogen is H; that of magnesium, Mg; that of sodium, Na; and so on. A complete list of the elements and their symbols can be found in any introductory textbook of chemistry.

Evidence indicates that atoms are composed of three primary building blocks: *protons, neutrons, and electrons.* Hydrogen, however, has no neutron. The protons and neutrons have almost 2,000 times the mass of an electron and are held together very tightly to form the compact nucleus of the atom. As shown by their names, a proton has a positive electrical charge and a neutron is neutral, so that the nucleus has a net positive charge. The arrangement of protons and neutrons in the atomic nucleus is not completely understood, nor is the nature of the energy that binds them together. An electron has a negative electrical charge. The electrons of an atom move at relatively high velocities about the positively charged nucleus at varying distances from it. The number of electrons in an atom is ordinarily equal to the number of protons, making the atom electrically neutral.

Variations in the numbers of protons, neutrons, and electrons composing atoms account for differences in the elements that they represent. Primarily, there are three ways of identifying an atom or the element to which it belongs. Probably the simplest and most orderly, at least for reference purposes, is to cite the *atomic number*. The atomic number of an atom is equal to the number of protons in the nucleus. Atomic numbers, therefore, range from 1 for hydrogen, the simplest atom, to 92 for uranium, the most complex of the naturally occurring atoms. Atoms are also identified by *mass numbers,* in which case the protons and neutrons are considered to have a mass of 1 each, and the electrons are considered to have no mass. For example, carbon-12, which has six protons and six neutrons, has an atomic number of 6 and a mass number of 12. As an element, it is frequently represented by the symbol $_6C^{12}$, in which case the subscript is the atomic number and the superscript is the mass number. A third means of identifying an atom, and one closely related to the concept of atomic mass, is that of *atomic weight*. Atomic weights of atoms are relative values determined by comparison of a given element with that of carbon-12. Thus, the atomic weight of an element indicates whether it is lighter or heavier than carbon and by how much. For example, hydrogen (atomic weight 1.008) is approximately $\frac{1}{12}$ as heavy as carbon-12, and chlorine (atomic weight 35.453) is almost three times as heavy.

As recently as the year 1900, physical scientists assumed that the atoms composing a given element were identical. Because this assumption could not be reconciled with certain experimental data, however, special attention was given to the problem. It was soon learned that most elements are composed of two or more variant forms of atoms. The variant forms of a given element were named *isotopes* and are atoms of the *same element with the same atomic numbers but different mass numbers.* In other words, they have the same number of protons and electrons but not the same number of neutrons. For example, the element chlorine has two naturally occurring isotopic forms. One type of atom has a mass number of 35 (17 protons plus 18 neutrons) and the other type has a mass number of 37 (17 protons plus 20 neutrons). Precise analysis reveals that the proportions of these two isotopes in nature are about 75.4 per cent of the lighter atoms ($_{17}Cl^{35}$) to about 24.6 per cent of the heavier atoms ($_{17}Cl^{37}$). Consequently, the mass number averages out at 35.453. **The atomic weight of a particular element, therefore, is defined as the average of the mass number values of all the naturally occurring isotopic forms of that particular element.**

The fact that most elements are isotopic is very fortunate for biologists. For example, if an investigator wishes to trace the path of the element carbon in some living system, he may "label" some carbon compound with the relatively rare $_6C^{14}$ and determine its pathway or its ultimate fate by the use of instruments that are capable of detecting it. Within recent decades, isotopes have become widely used in biological research.

For our purposes, it is useful to view the atom as a miniature solar system in which the nucleus is analogous to the sun and the electrons to its planets (Fig. 4-4). Thus, an atom consists chiefly of space. Actually,

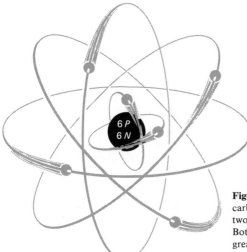

Figure 4.4. Theoretical structure of the carbon atom, whose six electrons occupy two separate "shells" around the nucleus. Both the electrons and the nucleus are greatly enlarged in terms of their actual sizes in relation to space within the atom.

it is impossible to illustrate by means of a diagram just how much space really exists in an atom. To draw an analogy, suppose that an atom were expanded in size until it measured a mile in diameter. The nucleus would then be about twice the size of a baseball; the electrons, smaller than golf balls.

Because electrons are located at varying distances from the nucleus, about which they travel at high velocities, they become directly involved in chemical reactions. Before considering the behavior of electrons, however, we need to understand some basic concepts regarding energy.

ENERGY

In contrast to matter, energy neither occupies space nor possesses mass. Therefore, it cannot be defined from a material or structural viewpoint; it must instead be defined in operational terms or in terms of its effect on matter. Energy is sometimes defined as the capacity to do work. Within this concept, it is useful to classify energy as either *potential* or *kinetic* energy. Potential energy is inactive or stored energy. It possesses the capacity to affect matter but it is not in the process of doing so. In contrast, kinetic energy is energy in action; that is, it is in the process of affecting matter. Figure 4-5 illustrates the difference in these two types

(a)   *(b)*

Figure 4.5.   (a) Potential energy represented by a boulder
at the top of a hill. (b) Kinetic energy represented by a
boulder in the process of rolling down a hill.

of energy. In the system represented by Fig. 4-5a, a certain amount
of potential energy is present. As the boulder rolls down the hill (Fig.
4-5b), this potential energy is converted to kinetic energy, and the amount
released is approximately equal to the amount originally expended in getting the boulder to the top of the hill. Thus, as one attempts to deal with
the concept of energy, one must think in terms of a particular system (for
example, our boulder on the hill) that has the inherent property of reversi-
bility.

Energy may exist in a number of different forms. The most common
of these are thermal energy (heat), radiant energy (visible light, infrared
and ultraviolet rays, X rays, gamma rays, cosmic rays), mechanical energy
(as illustrated in Fig. 4-5), electrical energy (the flow of electrons along
a conductor), and chemical energy (energy possessed by chemical compounds). In both living and nonliving systems, energy is converted from
one *type* to another (potential to kinetic and vice versa) and from one *form*
to another (for example, from chemical energy to mechanical energy). One
has only to consider a very common example of this conversion process
to realize that it occurs. In an automobile engine, potential chemical energy is present in the form of gasoline. Upon its ignition by kinetic electrical
energy, it is converted to kinetic thermal energy. This thermal energy is
then partially converted to mechanical energy, which is eventually dissipated as heat, and so on (Fig. 4-6).

As we shall see in a later chapter, these same types of conversions
and transformations occur in living systems. Thus, both living and nonliving systems exemplify the first law of thermodynamics, which states that
energy can neither be created nor destroyed but can be changed in form.
This principle is of considerable importance to biology, and we shall return to it.

The second law of thermodynamics is also basic to an understanding

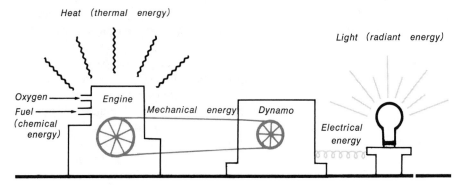

Figure 4.6. Some energy conversions, or transformations, from one type to another.

of chemical reactions in both living and nonliving systems. As a concept, this law accounts for a multitude of complex phenomena; stated simply, it holds that **energy tends to dissipate itself.** A good illustration of this principle may be seen in chemistry, where reactions proceed from high-energy to low-energy states. In other words, the second law relates energy changes in a system to the organization of that system. Placed in this context, it states that there is an increase in *entropy* (disorder or randomness)—that is, a decrease in organization. Since useful energy is organized energy, an increase in entropy means a decrease in useful energy.

How does this concept relate to the study of organisms? From one viewpoint, life itself might be regarded as an exception to the second law of thermodynamics. If there is a tendency in an isolated system to proceed toward disorder, the implication is that energy must be taken constantly into a living system in order for it to maintain its organization. As a matter of fact, this process is what actually occurs in living systems. The human body, for example, takes in potential chemical energy (food) that ultimately supplies kinetic chemical energy. These processes enable the body to maintain its organization; that is, the body is prevented from wasting away. Thermodynamically, a living system is not qualitatively different from a nonliving system in this respect; the difference is a quantitative one, leading to increased complexity in the living system. Energy conversions in living systems are fantastically numerous and varied; but *overall,* enough energy is supplied from external sources to delay its progress toward randomness. When the supply of energy is insufficient, the organism dies, of course. In brief, although a living system cannot presently be reduced to chemistry and physics, there is no reason to believe that it demonstrates a chemistry and physics different from that of nonliving systems. Thus, organisms exemplify not only the first and second laws of thermodynamics but many other laws of chemistry and physics as well.

As we shall emphasize later, the initial energy source for organisms is the sun. Green plants are capable of converting a portion of this radiant energy into chemical energy. Animals and microorganisms then use these plants as an energy source. At each step of energy transfer, there is a considerable loss. The energy lost, including the original radiant energy not utilized by green plants, goes on to a more disorganized state; that is, there is an overall increase in entropy. The universality of the second law of thermodynamics therefore hinges on whether or not the balance sheet of the entire earth-sun system shows a decrease in free or usable energy. Many physicists feel that there is a decrease; they consider our own solar system analogous to a huge clock that was initially wound up and will eventually unwind itself completely. According to this view, our sun will eventually "burn out."

THE MATTER-ENERGY COMPLEX

Armed with this brief and very simplified concept of energy, let us return to the nature of atomic structure. Previously, we depicted the atom as a miniature solar system in which the electrons travel about the nucleus (composed of protons and neutrons) in some fashion.

In order to understand the conditions making possible the combination of atoms and the transfer of electrons to and from atoms, it is necessary to recognize that electrons do not revolve about the nucleus in a haphazard fashion. According to one theory, there are "shells," "electron clouds," or "energy levels," which are restricted in the number of electrons that each can contain at a given time. The simplest atom, that of hydrogen, is characterized by the presence of only one proton in the nucleus and one electron in orbit (Fig. 4-7a). The helium atom possesses two protons and two neutrons in the nucleus and two electrons occupying the same shell (Fig. 4-7b).

Experimental evidence has indicated that the first shell surrounding the nucleus of an atom never contains more than two electrons. In the atom of lithium, for example, which possesses three protons in the nucleus and three electrons in orbit, two of these electrons orbit in the first shell and the third orbits in an outside shell. In any atom, this second shell may contain as many as eight electrons. When more than 10 electrons are present in the atom, a third shell is established outside the first two. This third shell may contain as many as 18 electrons. If more shells are present, the fourth shell may contain 32 electrons; the fifth shell, 32; the sixth shell, 18; and the seventh shell, 2. However, not more than eight electrons are contained in whichever is the outermost shell of an atom.

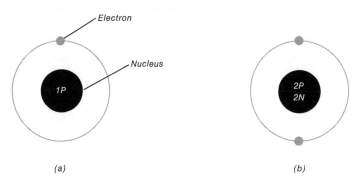

Figure 4.7. Two-dimensional representation of the hydrogen
atom (a) and the helium atom (b). The nucleus of the
hydrogen atom contains one proton and no neutrons; that
of the helium atom contains two protons and two neutrons.

The shells formed by orbiting electrons are not so much physical
entities as they are energy levels. According to this concept, electrons may
be viewed as units possessing certain amounts of potential energy; this
amount in any particular case is determined by the energy level that the
electron occupies in the atom. If one thinks of the nucleus with its net
positive charge as attracting the negatively charged electrons with a certain
force, then a theory can be presented in an effort to account for the elec-
tron-nucleus relationship: The farther the shell or energy level is from the
nucleus, the more potential energy it represents. Perhaps an analogy will
serve to clarify this theory. Let us suppose that we have seven stones at
the bottom of a stair and that we pick up a stone and place it on each of
the first seven steps. The topmost stone represents the *greatest* potential
energy of any, because it required more *kinetic* energy to get there in the
first place. In other words, the higher the stone, the more potential energy
it represents. If we let the stones represent electrons and the steps represent
the different energy levels of an atom, we can see something of the energetic relationships within an atom. The analogy breaks down somewhat
when we consider that electrons are in motion, but the principle is the
same. However, because they are in motion, those electrons farthest from
the nucleus can be removed from the influence of the nucleus more easily
than those electrons situated closer to the nucleus since the attracting force
is inversely proportional to the square of the distance of the electron from
the nucleus.

This concept of energy levels in the atom is basic to an understanding
of the interaction of atoms to form molecules. It is also essential to an
understanding of the energy transformations occurring in living systems,
where electron shifts from one level to another within atoms are accom-

panied by a gain or loss in energy. As we shall see in a later chapter, these mechanisms account for the ability of green plants to "capture" the energy of sunlight, and they enable all organisms to make certain energy transformations within their cells.

4.2B Molecules and Compounds

Thus far, in trying to understand matter, we have considered only single atoms. We have seen that energy is very much involved as a force within the atom itself. We shall now concern ourselves with a higher level of organization of matter and energy: particles composed of more than one atom. In fact, atoms generally do not exist singly but are most often joined with other atoms to form *compounds*. In compounds, atoms are held together by energy forces called *chemical bonds*. An analogy would be something like two ping-pong balls held together by a rubber band. Of, course, the bond does not really consist of a material substance; but, like a rubber band, it represents a certain amount of potential energy. To carry the analogy further, when either a rubber band *or* a chemical bond is broken, potential energy is converted into kinetic energy. A chemical bond is apparently an energy relationship between atoms. The amount of energy in chemical bonds is variable and is dependent upon the number and kinds of atoms that are associated together. The chemical energy or bond energy holding atoms together is equal to the amount of energy that must be put in to break the bond.

As we mentioned previously, the number of electrons in the outermost shell or energy level of an atom does not exceed eight. In atoms that have more than one shell, the presence of eight electrons in the outermost shell represents stability. As a general rule, one can predict that atoms will interact to form compounds when all participants are able to achieve stability by doing so. Essentially, we are saying that all chemical reactions involve an exchange of energy. This energy becomes kinetic as electrons interact in achieving stability, which means that bonds are either broken or formed, as the case may be.

For our purposes, there are two types of atomic interactions, based on the manner in which electrons of one atom relate to those of another atom. These types are *ionic* compounds and *covalent* compounds.

IONIC COMPOUNDS

Let us suppose that an atom has a second shell containing eight electrons and that a single electron occupies a third shell. It has a tendency to give up this single electron in achieving stability, and it will do so (under certain conditions) to any atom that will accept the electron. In contrast, if there is an atom with only seven electrons in its outermost shell, then it has a tendency to accept a single electron in achieving stability. If two such atoms are brought together, they make this exchange, and the result is an *ionic* or *electrovalent* bond. A number of similar interacting pairs of atoms comprise an ionic or electrovalent compound. For example, the sodium atom ($_{11}Na^{23}$) has 11 electrons, two of which form the first shell, eight of which form the second shell, while the remaining electron occupies a third shell. The chlorine atom ($_{17}Cl^{35}$), with 17 electrons, has seven of these in its third shell. The chlorine atom readily accepts the outermost electron of sodium—this electron actually transfers to the chlorine atom. The resulting compound, sodium chloride, consists of two types of stable but electrically imbalanced atoms. An atom achieving structural stability through the loss or gain of electrons is called an *ion*. Hence, sodium chloride consists of two types of ions, the sodium ions and the chloride ions. These ions are represented by the symbols Na^+ and Cl^-, respectively, and sodium chloride is represented by the formula Na^+Cl^-.

In such reactions as we have described, the total number of positive charges carried by one ion equals the total number of negative charges carried by the other. Since opposite charges attract each other, one should expect that the positive and negative ions exert a mutual attraction. This force of attraction is termed the ionic or electrovalent bond. For example, in Fig. 4-8, we have diagrammed the reaction $Na + Cl \rightarrow Na^+Cl^-$; the end

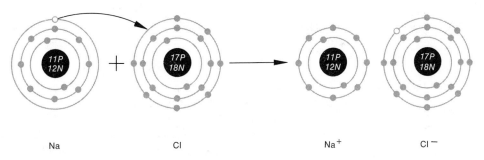

Na   Cl   Na$^+$ Cl$^-$

Figure 4.8.   Electron transfer from sodium (Na) to chlorine (Cl), resulting in sodium and chloride ions.

product is the ionic compound sodium chloride. In the compound, a single bond exists between the sodium ion and the chloride ion, formed by the electrical attraction that these two ions have for each other. The reaction resulting in this ionic situation is customarily called an electron-transfer reaction.*

Atoms do not always react in a one-to-one ratio in attaining stability. For example, consider the interaction between calcium ($_{20}Ca^{40}$) and chlorine in the formation of calcium chloride ($Ca^{++}2Cl^-$). Remember that one can get a reaction between calcium and chlorine if all participating atoms achieve stability. This reaction is accomplished quite readily in the interaction of calcium and chlorine, as shown in Fig. 4-9. In other words,

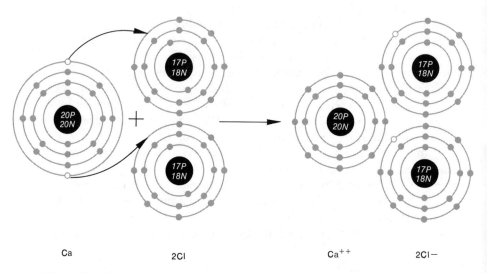

Ca   2Cl Ca^{++} $2Cl-$

Figure 4.9. The interaction of calcium and chlorine in a 1:2 ratio. Compare with the interaction of sodium and chlorine as shown in Figure 4.8.

the calcium atom has *two* electrons to donate in achieving stability, and so, in a manner of speaking, it does not "care" whether it donates both electrons to a single atom or to a pair of atoms.

To summarize ionic or electrovalent interactions, it is meaningful to say that atoms with more than four electrons in the outermost shell have a tendency to accept additional electrons, whereas those with fewer than four tend to give them up, thus presenting a satisfied shell to the outside. From a purely physical standpoint, atoms that have interacted to form ionic bonds may be only loosely associated, especially if the compound

---

* In most cases, 100-per cent ionization does not occur in ionic reactions, although the interaction of sodium and chlorine approaches it very closely. Electron transfer is usually incomplete, and the donated electron may occasionally be found in the shells of the donor atom.

formed is dissolved in some liquid such as water. This characteristic contrasts to the generally closer physical relationship of atoms involved in the second type of interaction, covalent compounds.

COVALENT COMPOUNDS

Under certain conditions, atoms may fill their outermost orbits by sharing electrons. In this case, an energy bond is formed, and it is called a *covalent* bond. Atoms held together by covalent bonds form a unit called a *molecule*.* A compound composed of similar molecules is called a *covalent* or *molecular compound*. Using chlorine ($_{17}Cl^{35}$) again as an example, let us consider how the atoms of this element might interact to achieve stability. Chlorine has seven electrons in its outer shell, but eight are required for stability. Whenever a chlorine atom comes close to another chlorine atom, each "tries" to wrest an electron from the other. However, the match is a draw, since each atom holds on to its electrons with equal tenacity. As a result, both atoms must share a pair of electrons that are found in the shells or electron clouds of either one of the atoms. By virtue of this arrangement, both atoms achieve stability and comprise a molecule, which we symbolize as Cl_2 (Fig. 4-10). Thus, chlorine does not

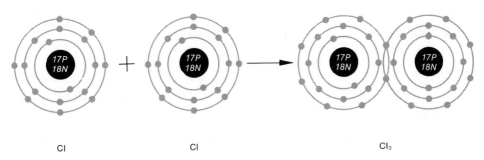

Cl   Cl Cl_2

Figure 4.10. The interaction of two atoms of chlorine in the formation of a molecule of chlorine.

exist naturally in the form of individual atoms but, rather, as molecular chlorine (Cl_2). In similar fashion, many elements exist as molecules; for example, two hydrogen atoms interact to form a molecule of hydrogen (H_2).

---

* Within molecules, especially those consisting of several types of atoms, one or more of the atoms may relate to the molecule ionically. As a result, a molecule may consist mostly of atoms that are held together by covalent bonds; some of these atoms are related to others by ionic bonds.

Let us consider the carbon atom ($_6C^{12}$), which has four electrons in its outer shell. We might question whether it tends to give them up or take on four more to achieve stability. Actually, it usually does neither but instead participates in the formation of molecules through sharing its electrons. Because of its outer shell configuration, carbon is a very versatile atom and can form an almost infinite number of different arrangements with other atoms. For example, carbon reacts in the presence of hydrogen to form methane (Fig. 4-11). In this case, each hydrogen atom shares a pair of electrons with the carbon atom.

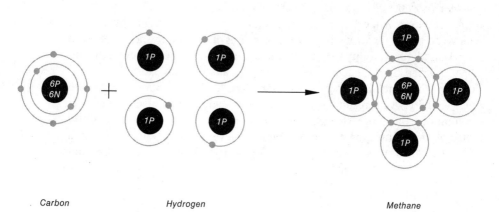

Carbon   Hydrogen   Methane

Figure 4.11. Formation of a molecule of methane by the combination of one carbon atom and four hydrogen atoms.

A number of ways may be used to present the relationship of shared electrons. For example,

Cl:Cl or Cl—Cl or Cl_2

H:H or H—H or H_2

$$
\begin{array}{ccc}
 & & H \\
H & & | \\
H\!:\!\overset{\cdot\cdot}{\underset{\cdot\cdot}{C}}\!:\!H & \text{or} & H\!-\!C\!-\!H \quad \text{or} \quad CH_4 \\
H & & | \\
 & & H
\end{array}
$$

The most common method of representing molecular relationships, especially for large molecules, is the second one shown above. Each line represents a pair of shared electrons, which form a chemical bond between the two atoms involved.

4.2C Chemical Reactions

When atoms unite to form compounds, the atoms themselves achieve stability. It might be concluded, therefore, that when a compound is formed, it is stable and nonreactive. However, this is not necessarily the case. Under certain conditions of temperature, pressure, and other factors, compounds may undergo alteration or may interact with other compounds. Whenever this interaction occurs, existing bonds are broken and new ones are formed.

BASIC TYPES OF CHEMICAL REACTIONS

By way of analogy, let us consider atoms as letters, molecules as words, and a chemical reaction as a sentence imparting a thought. Just as there are ways to classify sentences, so also are there methods of classifying chemical reactions. For our purposes, the five following types of reactions are fundamental ones.

SYNTHETIC REACTIONS   As the name implies, something is made in a reaction of this type. For example,

$$H_2 + Cl_2 \rightarrow 2HCl$$

Since two substances react to form a third, one can represent this reaction abstractly as follows:

$$A + B \rightarrow C$$

Synthetic reactions are quite common in living systems. For example, many of the reactions involved in growth, where new substances are being formed constantly, are synthetic in nature.

DECOMPOSITION REACTIONS   This type of reaction is the reverse of a synthetic reaction. To illustrate:

$$2HCl \rightarrow H_2 + Cl_2$$

As one would suppose, a decomposition reaction may be represented symbolically as

$$C \rightarrow A + B$$

Decomposition reactions are also quite common in living systems, particularly in such processes as digestion and respiration, where complex molecules are broken down into smaller molecules.

DISPLACEMENT, OR EXCHANGE, REACTIONS Displacement reactions involve the replacement of an atom or a group of atoms by another atom or another group. Let us consider the following typical reaction:

$$Zn + 2HCl \rightarrow ZnCl_2 + H_2$$

This type of reaction may be generalized as follows:

$$A + BC \rightarrow AC + B$$

Displacement reactions are very important to living systems. For example, in the body fluids of higher animals, various ions and molecules constantly displace each other as they are transported to and from tissues by certain compounds.

DOUBLE DISPLACEMENT REACTIONS These reactions involve a mutual exchange between compounds. For example,

$$NaOH + HCl \rightarrow NaCl + H_2O$$

This reaction may be symbolized as follows:

$$AB + CD \rightarrow AD + BC$$

Double displacement reactions are quite common in living systems.

REARRANGEMENT REACTIONS These reactions simply involve a change in the bonding pattern within a molecule where there is no change in the number or kinds of atoms. To illustrate:

$$
\begin{array}{c}
\overset{\displaystyle H\ H\ H\ H}{\underset{\displaystyle H\!-\!H\!-\!H\!-\!H}{\mid\ \mid\ \mid\ \mid}} \\
H\!-\!C\!-\!C\!-\!C\!-\!C\!-\!H
\end{array}
\rightarrow
\begin{array}{c}
H\ H\ H \\
\mid\ \mid\ \mid \\
H\!-\!C\!-\!C\!-\!C\!-\!H \\
\mid\quad\quad\mid \\
H\quad\mid\quad H \\
\quad H\!-\!C\!-\!H \\
\quad\quad\mid \\
\quad\quad H
\end{array}
$$

This reaction may be represented symbolically as shown by the following equation:

$$A \rightarrow B$$

Rearrangements of this sort are very common in living systems, especially in the breakdown of food molecules. For example, certain sugars are rearranged to form others without any quantitative change. There is simply a rearrangement of atoms within the molecule.

Any chemical reaction, regardless of its classification, has two basic features: direction and rate. In the illustrations we have presented, direction is indicated in each case by an arrow. How is one able to predict whether the reaction will proceed to the right (as we have symbolized it) or to the left? Or, if we consider rate, what determines how fast and how long a reaction will proceed? Certainly, it is beyond the scope of our study to attempt a thorough consideration of these questions, but perhaps we can gain some understanding of direction and rate in chemical reactions.

DIRECTION   We have already stated two laws that have been formulated as basic generalizations about matter and energy, namely, the first and second laws of thermodynamics. All matter and energy systems studied thus far, including chemical reactions, exemplify these laws. We have also presented the concept that the atoms composing chemical compounds (reactants) are held together by chemical bonds and that these bonds represent chemical energy. In any case, the amount of chemical (bond) energy is dependent upon the degree of attraction between the atoms involved. As a matter of fact, bond energy may be defined as the amount of kinetic energy, or work, required to break a given bond. Thus, the total chemical energy of a compound may be defined as the amount of energy necessary to break all of the bonds of that compound.

Since a given reaction between compounds is an energy system, the direction in which a reaction will proceed is that of minimal potential chemical energy—that is, a state in which the total energy content of the reactants will be the least and their arrangement in the system the most random. This phenomenon agrees with the second law of thermodynamics, since the end result represents the most stable condition of the system. Consider, for example, the following generalized reaction:

$$A + B \rightleftharpoons C + D$$

In which direction will this reaction go? If the total energy of all the bonds in compounds A and B together is more than the total energy of those in compounds C and D, thus making the potential energy on the left greater than that on the right, then the reaction will proceed from left to right. The difference in the energy will be lost from the system. Thus, the reaction is illustrated in the following manner:

$$A + B \rightarrow C + D + \text{energy} \uparrow$$

Such a reaction that gives off energy is termed an *exergonic* reaction. For the most part, decompositional reactions are of this type.

If one assumes the converse of this situation, where the total energy of all of the bonds in A and B together is less than that of those in C and D together, thus making the potential energy on the left less than that on the right, the reaction will proceed from right to left. If it were desired that the reaction proceed from left to right, the difference in potential energy would have to be supplied from an external source. This process would be an "uphill" reaction, in terms of the second law, since it would be proceeding from a more stable to a less stable condition. This reaction may be illustrated as follows:

$$\downarrow$$
$$A + B + energy \rightarrow C + D$$

Such a reaction that requires energy from an external source is termed an *endergonic* reaction. For the most part, synthetic reactions are of this type. As will become apparent later on, decompositional (exergonic) reactions are so coupled with synthetic (endergonic) reactions in living systems that the former provide the energy necessary to push the latter "uphill."

In summary, the direction of chemical reactions is determined primarily by the energetics of the chemical system.

RATE   The second basic attribute of chemical reactions, the rate, is determined by several factors that influence the frequency and precision of collisions between the reactants. The most important of these factors are pressure, temperature, concentration, and catalysis. The effects of temperature and pressure are much more obvious than those of concentration and catalysis, and so we shall deal with these first two factors only briefly. The effect of pressure is due mainly to the compression that it brings about, thus forcing reactants closer together and increasing the rate of collision. Pressure has a greater effect on reaction rates of gases than on those of liquids and solids, since gases are highly compressible whereas liquids and solids are not. For the most part, temperature is more significant in determining reaction rates than pressure. Since reaction rate is determined to a great extent by collision rate, and collision rate is determined by the degree of movement of particles, it is not surprising that temperature greatly affects reaction rates. Motion is expressed as heat, which is measured as temperature. The only condition under which motion and heat would be absent is at absolute zero ($-273°C$) temperature. As the temperature of a reaction is increased, the collision rate of reactants increases, and thus the rate of the reaction increases. In general, it has been found that for each 10-degree increase in temperature (on the centigrade scale), a reaction is speeded up two or three times.

Aside from considerations of pressure and temperature, the amount per volume (concentration) of reactants will determine the collision rate and therefore the reaction rate. It should be apparent that the more molecules there are to collide in a given space, the faster will be their rate of collision. For example, if a reaction system is started with only reactants A and B, which react to form C and D, it is obvious that at first the reaction can go in only one direction (A + B → C + D) and the rate of the reaction will be dependent to a great extent upon the concentrations of A and B. As the reaction proceeds, however, some concentration of C and D is accumulated and the possibility for the reverse reaction thus comes to exist:

$$A + B \rightleftharpoons C + D$$

If one assumes that the reaction is reversible, the rate of the reverse reaction will be determined by the concentrations of C and D. Of course, if products C and D are taken out of the reaction as fast as they are formed, the reaction to the right can go to completion, using up all of the reactants A and B. If the reverse reaction is endergonic and no energy is supplied, the reaction A + B → C + D may also go to completion.

In a reversible reaction (and all chemical reactions are at least potentially reversible), conditions may exist where the reaction rate to the right is equal to the reaction rate to the left. At this point, the reaction is said to be in equilibrium. Does this mean that when the reaction A + B ⇌ C + D is in equilibrium, then the concentration of all reactants is equal? Perhaps we can answer this question by means of an analogy.

Suppose we have a closed container with a partition in the center (Fig. 4-12a). We place a specific number of grasshoppers on one side of the partition, which represents A + B. As the grasshoppers begin to jump, some will go high enough to pass over the partition to the other side (C + D). Initially, therefore, the passage of the grasshoppers over the partition can occur in one direction only (A + B → C + D), and the rate will be at its maximum. However, as time passes, more and more grasshoppers accumulate on the other side (C + D), and these jump also. Since it takes as much energy to move across the partition in one direction as in the other, equilibrium will be reached; that is, the rate at which the grasshoppers pass from A + B → C + D and from C + D → A + B will be equal when there are equal numbers of grasshoppers on each side (equal concentrations of reactants). In this situation, there is no energetic bias for the reaction to go faster in one direction than in the other.

In contrast, if the container is so constructed that the bottom of the container on the C + D side is several inches lower than the bottom on the A + B side (Fig. 4-12b), the situation will not be the same. In this case, as the grasshoppers begin to accumulate on the C + D side, they have much farther to jump in crossing back to the A + B side (the energy requirement is greater). Thus, at equilibrium, the number of grasshoppers on the C + D side will be considerably greater than on the A + B side. This example illustrates a reaction in which equilibrium is attained at un-

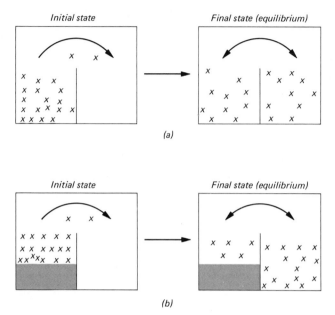

Figure 4.12. (a) Representation of a reversible reaction
in which equilibrium is reached at equal concentrations.
(b) Representation of a reversible reaction in which
equilibrium is reached at unequal concentrations. In terms
of the analogy (see text), the X's represent grasshoppers.

equal concentrations. In others words, equilibrium is a function of energetics as well as numbers of reactant particles.

The fourth factor that influences rate of reaction—catalysis—assumes
a special importance in living systems. For this reason, we shall consider it
at some length as a separate topic.

ACTIVATION ENERGY AND CATALYSIS

Regardless of whether a particular chemical reaction is exergonic or
endergonic, once it gets started, there may be an energy barrier to overcome
in starting the reaction. In such an event, a certain amount of energy must
be initially supplied to the reaction; this amount is termed *activation energy.*
Little or no activation energy is necessary in the case of some reactions;
those of biological importance, however, usually require considerable
amounts, especially if the reaction is to occur at a biologically significant
rate.

We have already emphasized the point that in order for a chemical
reaction to take place the reactants must come together, or collide. In the

case of large molecules, reactive sites may be restricted to a relatively small area of the molecule, in which case the collisions have to be quite precise. In addition, the collisions may have to be of sufficient force to overcome the initial repulsions of electrons surrounding the atoms of the interacting molecules. These are some of the reasons why activation energy is usually required in a reaction.

In order to create activation energy, students of chemistry use Bunsen burners, which are standard equipment in chemistry laboratories. In many cases, if two compounds are mixed together in a common solution with the expectation (based on thermodynamic principles) that they will react, they do so not simply because they are brought together. Even if there is a reaction, it may proceed at such a slow rate as to be imperceptible. However, when heat is applied, the reaction proceeds very rapidly. In this case, the heat serves as the energy of activation and enables the system (that is, the reactants in solution) to overcome the initial energy barrier. Heat increases the rate of movement of reacting molecules, thus increasing their chances for collision. It also increases the force of collision, thus enabling one reacting molecule to overcome any existing repulsion caused by the electrons of the other reacting molecule.

If such a reaction as that described is exergonic, the excess energy given off may be sufficient to keep the reaction going. This characteristic is analogous to starting a small gasoline engine with a pull cord. Once the initial energy is supplied, it manufactures its own spark, and the "reaction" is self-perpetuating. In contrast, if the reaction is endergonic, a continuous source of energy will have to be supplied as reaction energy. As an analogy, imagine using a large engine whose total energy output is utilized for manufacturing some product and whose "spark" must be supplied from an outside power source. To look at it another way, exergonic reactions go downhill once they get started, but there is an initial "hump" to overcome. In contrast, endergonic reactions are uphill all the way (Fig. 4-13).

In principle, living systems are so organized that excess energy from exergonic reactions supplies both the activation energy and the reaction energy for endergonic reactions. In applying this principle to living systems, however, one immediately encounters a high degree of complexity that demands a number of qualifications, one of which deserves attention at this point.

In the example of activation energy given above, heat was employed to give the exergonic reaction its initial push. However, a living system must operate, in most cases, within a rather narrow temperature range. The amount of heat required to serve as activation energy for many vital chemical reactions would completely destroy the living system. For this reason, one should expect to find some alternative mechanism for supplying activation energy. Such a mechanism does indeed exist in living systems in

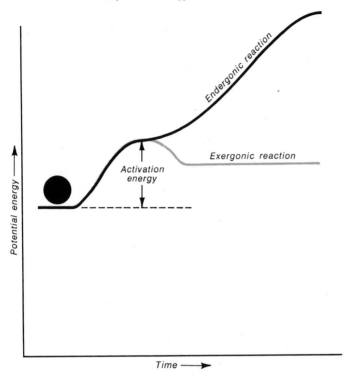

Figure 4.13. A contrast of endergonic and exergonic reactions from an energetic viewpoint. In each case, a reaction must be supplied with activation energy. Once it gets over the activation hump, an endergonic reaction still requires energy to be maintained. In contrast, an exergonic reaction proceeds downward, or on its own.

the form of substances called *catalysts*. Catalysts are substances that alter the rates of chemical reactions without being changed themselves in the process. They vary in structural complexity from simple ions to extremely large and complex molecules. The catalysts that are of greatest interest to biology are called *enzymes;* by chemical definition, they are protein molecules of considerable size and complexity. We shall defer a discussion of proteins to a later section of this chapter, but at this point, let us note a few characteristics of enzymes.

First of all, enzymes exhibit a high degree of specificity; that is, a given enzyme is able to catalyze only one type of reaction or, at most, a few related types. To draw an analogy, it is like a key specifically made for only one lock or one class of locks. Actually, this analogy is probably valid in a structural sense as well as a metaphorical one. A given enzyme apparently has a certain geometrical surface configuration on one part of the molecule into which only certain reactants fit. In an enzymatic reaction, the reactants are called *substrates*. The enzyme-substrate relationship is therefore very much like a key-lock relationship. When lock and key (substrate and enzyme) come into intimate contact, the substrate or substrates are altered in a highly specific manner (Fig. 4-14).

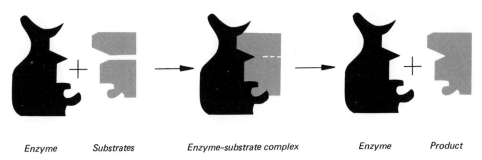

Enzyme   Substrates   Enzyme–substrate complex   Enzyme   Product

Figure 4.14. Diagrammatic representation of an enzyme-substrate reaction. According to this concept, the enzyme is geometrically specific for these two substrate molecules, which are combined into a single product molecule. The enzyme remains unchanged at the end ʹand may be involved over and over in identical reactions. The reaction illustrated is a synthetic reaction. How would you alter the diagram to show decomposition and rearrangement reactions?

Experimental evidence indicates that an enzyme first combines with a substrate or substrates to form an enzyme-substrate complex. Subsequently, the product or products of the reaction are released, and the enzyme molecule leaves the reaction in its original form. Thus, it can be used to catalyze the same reaction again, and it may serve millions of times before finally "wearing out." An enzymatic reaction can be illustrated symbolically as follows:

A + B + enzyme → AB-enzyme → AB + enzyme

This example shows a *synthetic* reaction, with A and B combining to form (synthesize) the product AB. The same type of reaction is illustrated in Fig. 4-14. In some cases, the enzyme forms a complex with only one substrate and the reaction yields two products; then it is called a *decomposition* reaction. A third type of enzymatic reaction is one in which the product is simply a rearranged substrate molecule. In this case, one has a *rearrangement* reaction.

As we have mentioned previously, the amount of heat ordinarily required to serve as activation energy for chemical reactions is incompatible with living systems. It appears that the chief function of enzymes, from a thermodynamic standpoint, is that of reducing the thermal energy of activation to a minimum. Instead of increasing the rate of movement of reactant molecules, the enzyme molecule offers a specific surface onto which the reactant molecules fit. If we repeat our earlier analogy, a locked door could be opened by melting the lock with a blowtorch, but this action would ruin the whole door—it is much more efficient to use a key.

There are many aspects of enzyme activity other than those related to specificity. We have concentrated on this particular characteristic because it points up some of the difficulties inherent in studying reactions occurring in living systems. Nevertheless, we must also mention that enzymatic activity is temperature-dependent and that the direction, rate, and duration of enzymatic reactions depend primarily upon the concentration of enzymes and/or the concentration of substrates, and upon the energy relationships existing between substrates and products.

The sum total of the chemical reactions in a living system is called *metabolism*. As an overall process, metabolism consists of ordered sequences of chemical reactions in which the product of one reaction is carried into another reaction (Fig. 4-15). Thus, equilibrium in the ordi-

Figure 4.15. Diagrammatic representation of a metabolic sequence in which products of a specific reaction are utilized in subsequent reactions to form a final end product used by the system. Thus, reaction $A + B \rightarrow C$ is not reversed. It should be understood that substances A, B and D are all fed into the system as raw materials, i.e., substrates.

nary sense of chemical reactions does not occur, because each reaction is like a step in an assembly line. In fact, "life" is partially defined by calling it a fight *against* chemical equilibrium.

Now that we have gained some understanding of matter and energy, as well as their interaction, let us proceed to investigate some of the major types of molecules that are basic to living systems.

4.2D Organic Molecules

For many years, it was supposed that living organisms were characterized by the presence of compounds fundamentally different from those found in matter not part of a living system. Many such compounds known to associate only with living organisms were called *organic* compounds, all others being designated *inorganic* compounds.

Although it is still a good rule in biology to associate organic compounds with organisms and their chemical activities, the original distinction is no longer valid in chemistry. To qualify according to present-day general usage, a compound need only be characterized by having one or more carbon atoms in its molecules to be considered organic, with the exception that one group of carbon compounds, the carbonates, are classed as inorganic. Thus, one now classifies as organic compounds many substances that are never associated with living organisms at all. In fact, thousands of such compounds that do not occur naturally have been synthesized in the laboratory. Furthermore, many inorganic compounds are quite closely associated with living systems, as will be made apparent in later chapters. Nevertheless, organic compounds, other than those produced synthetically in the laboratory, are the products of living systems. Thus, the original distinction is valid to a degree.

It should be pointed out again that carbon is a fundamental element of living matter. Its covalence (4) permits carbon to attach to various atoms and groups of atoms in a large number of different combinations. The relatively low potential energy of the carbon-carbon bond makes it possible for carbon atoms to form chains of almost unlimited length.* The number of carbon compounds known today exceeds that of all other compounds, indicating something of its versatility.

A vast array of organic molecules is found in living systems, and these molecules may be classified in a number of ways. However, for our purposes, we shall emphasize four basic types: *carbohydrates, lipids, proteins,* and *nucleic acids.* Because of their importance to living systems, they might be called the basic molecules of life.

Fundamentally, activities in a living system center around the synthesis of large molecules (*macromolecules* †) from small ones (*micro-*

---

* Paradoxical as it might seem, a chemical bond representing relatively little potential energy is very strong, whereas one that we call a high-energy bond is relatively weak. Can you advance a possible explanation for this?

† The term "macromolecule" is usually restricted to the extremely complex protein and nucleic acid molecules. We shall use it in a more general sense to describe a molecule that may be decomposed into several smaller units. We shall apply the term "micromolecule" to such units as are produced in decomposition or which may be "multiplied" in synthesis to form macromolecules.

molecules), and the decomposition of macromolecules to micromolecules (Fig. 4-16). Most of the molecules involved in these activities belong to one of the four listed types.

Macromolecule   Micromolecules

Figure 4.16. A diagrammatic representation of decompositional and synthetic reactions characteristic of living systems.

CARBOHYDRATES

As the name "carbohydrate" implies, these compounds contain the elements carbon, hydrogen, and oxygen according to the general formula $(CH_2O)_n$, where *n* may be any number. The carbohydrates are extremely important components of living matter. In addition to constituting the major fuel substances (sources of energy) in living systems, they play an important structural role, especially in plants.

Although there are carbohydrates whose molecules contain three, four, or five carbon atoms, the most common micromolecules are the six-carbon sugars called *monosaccharides*. It is from these six-carbon micromolecules that the complex macromolecules (*polysaccharides*) are built. Conversely, in a living system, the large polysaccharides must be broken down into the smaller monosaccharides in order to be utilized.

In the process of building the macromolecular polysaccharides from the micromolecular monosaccharides and in the decomposition of polysaccharides to monosaccharides, intermediate carbohydrate units called *oligosaccharides, trisaccharides,* and *disaccharides* are formed. The prefix *oligo-* means "a few" and describes a carbohydrate containing a few or several monosaccharide units joined together. The prefixes *tri-* and *di-* refer to "three" and "two," respectively. From the standpoint of increasing complexity, therefore, one can classify carbohydrates as monosaccharides, disaccharides, oligosaccharides, and polysaccharides.

The names of the simpler carbohydrates end in -*ose*. They either contain an *aldehyde* structure

$$\left(R - C \underset{H}{\overset{O}{\Big\Vert}} \right)$$

or a *ketone* structure,

$$\left(\overset{R}{\underset{R}{>}} C = O \right)$$

in which case they are called *aldoses* or *ketoses,* respectively. The number of carbon atoms in the molecule is sometimes designated by a prefix. Thus, a simple carbohydrate containing four carbon atoms is called a *tetrose;* one with five, a *pentose;* and one with six, a *hexose.*

Among the monosaccharides are the biochemically important compounds glucose, fructose, galactose, and ribose (Fig. 4-17). As shown by their structural formulas, glucose, fructose, and galactose are hexoses (six-carbon chain), whereas ribose is a pentose (five-carbon chain). Notice also that glucose, galactose, and ribose are aldoses, whereas fructose is a ketose.

Glucose is by far the most abundant monosaccharide in nature; that is, it is the most common micromolecular carbohydrate unit used as fuel by living cells. Fructose and galactose may also be used as fuel for cells; in fact, when glucose is broken down in living systems, it is changed to a form of fructose. In addition to its function as a fuel substance, ribose is one constituent of the nucleic acids, which we will discuss later.

Because of the relative importance of glucose to living systems, let us use it to illustrate the manner in which micromolecular carbohydrate units are linked together to form di-, tri-, oligo-, and polysaccharide carbohydrate structures. It should be understood, of course, that other micromolecules may be involved in a similar fashion.

In Fig. 4-17, the glucose molecule is illustrated as a straight or open chain. Actually, evidence indicates that it exists primarily as a cyclic or ring structure as shown in Fig. 4-18a. Notice that carbons 1 and 5 are connected to either side of an oxygen atom, thus forming a five-membered ring (pyranose form). A more convenient and realistic way of illustrating glucose is shown in Fig. 4-18b, where the pyranose ring can be seen more clearly.

Under certain conditions, two glucose units ·may bond together to form the disaccharide maltose, as shown in Fig. 4-19. Notice that this

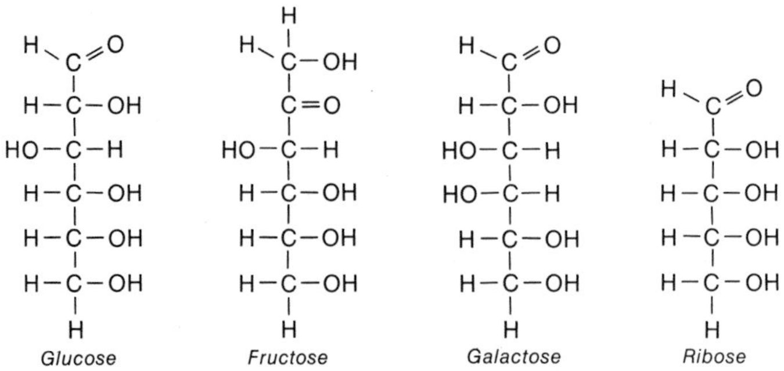

Figure 4.17. Open-chain structural formulas of four monosaccharides commonly found in living systems.

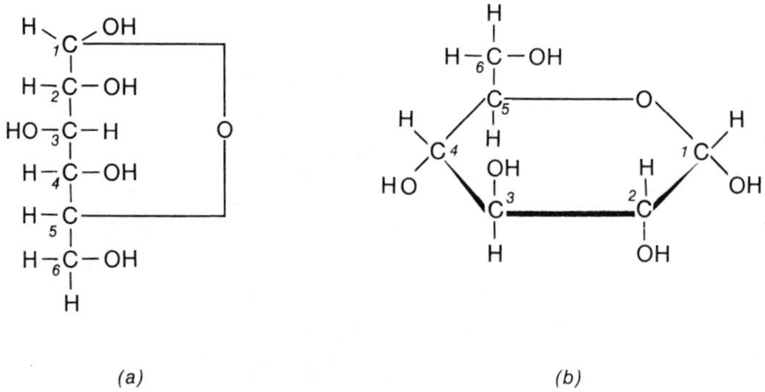

(a)   (b)

Figure 4.18. Two representations of the ring-form structure of the glucose molecule. For reference purposes, carbon atoms are numbered in order.

figure shows water being removed during the reaction and adjacent carbons (1 and 4) being bonded by an oxygen atom. In similar fashion, another glucose unit may be added to form a trisaccharide. The addition of still others would form an oligosaccharide; finally, a large macromolecular polysaccharide would result. This process occurs in many animals when the polysaccharide glycogen is formed and stored; in plants, the multiplication of glucose units produces starch as a polysaccharide. A reversal of the process just illustrated results in the breakdown of glycogen and starch to their component glucose molecules. This breakdown occurs in plant and animal digestion, for example, when the 1-4 carbon linkages are broken by enzymatic action and a molecule of water is split (H + OH) and added to each linkage site. Reactions involving a breakage of bonds with the addition of water are called *hydrolytic* reactions.

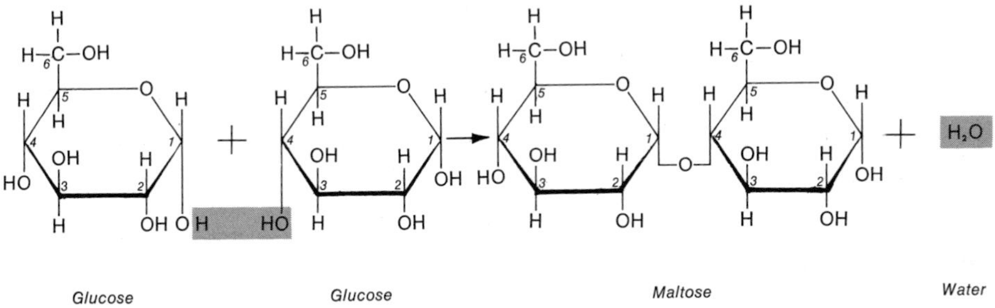

Figure 4.19. The combination of two glucose molecules in the formation of maltose, a disaccharide. In this representation, carbon atoms 1 through 5 are not drawn, although their respective locations are indicated by number.

LIPIDS

Lipids are a very diverse group of organic substances that are classified together because they are all soluble in such fat solvents as ether and chloroform. As a rule, they are insoluble in water. The lipids are generally divided into three main groups, as follows: simple lipids (fats and waxes), compound lipids (glycolipids and phospholipids), and steroids.

Let us concentrate first upon one of the simpler types, the fats. As is the case with so many of the biologically important organic compounds, fats are macromolecular complexes composed of smaller micromolecules, or building blocks. Specifically, a fat molecule is composed of the three-carbon micromolecule glycerol, to which are attached three fatty acids of varying length. Figure 4-20 shows the structure of a common animal fat, tristearin, which is formed by the combination of three molecules of stearic acid, a fatty acid, with one molecule of glycerol. As Fig. 4-20 shows, the hydrogens from the three alcohol ($-CH_2OH$) groups of the glycerol molecule break off with the hydroxyl (OH) radical from the three acid groups

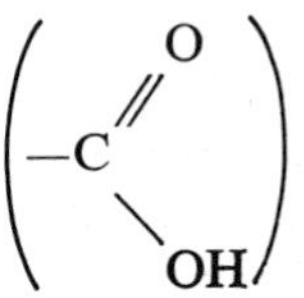

of the stearic acid to form three molecules of water, thus leaving the adjacent carbons bonded together by oxygen. This type of linkage

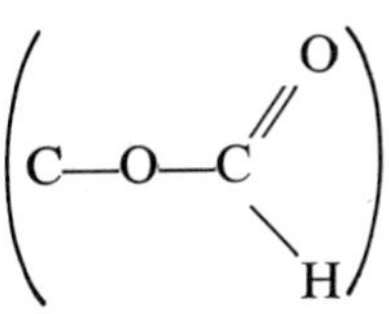

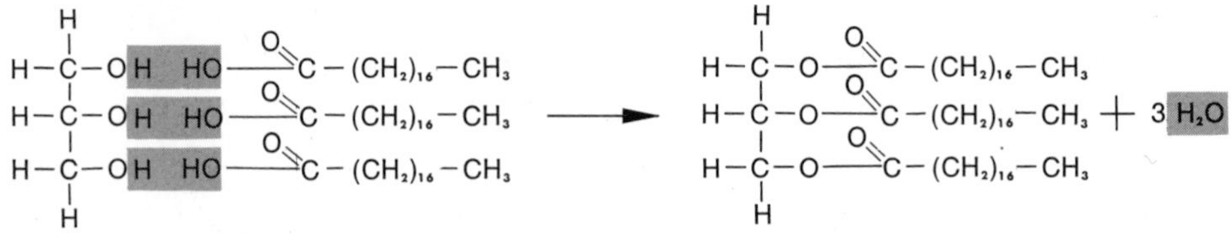

1 Glycerol   3 Stearic acid   1 Tristearin   3 Water

Figure 4.20. Synthesis of the animal fat stearin from glycerol and stearic acid.

is called an *ester linkage* and the true fats are termed *glycerol esters* or *triglycerides.*

Fats are quite common in the bodies of animals and are found to a lesser degree in plants. They represent stored energy; and, gram for gram, they yield the most energy of any foodstuff. Stored fats are broken down by a reversal of the process shown in Fig. 4-20. By this means, fatty acids and glycerol are made available to the body as fuel substances. This breakdown also occurs in the digestion of fats. As a process, it involves the addition of water at existing ester linkages, which are broken in the process. In other words, the breakdown of fats, like that of macromolecular carbohydrates, is hydrolytic.

The waxes, which we shall mention only in passing, are similar to the fats since they are fatty acid esters. However, instead of being esters of glycerol, they are esters of long-chain alcohols. They are found as protective coatings on the skins and furs of animals and on the leaves and fruits of plants.

The compound lipids (glycolipids and phospholipids) are important structural compounds in living systems. Chemical analysis and electron microscope studies strongly indicate that a double layer of phospholipids makes up a large part of the membranes of cells. In addition, they are thought to play a role in a number of metabolic processes, including fat metabolism, respiration, and enzyme activation. The glycolipids are quite common in certain nervous tissues of the more complex animals.

The steroids are chemically related to the triglycerides and compound lipids, although their molecular structure is quite different from that of other lipids. They are classified as lipids primarily because of their solubility in fat solvents. Steroids are very important molecules in the bodies of complex animals, where they are found primarily in the heart, blood vessels, and liver. In addition, certain vitamins and hormones produced in animal bodies are steroids.

Many biologists regard proteins as the fundamental compounds of living systems. Whether or not any one type of molecule may be singled out as "fundamental" is open to question, but proteins play many extremely important roles. Although they are structurally and functionally diverse, they exhibit certain characteristics that enable us to make some generalizations about them.

In terms of elementary chemical composition, proteins always contain carbon, hydrogen, oxygen, and nitrogen, and they usually contain sulfur as well. The micromolecular units are called *amino acids,* and a given protein molecule may consist of several hundred or even thousands of these units.* The structure of a typical amino acid is shown in Fig. 4-21, where R represents a chemical group that is specific for a particular

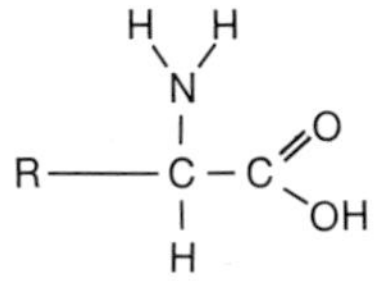

Figure 4.21. Generalized structure of an amino acid. Note the relative positions of the carboxyl (COOH) and amino (NH$_2$) groups.

amino acid. The feature shared by all amino acids is a carbon atom (called the alpha carbon) to which is attached a carboxyl (COOH), or acid, group and an amino (NH$_2$) group—hence the name amino acids. Figure 4-22 illustrates some of the diversity exhibited by the amino acids. A complete listing and illustration of their structure may be found in most textbooks concerned with organic chemistry.

When amino acids link together, they do so in such a way that the acid (COOH) group of one is attached to the amino (NH$_2$) group of another. The bond thus formed between the carbon of the acid group and the nitrogen group is termed a peptide bond. This linkage can be illustrated by showing how two amino acids are joined together (Fig.

---

* Of the many amino acids known to chemistry, only 20 are commonly found in proteins. In referring to the total number of amino acids, we mean those 20.

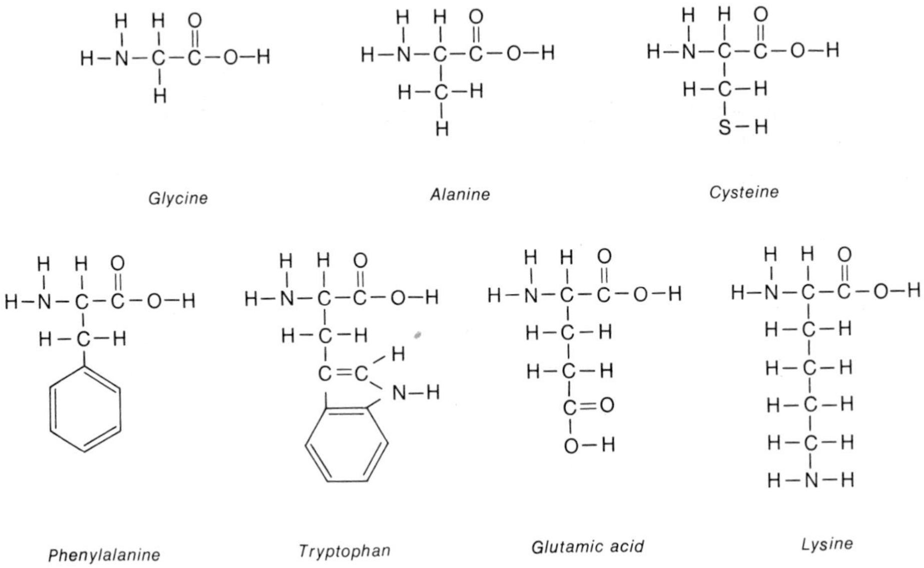

Glycine   Alanine   Cysteine

Phenylalanine   Tryptophan   Glutamic acid   Lysine

Figure 4.22.   Structural formulas of several representative amino acids.

4-23). In this particular example, the two simplest amino acids, glycine and alanine, are subjected to dehydration (water removal). As shown, the carboxyl group of one molecule gives up its OH and the amino group of

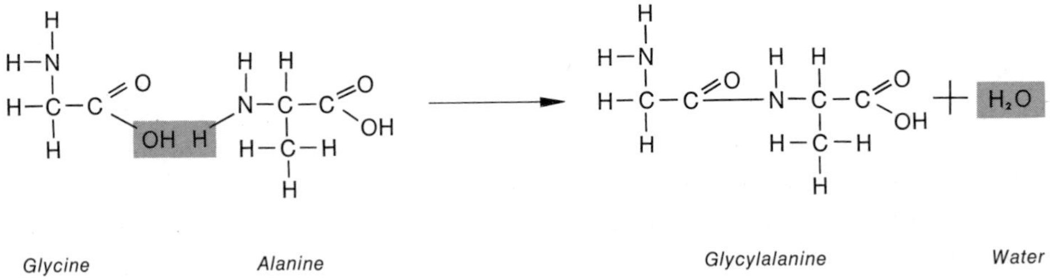

Glycine   Alanine   Glycylalanine   Water

Figure 4.23.   The combination of glycine and alanine by dehydration. Note the peptide bond formed between these two molecules by the splitting off of water.

the other reacting molecule gives up one H. Water is thus formed, and the two molecules are linked from carbon to nitrogen. By addition of any one of the 20 amino acids to this dipeptide, a tripeptide would be formed. In similar fashion, continued addition to the chain would lead to the formation of a large polypeptide chain—that is, a large protein molecule. The specific amino acid sequence of any given protein molecule is called its *primary structure*.

In the formation of a single protein molecule, there are 20 different amino acids that may be arranged in any order to form hundreds of sequences (or thousands of sequences in the largest protein molecules). Obviously, a vast number of different protein molecules can exist. This situation is analogous to forming words from an alphabet of 20 letters. If there is no prescribed sequence in which the letters must appear, then the number of words that can be formed becomes almost infinite. As we shall see, this high degree of structural diversity is very important in the many and varied functional roles fulfilled by proteins in living systems.

The protein molecule owes its ultimate configuration to the diversity of exposed chemical (R) groups comprising the amino acids that determine the primary structure of the molecule. Some of this diversity is illustrated in Fig. 4-22, where the R groups may represent ring structures, acid groups, amino groups, or sulfhydryl (SH) groups. This diversity makes it possible for a number of bonding situations (including the hydrogen bond) to develop between adjacent groups. These interactions cause the molecule to fold upon itself, producing what is termed the *secondary* and *tertiary* structure of the molecule. The tertiary structure gives the molecule a final and specific surface configuration, leaving certain active groups exposed to react with other molecules and also shielding certain groups from reaction with other molecules.

Earlier, we discussed enzymes and the role that they play as organic catalysts in living systems. You will recall that we defined enzymes as proteins. In the light of this discussion on the structure of protein molecules, perhaps we are now in a better position to understand the specificity of enzymes as well as certain other aspects of their activity.

Enzymes belong to the group of globular or spherical proteins. Each type of enzyme molecule has a very specific surface configuration due to its primary, secondary, and tertiary structure. The specific configuration exposes certain chemical groups that will react quite readily with certain other chemical groups upon contact. Thus, it is not difficult to understand that an almost infinite number of different and quite specific enzymes having certain active sites (exposed chemical groups) may exist. Perhaps our previous analogy of a lock-and-key type of relationship between an enzyme and substrate molecule is now clearer and more meaningful.

NUCLEIC ACIDS

Although the nucleic acids have been known to chemistry since the 19th century, their importance to living systems was not appreciated until recently. Of the four basic molecules of life that we have mentioned, there is more research being done at the present time in the nucleic acids than in any of the others. In fact, one of the nucleic acids, deoxyribonucleic acid (DNA), is sometimes called "the basic molecule of life." The role of the nucleic acids as genetic material directing and controlling the metabolism of living systems will be discussed in a later chapter. We aim here to gain some insight into the structure of these large organic molecules. Such insight is essential to an understanding of their functional roles in living systems.

The nucleic acids are threadlike macromolecules composed of thousands of atoms. There are two different types of nucleic acids: *deoxyribonucleic acid* (DNA) and *ribonucleic acid* (RNA). The difference between the two will become apparent as we consider the micromolecular units that make up these large macromolecules.

By treating DNA or RNA with mild hydrolytic agents (acids, bases, etc.), one can hydrolyze them into smaller units called *nucleotides*. The nucleotides may be considered the micromolecular building blocks of the large macromolecular nucleic acids. However, the nucleotides themselves are relatively large molecules; and when they are hydrolyzed further, they break down into *nucleosides* and *phosphoric acid*. The nucleosides, under treatment with still stronger hydrolytic agents, break down into *pentose sugars* and *nitrogen-rich bases*. This sequence of events is illustrated in Fig. 4-24. Thus, a nucleotide is composed of one molecule of phosphoric

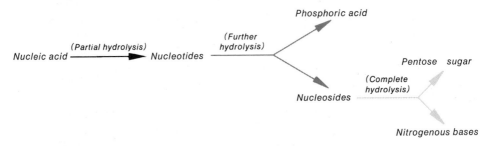

Figure 4.24. The degradation (breakdown) sequence in the hydrolysis of nucleic acids.

acid; one, of a pentose sugar; and one, of a nitrogenous base. There are five major nitrogenous bases involved, and these fall into two categories, the *pyrimidines* and the *purines*. Three of the five (*cytosine, uracil, and thymine*) are pyrimidines; the other two (*adenine and guanine*) are purines. Although it is not essential at this point that we distinguish between pyrimidines and purines from a technical standpoint, it will be helpful to look at the formula of each base (Fig. 4-25). As you can see, the three pyrimidines are single rings, and the two purines are double-ringed molecules.

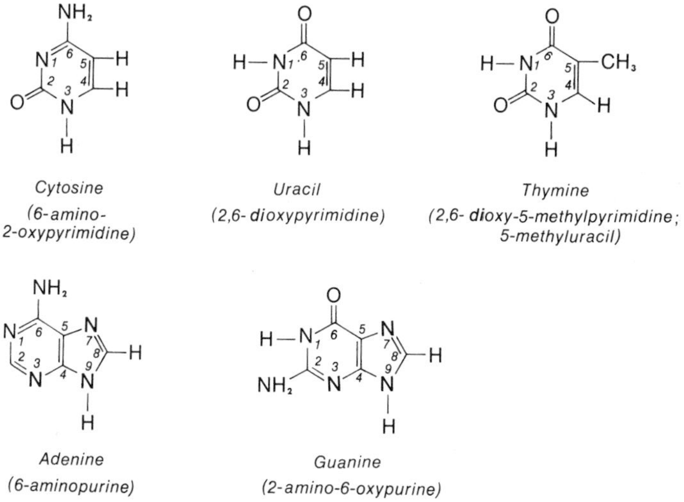

Cytosine
*(6-amino-
2-oxypyrimidine)*

Uracil
(2,6-dioxypyrimidine)

Thymine
*(2,6-dioxy-5-methylpyrimidine;
5-methyluracil)*

Adenine
(6-aminopurine)

Guanine
(2-amino-6-oxypurine)

Figure 4.25. Structural formulas of the five nitrogenous bases found in nucleic acids. The upper three are pyrimidines, and the lower two are purines.

The two basic types of nucleic acid, DNA and RNA, differ in the kinds of pyrimidine bases composing them. The nucleotides of DNA contain cytosine and thymine, while those of RNA contain cytosine and uracil. Both contain the purine bases adenine and guanine.

The two pentose sugars found in nucleic acids are *ribose* and *deoxyribose*. You will recall that we gave the formula for ribose when we discussed carbohydrates (Fig. 4-17), and we mentioned its presence in the nucleic acid molecule at that point. The ring structure for ribose and deoxyribose along with the structure of a nucleoside (nitrogenous base and ribose bonded together) are shown in Fig. 4-26. The difference between the structure of ribose and that of deoxyribose is the absence of oxygen at position 2 in the deoxyribose molecule. The absence of an oxygen atom is implied in the prefix *deoxy-,* which means "take away oxygen." The pentose sugar found in RNA is ribose; that found in DNA is deoxyribose. This difference and the substitution of uracil for thymine in RNA constitute the primary structural differences between DNA and RNA.

A nucleotide is formed by adding phosphoric acid to a nucleoside,

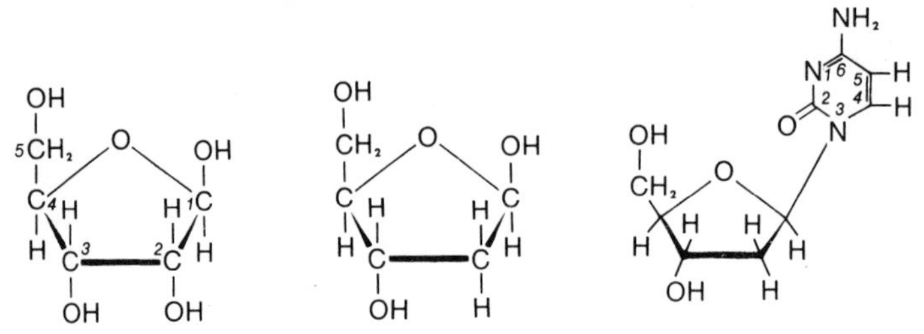

Ribose *2-Deoxyribose* *Deoxycytidine (a nucleoside)*

Figure 4.26. Structural formulas of ribose, deoxyribose, and a nucleoside. This particular nucleoside consists of deoxyribose and cytosine bonded together.

as shown in Fig. 4-27. By this means, a nucleotide may be formed involving any of the nucleosides—that is, a given nitrogenous base bonded to either ribose or deoxyribose.

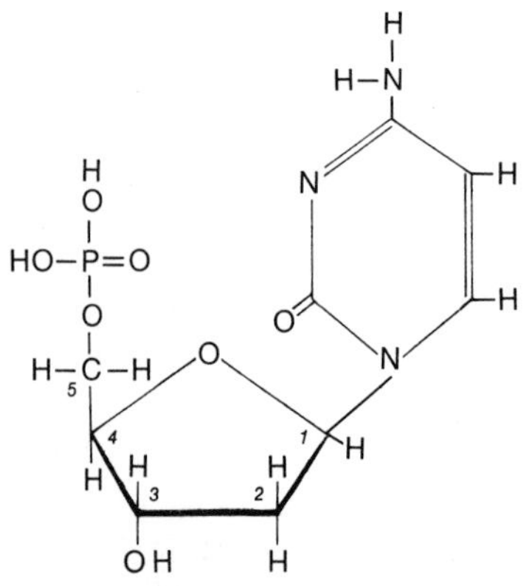

Deoxycytidine-3-monophosphate (a nucleotide)

Figure 4.27. Structural formula of a nucleotide. Compare with Figure 4.26.

As shown in Fig. 4-28a, DNA and RNA molecules consist of chains of nucleotides linked together by a phosphate group between position 5 of the ribose of one nucleotide and position 3 of the ribose of another nucleotide. Thus, nucleic acid molecules exist as long chains of nucleotides, possessing a sugar-phosphate "backbone" from which various bases extend. This structure is represented diagrammatically in Fig. 4-28b.

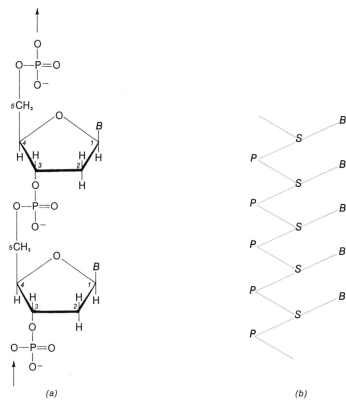

Figure 4.28. (a) Nucleotide linkage in the formation of a nucleic acid molecule. Is this DNA or RNA? What compounds might be attached at B? (b) Diagrammatic representation of the relationship among the sugar, phosphate, and base (purine or pyrimidine) molecules comprising a nucleic acid.

It is important to note that the linking of nucleotides by phosphate in a nucleic acid molecule is of a nonspecific type. The specific base in each nucleotide is not directly involved in the linkage. Therefore, the bases may occur in a variety of sequences, forming chains of varying lengths. This structural feature imparts a great deal of variety to the nucleic acid molecule. When we consider that thousands of nucleotides may be present in any sequence in the nucleic acid molecule, it becomes apparent that an almost infinite variety of molecular types might exist. We shall show in a later chapter that this structural feature of the nucleic acids is directly related to their physiological role in living systems.

For a number of years after most of these details regarding nucleic acids were known, the precise structure of the nucleic acid molecule was still a matter of almost pure speculation. However, in 1953, M. H. F. Wilkins, J. D. Watson, and F. H. C. Crick proposed a model for the structure of the DNA molecule based on information from X-ray diffraction and electron microscope studies. They surmised that the nucleotides composing a DNA molecule do not exist as straight chains but that each nucleotide has about a 36-degree turn in its structure, causing the chain to coil into an alpha helix. Thus, a length of 10 nucleotides makes a complete 360-degree turn. They also determined that the diameter across the molecule is consistently about 20 Å * throughout the length of the molecule and that the molecule is therefore not a single chain or helix, but a double helix, with the two chains paralleling each other like the coils in a rope. The two coils are held together by hydrogen bonds, which link the bases together across the double helix (Fig. 4-29). Let us imagine a long, flexible ladder that is twisted from either end until a 360-degree turn is taken at every 10th rung. In this analogy, the sides of the ladder represent sugar-phosphate linkages, and the rungs represent the hydrogen-bonded base pairs. This concept of the DNA molecule is generally accepted in biochemistry and biology, and it is frequently termed the *Watson-Crick model.*

It was further determined by physical and chemical analysis that there is a precise or specific quality in the bonding across the double helix —that is, that certain bases must pair off with certain other bases. The diameter of 20 Å across the helix suggested that a pyrimidine bonds with a purine. You will recall that a purine molecule involves a double ring; and, as a consequence, it is of greater diameter than a pyrimidine molecule. According to size estimates, a distance of 20 Å would not accommodate two purines, and it appeared to be too great a distance for a pair of pyrimidines. However, it was estimated that a purine bonded to a pyrimidine ought to fit the space very nicely. After any given type of DNA is hydrolyzed completely, the relative proportions of the four nitrogenous bases may be determined. Then the following relationships are evident: †

$$
\begin{aligned}
\text{Adenine (A)} &= \text{thymine (T)} \\
\text{Guanine (G)} &= \text{cytosine (C)} \\
A &\neq G \\
T &\neq C \\
A + G &= T + C \\
A + T &\neq G + C
\end{aligned}
$$

---

* Below the level of the millimeter, there are three units of linear measurement that should be defined at this point: A millimeter (mm) equals 1,000 microns (μ); a micron equals 1,000 millimicrons (mμ); and a millimicron equals 10 angstroms (Å). Therefore, 1 Å = 0.1 mμ = 0.0001 μ = 0.0000001 mm.

† By substituting numerical values (for example, let A = 15 per cent, G = 35 per cent), these relationships may be made clearer.

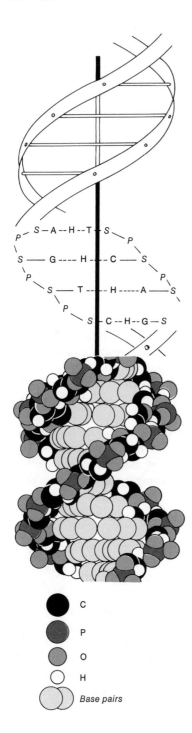

C

P

O

H

Base pairs

Figure 4.29. The helix of DNA, with
three different ways of representing the
molecular arrangement. **Top,** general picture of the double helix, with the phos-
phate-sugar combinations making up the
outside spirals. The cross bars represent
base pairs. **Middle,** a somewhat more detailed representation: phosphate (P), sugar
(S), adenine (A), thymine (T), guanine
(G), cytosine (C), and hydrogen (H).
Bottom, detailed structure showing how
the space is filled with atoms: carbon
(C), oxygen (O), hydrogen (H), phos-
phorus (P), and the base pairs. [After
C.P. Swanson, **The Cell,** 3rd. ed. (Englewood Cliffs, N.J.: Prentice-Hall, Inc.,
1969).]

It is evident from these relationships that adenine must be bonded to thymine and cytosine must be bonded to guanine across the double helix. In other words, for every adenine in a DNA molecule there must be a thymine, and for every cytosine there must be a guanine. It is extremely important to note at this point, however, that this characteristic of the DNA molecule does not affect the possible wide variability in the sequence of nucleotides that may exist in the chain in an "up and down" direction. It should also be pointed out that there are a few cases in which DNA apparently exists as a single strand rather than as a double helix.

The Watson-Crick model has withstood the rigors of numerous experimental tests since 1953. It has emerged as the best working model available for the structure of DNA. In fact, Watson, Crick, and Wilkins were awarded the Nobel prize in physiology and medicine in 1962 for their formulation of this model.

The precise structure of RNA is much less clear than that of DNA. In some cases, it appears to be single-stranded; in others, double-stranded; and in still others, a combination of both. Its structural variability probably relates to its functional variability, which we shall discuss in a later chapter.

In summary, the basic organic molecules of living systems are classified as carbohydrates, lipids, proteins, and nucleic acids. Each of these types may be distinguished from the others according to chemical composition and structural characteristics. In general, carbohydrates and lipids are composed of relatively simple molecules, while those of proteins and nucleic acids are extremely complex.

Let us return to our earlier statement that life may be considered a set of properties that emerge within a matter-energy continuum. We have gained a degree of appreciation for the nature of matter and energy, their interaction, and the basic macromolecules of living systems. At this point, let us attempt to gain further understanding of the matter-energy continuum by considering the relationship that exists among its major physical components.

4.2E The Physical Nature of Living Systems

The physical material that constitutes living systems is called *protoplasm* (Greek *protos,* first + *plasma,* form). It is typically a more or less viscous, translucent kind of material that is a complex mixture of many substances, although there are variations in its physical and chemical composition. It may contain material that is not, within itself, a necessary accompaniment of life, such as fat or starch particles. Whenever the term "protoplasm" is used, however, it refers to a given quantity of matter in which the characteristics of life are manifested. By means of special chemical techniques, much has been learned about the nature and organization of this material. Such knowledge has shed considerable light on certain fundamental life processes. Furthermore, many important problems that are the concern of modern biology involve the physics and chemistry of protoplasm.

CHEMICAL COMPOSITION OF PROTOPLASM

From the chemical standpoint, it might logically be supposed that protoplasm should contain rare or unusual elements that are completely absent from nonliving matter. This is not the case. The most abundant elements found in protoplasm are also among the most abundant in the nonliving world. The major elements found in most protoplasmic systems, and their approximate relative percentages by weight, are shown in Table 4-1 in the appendix. In addition to those elements listed, traces of other elements (for example, iodine and boron) are usually present. These trace elements are highly variable quantitatively in different protoplasmic systems. They constitute only a small fraction of 1 per cent of the total matter in any given living system.

The elements found in protoplasm do not actually exist in elemental form, although some of them are present as ions. In ionic form, they are functional in such processes as energy transfer, enzymatic activity, nerve conduction, and membrane permeability. For the most part, elements are organized into compounds, both organic and inorganic. Hence, there is a range in complexity of organization all the way from ions to the large macromolecules discussed in the preceding section.

The inorganic compounds of protoplasm are water and a variety of electrolytes (acids, bases, and salts). The organic compounds include carbohydrates, lipids, proteins, and nucleic acids. The average relative amounts of these substances in protoplasmic systems are as shown in Table 4-2.

It should be pointed out that "average" or "typical" protoplasm does not exist, since protoplasmic systems vary so widely. However, the approximations listed in the table give some idea of the relative abundance of these substances in protoplasmic systems and may generally be considered typical.

THE PHYSICAL NATURE OF PROTOPLASM [6]

From the foregoing discussion, it might be inferred that the most outstanding feature of protoplasm is its chemical makeup. Although protoplasm does contain unique materials such as enzymes and nucleic acids, the compounds and elements might be mixed together in the exact proportions found in any given unit of protoplasm, but the resulting material would not be alive. Even after a unit of protoplasm has died, it is no longer protoplasm by correct definition. The ingredients are still all present, but the organization is lacking. The one factor that renders such a chemical mixture living, therefore, is the physical relationship that the various components bear to each other.

A protoplasmic system is a *multiphasic* system; that is, it consists of molecular aggregates and particles of various sizes, all of which are contained in a liquid medium. Multiphasic systems may be classified on the basis of the size of the particles involved. If the particles are sufficiently small to form a homogeneous dispersion throughout the medium, they are said to be *in solution*. If their size is such that they settle out of the medium in response to gravity, they are said to be *in suspension*. Finally, if the particles in such a system are intermediate in size—that is, too large to go into solution and too small to settle out—they are said to be *colloidal*. The range in size of colloidal particles is 0.001 to 0.1 μ. Thus, particles as small as 0.001 μ or smaller go into solution, while those as large as 0.1 μ or larger settle out. Particles of intermediate size are dispersed in the medium, forming a colloidal system.

A protoplasmic system is a combination of several substances in solution and several types of particles in suspension. The solvent, of course, is water, which is also the liquid medium or phase in which colloidal particles are dispersed.

It is beyond the scope of our treatment here to discuss the various types of colloidal systems that may exist in protoplasm. It is sufficient for our purposes to understand that protoplasm is a colloidal system involving solids (for example, fibrous protein aggregations) and liquids (for example, oil or fat droplets) dispersed within a liquid. In such a system, many reactions occur at the surfaces of particles or aggregations rather than between individual molecules. Furthermore, the direction or rate of such reactions depends to a great degree not only upon the electrical charges at the surfaces of the highly polarized particles but also upon the size and shape of each particle.

Many characteristics of protoplasm, including the formation of large macromolecular complexes called *organelles,* may at least partially be explained on the basis of the characteristics of a colloidal system. However, it may be a mistake to assume that all properties of protoplasm can be duplicated by any test-tube colloidal complex.

Let us return to our earlier statement that physical relationships within protoplasmic systems are ultimately responsible for those characteristics that we summarize by the term "living." Perhaps an analogy will clarify this point.

Suppose a master watchmaker invents a clock whose parts are so intricately arranged that only he knows the secret of its operation. Suppose that he dies, and the clock is given to a novice. Upon observing the clock and its parts, this second person might well conclude that the clock operates successfully because it is composed of certain wheels and gears. In a sense, of course, this is true. It could hardly operate without them. However, many things are composed of wheels and gears that do not keep time. In the final analysis, it is the physical relationship that these parts bear to each other that makes the instrument a clock. If the novice tries to take it apart, he will have wheels and gears, but he will not have a clock and never will again unless he can learn the secret of the original relationships. There is yet another point to be made from this analogy. When the master craftsman originally made the clock, he put a great deal of his "genius" into it. Does this mean that there is some mysterious influence, undefinable in physical and chemical terms, still floating around inside the clock? Not at all. His genius is measurable only by its results and does not constitute a vitalistic factor in the operation of the clock.

Let us carry our analogy of the clock one step further. Suppose that the novice to whom the clock is given has great difficulty in taking it apart in order to observe its inner workings. In exasperation, he finally takes a sledge hammer and smashes the clock. Because of this drastic action, a random dispersal results. The task of the novice in understanding the inner structure of the clock is now complicated by the fact that it is greatly distorted. One is faced with something of the same difficulty in studying protoplasm. In getting at the contents of living systems, one must use drastic treatments to break them down to their component parts. Thus, when either a chemical or a physical analysis of protoplasm is made, one cannot get a very accurate picture of the actual relationships existing in the functional or living state.

Obviously, this approach is a mechanistic one; in philosophical terms, it is thoroughly Cartesian. This view of living systems may not be sufficient to explain *all* life phenomena, but it is an exceedingly fruitful viewpoint at this level of consideration. Thus, in formulating a conceptual scheme, the biochemist and the biophysicist make their greatest gains by *acting as if* a unit of protoplasm is like a miniature clock. Cartesian reductionism can be a very useful viewpoint at certain levels of consideration in the study of living systems.

Because the machinery of protoplasmic systems is quite intricate, there are formidable barriers standing in the way of understanding it, to say nothing of the immense task of putting it together synthetically. Hence, most biologists are not overly optimistic that either the goal of complete understanding or the goal of artificial production of living protoplasm are near accomplishment, although great strides have been made toward both. **Thus far, life seems to come only from previous life in an unbroken chain, at least under conditions that prevail at present on earth.** In other words, the conceptual scheme of biogenesis is vindicated by modern biochemical and biophysical research.

4.3 THE CONCEPT OF BIOGENESIS REVISITED

As you recall, the Aristotelian concept of abiogenesis (the notion that spontaneous generation of organisms occurs in nature) was widely accepted as late as the mid-17th century. In 1668, however, Francesco Redi refuted it, at least as it applied to the world of visible organisms, by means of his elegant experiments. Then in the mid-18th century, after the discovery of microorganisms, Needham rejuvenated the concept of abiogenesis. In spite of the contributions of Spallanzani (1769) and Schwann (1838), it was not fully discredited until Louis Pasteur did his definitive research in the early 1860's. Even then, abiogenesis was not "disproved." It can never be disproved in the strict sense; yet, the scientific community as a whole repudiated it, because the alternate conceptual scheme, biogenesis, became a better instrument of explanation and predictability. In an operational sense, it has remained so to the present time.

However, the concept of biogenesis ignores at least one nagging problem: Where and how did life begin in the first place? [7] This question presents the biologist with something of an embarrassing dilemma: If he attempts to account for the origin of life in naturalistic terms, he reverts in effect to abiogenesis; and if he falls back upon metaphysical explanations, he risks a violation of the first principle of science. This dilemma is particularly significant because biology underwent a long struggle before it finally repudiated abiogenesis, and the history of science as a whole is virtually one continuous battle to clarify its first principle. Quite understandably, there is a general reluctance to yield the hard-won gains either way.

For many decades after Pasteur's work was performed, there was no satisfactory way to answer the question about the origin of life. In the first place, biologists tended to think of life in very discontinuous terms—that is, as though there is an abrupt and discernible difference between living and nonliving entities. Secondly, little was known about physical conditions that may have existed many eons ago on earth.

At this point, let us review some of what we have learned about the phenomenon called life. Its physical basis, protoplasm, is composed of many substances held together in a highly organized chemical and physical state. Obviously, the task of synthesizing an organism *de novo* would be an immense one and would demand the proper substances in exact proportions with just the right physical arrangement. The fundamental compounds required would be water, a variety of inorganic salts, and such organic compounds as carbohydrates, lipids, proteins, and nucleic acids (see Table 4-2 in the appendix), not to mention a host of substances that we have not mentioned at all. Regardless of other chemical requirements, the large and complex proteins and nucleic acids would seem to be absolutely essential, since they are the only information-carrying molecules of which we know. To say the very least, the origin of these large molecules and their physical interaction must be accounted for before we can even begin to think about the origin of a living system. Obviously, the problem is an immense one, since the probability of the right substances coming together at the right time would seem to be extremely low.

However, let us conceive of the process in stepwise terms. Ions *do* interact with other ions and with molecules, and complexes do eventually form, however slowly. Thus, over a long enough period of time, a complex of substances could conceivably build up.

Present evidence indicates that the earth is at least 5 billion years old and that life in *some* form has been present on earth for at least 3 billion of those years. Thus, we are talking about a magnitude of time that defies human imagination. Our point is simply this: If events are possible, no matter how improbable for any given short space of time, they are probably inevitable eventually. Let us say (conservatively) that 2 billion years were required for the stepwise process of chemical and physical interaction to produce a self-perpetuating system. Although highly improbable in terms of any given reaction at a given period of time, the overall process becomes quite probable indeed. In fact, unless we abandon all attempts to explain the origin of life by naturalistic means, it *must* have happened.

This line of reasoning had occurred to a number of biologists and geologists well before the mid-1900's. By that time, sufficient evidence had accumulated that workers in this field were able to construct a general picture of chemical and physical conditions that characterized the primeval earth. Apparently, there was little or no oxygen; the atmosphere was heavy with water vapor, ammonia (NH_3), hydrogen (H_2), and methane (CH_4). The temperature was apparently rather high, and conditions were such that frequent electrical discharges in the form of lightning were released into this atmosphere, which means that large amounts of energy were available to activate chemical reactions.

In 1953, it occurred to Stanley Miller, who was a graduate student at the University of Chicago, that a primeval atmosphere might actually be created in a closed container. If the geophysicists were right about the constitution of the primeval atmosphere, Miller reasoned, then one might actually be able to obtain organic substances, synthesized at random within the container. Accordingly, Miller built a relatively simple apparatus (Fig. 4-30), enclosed the proper compounds, provided for maintenance of an

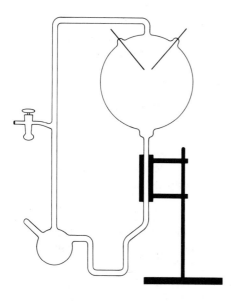

Figure 4.30.   Miller's closed-chamber apparatus used in his original work on the random synthesis of organic compounds. [Adapted from S. L. Miller, *Journal of the American Chemical Society* 77:2351 (1955).]

elevated temperature, flashed a spark of electricity (simulated lightning) through it for a week, and then analyzed his results. Amazingly, he had produced a number of compounds that are presently associated only with living systems: several amino acids, a variety of organic acids, and certain miscellaneous compounds. Miller's work was repeated and corroborated by others; and subsequently, variations in the technique produced still other compounds. Step by step, such complex molecules as nucleotides were ultimately synthesized.

The implication of Miller's work should be clear. It provided experimental evidence that the basic micromolecules essential to the synthesis of a living system *could* have arisen under conditions thought to have been present in the primeval atmosphere, thus lending great weight to a naturalistic hypothesis for the origin of life. Furthermore, the probability of these events was greatly increased over the probability that had been assumed by many scientists, who tended to think in terms of present-day conditions.

At this point, a number of objections might be raised. First, it is difficult to imagine the synthesis of large macromolecules in the absence of enzymes, and enzymes are themselves macromolecules. However, let us remember that enzymes are concerned only with the *rate* of chemical reactions; they do not initiate them. Here again, we can see that the crux of the argument is time. Given the long period of time that was available, it was probably inevitable that these reactions would occur. But, it might be asked, are not such macromolecules as enzymes highly perishable? Long periods of time would seem to work against the sufficient accumulation of all substances involved for there to be any appreciable probability of their interacting together.

There are two major factors that are responsible for the perishable nature of organic molecules: heterotrophic microorganisms * and the process of chemical oxidation. It is relatively easy to dismiss the first of these factors, since microorganisms are living systems and we are talking about a time when such systems were only evolving. The second factor, oxidation, must be considered in the light of authority. Geologists and astronomers are in fair agreement that the early atmosphere contained practically no free oxygen or, for that matter, carbon dioxide. Both of these gases were evidently put into our atmosphere by living systems themselves through the processes of photosynthesis and respiration, which we shall discuss later. The oxygen of the early atmosphere is thought to have been bound up in metal oxides and water. Thus, organic compounds could have been stable over long periods of time in an atmosphere that was free of molecular oxygen and devoid of living systems. This explanation partly accounts for why life evidently originated from nonliving antecedents at least one time but apparently does so no longer.

Let us consider yet another objection to the argument that life originated on this planet by natural means. As you will recall, chemical reactions are reversible; that is, they can go in the direction of synthesis and they can also go in the direction of decomposition. In fact, the latter is more likely from an energetic standpoint, and an equilibrium would probably be reached in which there would be a very low concentration of the synthesized product (remember our analogy of the grasshoppers in Section 4.2C). In a living system, the product is taken immediately into other reactions so that an equilibrium cannot be reached. How, therefore, could enough macromolecules ever accumulate in one place to start a living system? Furthermore, present living systems are obliged to expend tremendous amounts of energy in synthesis to offset the forces of decomposition; as a matter of fact, their growth is dependent on their ability to oppose these forces successfully. How could a system ever accomplish this task if it did not as yet possess any machinery for synthesis?

---

* Microorganisms (for example, bacteria) that break down macromolecules in their environment through enzymatic action.

In consideration of the first question, we must remember that long periods of time were available, which might allow for the accumulation of even small yields from synthetic reactions. As for the second question, it must be pointed out that external energy (sunlight, electricity in the form of lightning, perhaps other sources) was available and might well have supplied the energy required to drive synthetic reactions. In fact, this process is apparently what happened in Miller's experiments. There is also evidence that organic molecules derive some protection from decomposition by complexing together; and, in general, large macromolecules tend to be more resistant to decomposition than small ones. In fact, many organic molecules tend to gain a higher degree of organization spontaneously. In any event, the thermodynamic objections to the possibility of the origin of life are not insurmountable.

Other objections to the naturalistic hypothesis of the origin of life have been raised, and some of these have been met by experimentation. But regardless of the plausibility, feasibility, or degree of evidence, most scientists feel that it is a reasonable conceptual scheme.

In the light of evidence that has been forthcoming since about 1950, and considering the fact that biologists have changed their ways of thinking about life, the dilemma of "spontaneous generation or supernatural explanation" no longer seems necessary. To summarize, the evidence indicates with a fair degree of clarity that life had a naturalistic origin on this planet some three to four billion years ago. Many biologists prefer to call this process *biopoiesis* (Greek *bios,* life + *poiesis,* creation) in order to avoid the unpleasant connotations of the term "spontaneous generation." The latter term has always carried with it the implication of sudden organismic production (for example, flies from carcasses or bacteria from sterile broth within two or three days) and is a simplistic holdover from a time when the fantastic complexity of living systems was not even imaginable. Regardless of the term used, it seems most unlikely that a process like biopoiesis could occur at the present time. First of all, conditions favorable to the origin of life no longer exist on our planet; and, secondly, any developing macromolecule or chemical complex probably would not last long in a world filled with microorganisms.

Thus, we are justified in considering biogenesis a fruitful conceptual scheme. Remember, it merely states that life comes only from life *under conditions now prevailing on earth.* It does not commit us to any exceptions from the past. Hence, biogenesis and biopoiesis are two entirely different conceptual schemes.

What are the chances that biologists will "create life" some day? If one goes by past experience and follows the concept that "life" is some point on a physicochemical continuum of complexity, such an event seems inevitable. Already, some very complex macromolecules have been synthesized using less complex precursor materials, and it may be only a matter of time until a metabolizing, self-perpetuating unit is constructed in some laboratory. Perhaps this event, if achieved, will seem more epochal to lay persons than to biologists, who have grown accustomed to thinking in terms of a continuum. Why, for example, should this additional triumph of science have any more profound implications for mankind than the creation of a complex macromolecule? The answer probably lies in the general tendency to equate "life" with "God," a vitalistic train of thought that does neither science nor theology any service. But whatever the implications, they may have to be faced at some future point of time.

In a more practical vein, the conceptual scheme of biogenesis and its modern extension, the concept of life as a phenomenon resulting from complex organization, have proved very fruitful indeed. Studies on the nature of cancer, the nature of viruses and viral diseases, the biological process of aging, and a host of other problems are directly related to this theoretical consideration. We shall gain more insight into its fruitfulness as we pursue the subject of the cell in the next chapter.

QUESTIONS FOR REVIEW AND DISCUSSION

1. What is the most fruitful approach in attempting to define or explain the basis of a living system? Why? Is the "either-or" approach very fruitful? Explain.

2. Discuss the contributions of Redi, Needham, Spallanzani, and Pasteur to the biogenesis-abiogenesis controversy.

3. What is meant by a mechanistic approach to the nature of life?

4. Is it always valid to make a distinction between matter and energy? Explain.

5. Illustrate by diagram the atomic and molecular levels of organization. At the molecular level, illustrate both ionic and covalent compounds.

6. What is meant by the term "chemical bond"?

7. List and explain three approaches to the description of an atom.

8. Relate the first and second laws of thermodynamics to chemical reactions.

9. List four basic types of chemical reaction and illustrate each type.

10. Distinguish between an exergonic and an endergonic reaction.

11. What is meant by an enzyme-substrate complex? What is the relevance of this complex to enzyme activity?

12. Why are enzymes necessary in a living system as we know it?

13. Explain why different reactions reach equilibrium at varying concentrations of reactants.
14. Define briefly and illustrate the four basic organic molecules present in a living system.
15. Define and illustrate the following: (1) glycosidic linkage, (2) peptide bond, (3) ester linkage, (4) phospho-diester linkage.
16. Discuss the Watson-Crick model for the DNA molecule. What are the basic micromolecules? What are the basic units of the micromolecule? What is specific about the double helical nature of the molecule?
17. List three lines of evidence that were instrumental in the formulation of the DNA model by Watson and Crick.
18. List three structural differences between DNA and RNA.
19. Discuss briefly the physical nature of protoplasm.
20. Discuss the concept of biopoiesis as a possible process for the origin of life. If you accept this concept as an explanation of the way life originated, how do you reconcile this hypothesis with the concept of biogenesis?

REFERENCES

Baker, J. J., and E. A. Allen. *Matter,,Energy, and Life.* Palo Alto, California: Addison-Wesley Publishing Company, Inc., 1965. A clear and concise little book that deals with the entire spectrum of organization from energy and atoms through enzymes and nucleic acids. This short book provides the chemical models needed to explain the emergent properties of higher levels of organization.

Beck, W. S. *Modern Science and the Nature of Life.* Garden City, N.J.: Doubleday and Company, Inc., 1961. This book, published in cooperation with The American Museum of Natural History, is a part of The Natural History Library, which makes available books of enduring interest in the life and earth sciences.

Giese, A. C. *Cell Physiology.* Philadelphia, London, Toronto: W. B. Saunders Company, 1968. An excellent and rather comprehensive treatment of cell physiology for the student desiring more in-depth treatment of this area.

Haynes, R. H. and P. C. Hanawalt (eds.). *The Molecular Basis of Life, Readings From Scientific American.* San Francisco: W. H. Freeman and Company, 1968. This book consists of a series of articles appearing in *Scientific American* dealing with the molecular basis of living systems. The paper that is most pertinent to this chapter is entitled "The Origin of Life."

Knobloch, I. W. (ed.). *Readings in Biological Science.* New York: Appleton-Century-Crofts, 1967. This book consists of a collection of papers by prominent research biologists and theoretical biologists concerning several aspects of biology.

Waddington, C. H. *The Nature of Life.* New York: Harper and Row, Publishers, 1961. C. H. Waddington is a developmental biologist with a considerable interest in the philosophy of science and scientific generalization. This short paperback presents the main problems and trends of thought in modern biology.

FIVE

Life and Cell

In the preceding chapter, we emphasized the difficulty of trying to define or delimit "life" as a biological phenomenon, although we attempted to gain some insight into this phenomenon by discussing its physical nature (a multiphasic complex), its origin (the conceptual scheme of biopoiesis), and its continuity (the conceptual scheme of biogenesis). We have taken the position that as scientists we are obliged to view the life phenomenon mechanistically, and so we dealt with the chemical and physical nature of the substance of life (protoplasm). Thus, we have felt it permissible to make some semidefinitional statements—for example, a living system is an open one that fights successfully against entropy and against the establishment of chemical equilibrium, because it continually receives energy and matter from its environment. We mentioned further that in terms of basic properties, "life" reflects a level of organization that is capable of metabolism and self-perpetuation, and we shall discuss these two properties in more detail later.

Now let us view the life phenomenon from a somewhat different operational viewpoint in order to answer certain questions that follow logically from our preceding discussion. At what point on the continuum of the organization of energy and matter do the properties of metabolism and self-perpetuation (basic properties of life) emerge (Fig. 4-1)? Can we point to a specific structural or functional unit as the basic unit of life? Such a unit does indeed exist, and we call it a *cell*. This chapter is devoted to the historical development of the cell theory and to a consideration of the cell as a unit of structure, function, and reproduction.

5.1 A GREAT CONCEPTUAL SCHEME: THE CELL THEORY [1]

The history of science reveals numerous instances in which an important conceptual development was postponed until the technological means for achieving it were invented. For example, extension of the fine work done by Copernicus, Kepler, and Brahe in astronomy awaited the invention of the telescope; after its invention in 1608, Galileo and others were able to carry astronomical work forward at a rapid pace. Much the same was true in the case of the cell theory. Cells are microscopic entities, and their discovery awaited the invention and development of the microscope about 1590. The invention of this instrument is generally credited to two Dutchmen named Janssen, who were father and son. They were lens-grinders, not scientists, and if they put their microscope to good use in the study of organisms, history does not record it. However, a succession of individuals who were more inclined toward biology effected improvements in this instrument (Fig. 5-1), and gradually, their observations led to valuable generalizations about the world of life.

Discovery of cells is credited to a 17th-century Englishman, Robert Hooke (1635–1703), who focused his primitive microscope on a thin section of cork and observed that the material was composed of numerous box-like compartments (Fig. 5-2). He reported his observations in 1665 and coined the term *cell* for the unit of structure he had observed.[2] Hooke was a thorough investigator, and he extended his observations to the tissues

(c)

(b)

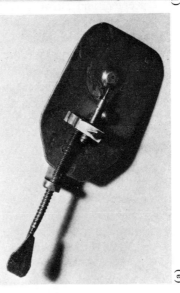

(a)

Figure 5.1. (a) A replica model of the microscope used by Leeuwenhoek in his observations. The original is located at the University of Utrecht. (b) The microscope used by Robert Hooke, constructed by Christapher Cook of London in the latter part of the 17th century. See also Figure 5.2. (c) A modern research compound microscope. [Figures (a) and (b) courtesy Armed Forces Institute of Pathology, Negative numbers 53-662-3-A and 53-662-41, respectively. Figure (c) courtesy American Optical Corporation.]

124

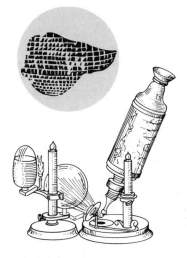

Figure 5.2. Drawing made by Robert Hooke showing "cells" of cork (encircled) and the microscope he used in his observations. [From C. P. Swanson, *The Cell* (Englewood Cliffs, N.J.: Prentice-Hall, Inc., 1970.)]

of other plants. Everywhere he turned, there were cells. As a consequence, he concluded that the cell is fundamental to the structure of organisms. His observations were reinforced by those of Nehemiah Grew, whose illustrations in a publication of 1674 indicate quite clearly that he recognized the cellular structure of his materials. Two years later, the Dutchman Anton van Leeuwenhoek reported his observations of microorganisms, to which we referred in the preceding chapter. Actually, at least a half-dozen microscopists made significant contributions to biological knowledge during the 17th century; however, only Hooke was primarily concerned with the cell itself as a unit of structure.

Rather strangely, very few important developments in microscopic biology occurred during the 18th century. One reason may be traced to the fact that biology had begun to develop along other lines, and these new and exciting developments served to divert the interest of the relative handful of men who might otherwise have continued the work of the 17th-century microscopists. Another reason may be that little technical improvement was made during that time in the quality of lens systems. However, shortly after the year 1800, when great improvements were made in the quality of microscopes, there occurred a renewed interest in microscopical observations. This great burst of activity is typical of the way a particular scientific discipline surges forward whenever some new technological development is forthcoming. In this case, it was the invention of the achromatic lens system, which eliminated the distortions and prismatic color effects that were characteristic of the older microscopes.

During the 19th century, Europeans dominated cytology, along with most areas of biological science. Notable among the European biologists who seized upon the opportunities provided by the new microscopes was the physiologist-cytologist Johannes Müller (1801–1858) of Germany, who is often called the father of European cytology. He and his students were responsible for a great deal of the cytological discovery that occurred during the 19th century, and their combined activities spanned many decades. However, the time was ripe by the 1830's for a sweeping generalization that would focus upon the cell as the basic unit of living systems. The French biologist Henri Dutrochet (1776–1847) came very close to enunciating the cell theory when he stated, in 1824, that "All organic tissues are actually globular cells of exceeding smallness. . . ." [3]

However, it remained for two German scientists, M. J. Schleiden (1804–1881) and Theodor Schwann, the former a botanist and the latter a zoologist, to bring all of the observations together into a single generalization that has caused them to be remembered ever since as the authors of the cell theory. Schleiden was a somewhat erratic man who turned to biology in 1831 after having attempted suicide over his failure as a lawyer; and at the time they collaborated, Schwann (whom you will remember from the preceding chapter) was a promising young physiologist. As the story goes, Schleiden described his recently published work on the microscopic anatomy of plants to Schwann in October of 1838 during the course of a dinner conversation. Schwann recognized the similarity of Schleiden's plant cell nuclei to structures he had seen in the nervous tissues of animals. The two men went immediately to Schwann's laboratory where Schleiden viewed these animal materials and recognized the basic similarities to his plant tissues. Thus, the cell theory was born as a joint endeavor. [4]

In his famous monograph of 1838 (obviously, he wasted no time in publishing his views), Schleiden proposed three major premises: (1) Plants are composed of cells that are units of structure, function, and organization. (2) These cells play a dual biological role; they are independent living entities, but collectively, they are a complex living system. (3) New cells form within a tissue in much the same manner as granules accumulate around a crystal. Note that Schleiden accounted for growth by making an analogy, thus formulating a conceptual scheme.

Schleiden's first two premises were not original with him or with Schwann. They had been stated or implied by workers before them, and Schleiden failed to acknowledge the credit due his predecessors. His third premise was not original either. It was one of two conceptual schemes that had been postulated earlier to account for growth in organisms (we shall examine the other presently); and, as it turned out, Schleiden chose the wrong one. Apparently, Schwann agreed with him in all of these premises; and taking Schleiden's treatise as his starting point, he published his own views during the following year (1839). For the most part, his monograph simply reinforced Schleiden's views. This double statement of the cell theory was received enthusiastically by the scientific community and provided an immediate stimulus for many varieties of biological investigation.

It is somewhat surprising in the light of history that most textbooks of biology attribute the cell theory entirely to Schleiden and Schwann. Perhaps this is an indication that history is kinder to those who fit the last piece of a puzzle into place or to those who formulate a successful generalized statement, than to their predecessors who bear the main heat of the battle. In any event, the Schleiden-Schwann concept that the cell is the fundamental unit of living systems, having an independent existence but at the same time being the basic unit of higher levels of organization, summarized a considerable amount of cytological work that had been done up to the late 1830's. Their summary conceptual scheme was to exert a profound influence upon all subsequent biological research.

One of the immediate effects of the cell theory was essentially philosophical. The concept of the nature of life was shifted from the organismic to the cellular level, thus resurrecting the age-old question first posed by Democritus as to whether the universe is built according to a system of fundamental units. This view of matter had been generally accepted in chemistry by the 1830's, due chiefly to the influence of John Dalton and J. J. Berzelius. Despite the fact that the atomic concept in chemistry encountered serious difficulties during the 1840's and 1850's, the scientific world was conditioned to thinking in terms of fundamental units. The shift of emphasis from the organism to the cell as the seat of life, with the mechanistic implication that one might even be able to reduce the life phenomenon to an even lower level than the cell, played an important role in clearing the way for a thoroughgoing mechanistic outlook in biology. At the very least, faith in the power of the microscope to unlock the ultimate secrets of life became very great indeed. It began to appear that Cartesian reductionism was the correct philosophy for biology after all.

The cell theory was extended to the world of microorganisms in 1845 when the German biologist Karl von Siebold declared that protozoa are simply animals that consist of single cells. By 1858, the German biologist Rudolf Virchow had decided that Schleiden and Schwann had erred in their conclusion on the origin of cells. He championed the alternative hypothesis that every cell is formed by the division of a cell: *"Omnis cellula e cellula;"* that is, all cells come from cells. Thus, if one combines von Siebold's concept that microorganisms are cells with Virchow's concept that cells come only from preexisting cells, one has a fair statement of the principle of biogenesis. It was not long after Virchow's statement, of course, that Louis Pasteur was able to establish the biogenetic viewpoint to the almost complete satisfaction of the scientific community.

Although by the middle of the 19th century much had been learned about cells through direct microscopical observation, developments during the latter half of the century were perhaps even more fruitful. There were several parallel developments, foremost among which were the use of staining techniques; improvements in the microtome, which made it possible to obtain thinner tissue slices; and the identification and localization of specific chemical substances in cells by the use of chemical reagents. Cytology continued to be almost exclusively the province of German biologists, partly because of the early influence of Johannes Müller (most of the men we have discussed were his pupils). Furthermore, the field of chemistry was also dominated throughout the latter half of the 19th century by Germans. Since German biologists were not slow to utilize the chemical knowledge that was at their immediate disposal, they were able to make such great advances in cytology during this time. German cytologists discovered many of the organelles, or parts that characterize cells, and in some cases correctly identified their respective functions. German scientists also elucidated the mechanics of cell division, and they identified some of the important macromolecules that we considered in the preceding chapter. Thus, by the turn of the century, cytology was well established as a leading branch of biology. This development originated in a broad conceptual scheme that had been exceedingly fruitful in the hands of skilled workers, and it was their extension of this conceptual scheme that had produced such a large and significant body of empirical data.

During the first half of the 20th century, most cytologists became concerned with nuclei and the chromosomes located within them, and very little attention was devoted to the remainder of the cell. This attitude was due primarily to the great interest that surrounded the precise mechanics of chromosomal behavior in cell division (elucidated in the 1880's) and to the stimulus provided cytology by the field of genetics (which, for all practical purposes, was born in the year 1900). Furthermore, even though compound microscopes of that day were very nearly as functional as present-day microscopes, they were not adequate for the study of most of the cellular organelles located outside the nucleus.

By the 1940's, several technological advances contributed greatly to a radical shift in emphasis within cytology. Foremost among these advances was the electron microscope (Fig. 5-3), invented during the 1930's and made generally available during the 1940's. There was also improvement in techniques for killing, fixing, sectioning, and staining cells; and biochemical techniques for isolating and studying cellular organelles were developed. Furthermore, the fields of biochemistry and biophysics had expanded rapidly since the turn of the century and began to influence cytology profoundly. The net result was a great upsurge of interest at the *subcellular* and molecular levels, with the result that the whole field of biology became influenced by molecular cytology. As a matter of fact, this emphasis has been so strong and has produced so many changes in bio-

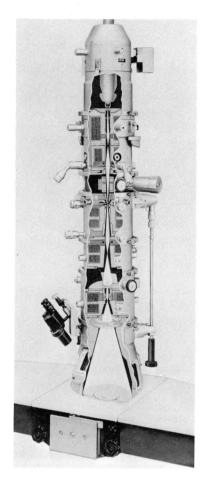

Figure 5.3. A modern electron microscope shown in cutaway view. (Courtesy Siemens Corporation.)

logical thought that it has frequently been termed the "new" biology. Thus, the original conceptual scheme of Schleiden and Schwann has been exceedingly fruitful even to the present time. However, as we shall see, their statement of the cell theory has been subject to reconsideration in biology.

It must be remembered that the Schleiden-Schwann concept was developed during a time when it was universally supposed that living systems are discontinuous with nonliving entities. In the light of information gained by the use of such instruments as the electron microscope, and by refined biochemical techniques, it has become obvious that this is not the case. Thus, the Schleiden-Schwann straightforward statement of the cell theory has become recognized as an oversimplification, because any distinction between the "living" and the "nonliving" is nebulous. Actually, the difficulty resides in deciding what the functional properties of life are, and to what extent they must be exhibited by a system before it may be termed "living." Once this decision is made, it becomes much easier to decide what constitutes a cell from a structural viewpoint. The standard unit would be that point along the continuum of the organization of matter at which these properties emerge.

As a case in point, let us consider the viruses (Fig. 5-4). These

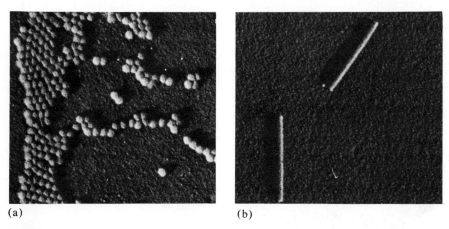

(a)   (b)

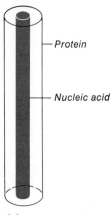

(c)

—Protein

—Nucleic acid

Figure 5.4. Some representative viruses. (a) Electron photomicrograph of tomato bushy stunt virus, magnified 48,000 times. (b) Electron photomicrograph of tobacco mosaic virus, magnified 63,000 times. (c) Diagram of a virus, showing typical structure. A core of nucleic acid is surrounded by an "overcoat" of protein. (Electron photomicrographs courtesy of Dr. R. C. Williams.)

entities, some of which are causative agents of diseases in various plants and animals, are extremely small units of matter that manifest certain characteristics associated with protoplasm. Typically, they consist of nucleic acid coated with protein. Although they reproduce (perpetuate), this function is achieved only in association with the more complex units (cells) of some host organism. Apart from these more complex units, they cannot carry on the chemical activities (metabolism) associated with protoplasm. Are they living? The answer to this question depends entirely on where one wishes to draw the line relative to the functional properties that emerge in the continuum of organization of matter and energy. Many biologists consider them to be living, even though they are not self-perpetuating and cannot carry out the phases of metabolism (which we shall consider presently) in isolation—that is, as independent units. Biologists generally consider the cellular level to be the point at which the properties of metabolism and self-perpetuation emerge. The simplest organization of matter to which these properties can be ascribed is the pleuropneumonia organism (which will be mentioned later). Thus, according to this concept, viruses—whatever they may or may not be in terms of identifiable entities—are not cells. If they are living, then the basic unit of life is something below the cellular level.

The Canadian endocrinologist Hans Selye stated in 1954 that the cell theory has become "too deeply engrained in the minds of biologists to be displaced by other concepts," and it may well be that we need to lose some of our attachment for it.[5] Selye went so far as to suggest a new conceptual unit of life, the *reacton,* which he defined as the smallest unit of biological reactivity. Selye's proposal has received very little attention, and perhaps justifiably so, since there is nothing "real," or concrete, that can specifically be labeled a "reacton." However, it may well be that a conceptual scheme of this type will eventually become useful; after all, the ability to delimit a physical unit is not requisite to recognize it conceptually. We have used the terms "gene" and "atom" for years without understanding a great deal about what either "really" is, thus upholding our contention that it makes little difference whether a conceptual scheme is "true" or whether it refers to "real" entities. The ultimate test is whether it is more useful than any available alternate conceptual scheme.

Notwithstanding the changes in viewpoint that we have reviewed, the Schleiden-Schwann concept has been extremely fruitful in biology. Regardless of whether the cell is the fundamental unit of structure and function in a living system, a great many biological phenomena are basically cellular. For example, let us consider the secretion into the human stomach of the protein-digesting enzyme, pepsin. It carries on its work *outside* cells—that is, in the stomach cavity. But it originates *inside* cells that lie deep within the stomach wall. This powerful enzyme is produced within these specialized cells in an inactive form called pepsinogen; were this not so, it would digest the proteins within the very cells that produce it. It becomes pepsin only when it reaches the acid environment of the stomach. However, our point is this: Even the extracellular process of human digestion is cellular in its starting point. Regardless of what they may think at the present time of the Schleiden-Schwann concept, most biologists are profoundly committed to the principle that **if one cares to understand a biological process, at whatever level of organization, he must, at some point, study that process at the cellular level.**

Consequently, the cell is a very important biological entity, and we shall concentrate on the cell as a biological unit in the remainder of this chapter. For our purposes, we shall act as if the cell is the smallest unit of life (viruses notwithstanding), and our approach will be thoroughly mechanistic.

5.2 THE CELL AS A BIOLOGICAL UNIT

As a unit, the cell is considered by most biologists to represent the level of organization in the continuum of matter and energy that constitutes the simplest living system. From a structural viewpoint, the cell constitutes a kind of building block for the more complex (multicellular) living systems. Although some organisms consist of only one complete unit of protoplasm and hence are said to be *unicellular,* the great majority of organisms are made up of more than one protoplasmic unit and thus are *multicellular.*

Let us note once again that the cell is the smallest and least complex unit of matter that can *unquestionably* be called living. This definition means that, within limits of specialization, the cell can carry on all the basic activities characterizing organisms. In other words, the activities to which we refer as metabolism and self-perpetuation are, in the final analysis, carried on by protoplasm. It should be kept in mind as one considers these fundamental activities that a cell is a highly organized entity whose material substance is so ordered as to warrant its being considered "living." *In its own right,* therefore, and not simply by virtue of its association with other such units in a complex organism, the cell holds this unique distinction. More precisely, a cell is a system of supramolecular complexes organized in a certain way to take in free energy and matter. By so doing, it is able to maintain and extend its organization and exhibit the properties of metabolism and self-perpetuation.

5.2A The Cell as a Unit of Structure [6]

Cells show a great deal of variability in size, shape, structure, and function. This characteristic is especially true of the various cells making up a complex multicellular organism, where the association of cells in the formation of tissues is accompanied by a division of labor. Some of this diversity is shown in Fig. 5-5. On the other hand, there are many structural and functional features that most cells have in common. Because of these common features, one can speak of a "typical," or "generalized," cell, although such a cell is quite mythical.

When viewed with an ordinary light microscope, the typical cell (Fig. 5-6) appears as a unit separated from its environment by a *plasma membrane* enclosing the protoplasm (which consists of a *nucleus* and *cytoplasm*). In plants, a rigid *cell wall,* composed chiefly of cellulose, typically surrounds the cell and delimits it as a unit from others. This wall is nonliving and is not strictly a part of the cell, having been formed by the cytoplasm during its inception and growth. The plasma membrane lies just within this wall. Most animal cells, in contrast, are simply limited by their plasma membranes, although some possess a flexible, nonliving pellicle that corresponds to the plant cell wall.* Inside the cell, the nucleus appears to be separated from the cytoplasm by a *nuclear membrane.* It should be pointed out that in a few types of cells this definite nucleus-cytoplasm relationship does not exist. For example, the pleuropneumonia organism (Fig. 5-5) has no organized nucleus as such; rather, nuclear materials are scattered throughout the cytoplasm.[7] This organism is approximately 100 $m\mu$ (1,000 Å) in diameter and may represent the lowest organizational level of protoplasm that can be considered a living cell. At the other extreme, one of the largest cells known is that of the giant amoeba, *Chaos chaos* (Fig. 5-5), which is approximately 100 μ (1,000,000 Å) in diameter and is multinuclear. But the typical nucleus-cytoplasm ratio is one nucleus per cell.

The protoplasm within the nucleus is called *nucleoplasm,* and it contains one or more dense bodies known as *nucleoli,* as well as a granular mass called the *chromatin network,* or simply chromatin material. When a cell enters into a divisional cycle, the chromatin assumes the form of discrete *chromosomes.* The number of chromosomes thus formed is usually constant for a given species of organism. When viewed in the living condition with an ordinary light microscope, cytoplasm appears as a somewhat homogenous, translucent material containing refractile bodies of different sizes. In many cells, the cytoplasm appears to be thicker or more viscous (*gel* state) around the periphery and less viscous (*sol* state) toward the center of the cell. Whenever such a distinction is made, the outer portion is called the *ectoplasm* and the inner portion is called the *endoplasm.* The sol-gel change that occurs as cytoplasm alternates between these two physical phases is a reflection of its colloidal nature. Although several bodies lie within the cytoplasm, most of them are difficult to see in the living cell with an ordinary light microscope. These bodies include

---

* Since there is some confusion as to whether or not one includes the cell wall or pellicle when he speaks of a cell, the term *protoplast* is widely used to describe the entire unit lying within any such nonliving structure. Some biologists use the terms "protoplast" and "cell" synonymously.

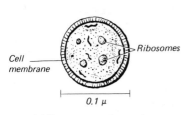

Cell membrane

Ribosomes

0.1 μ

(a) Pleuropneumonia organism
(anucleate)

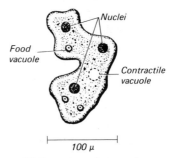

Nuclei

Food vacuole

Contractile vacuole

100 μ

(b) Chaos chaos, giant amoeba
(multinucleate)

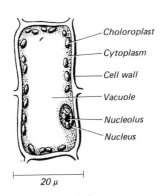

Choloroplast

Cytoplasm

Cell wall

Vacuole

Nucleolus

Nucleus

20 μ

(c) Cell from the leaf of a
water plant, Elodea

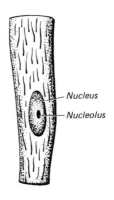

Nucleus

Nucleolus

(d) Cell from intestinal tract

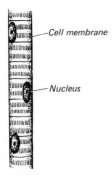

Cell membrane

Nucleus

(e) Striated muscle cell

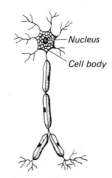

Nucleus

Cell body

(f) Nerve cell showing fibrous
extensions

Figure 5.5. Various types of cells. Note the many differences in size, shape, and structure, especially in cells (a), (b), and (c). Cells (d), (e), and (f) are all from the body of a complex animal.

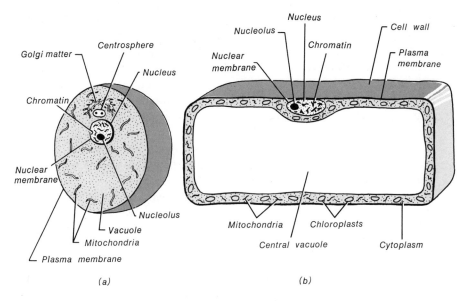

Figure 5.6. Representative cells in sectional view, magnified about 2,000 times. (a) Animal cell. (b) Plant cell.

mitochondria, a structure called the *Golgi complex,* and various granules, yolk bodies, and crystals. Under ideal conditions of observation, the *centrosphere* of the animal cell can be distinguished from the surrounding cytoplasm. Less difficult to see are the *plastids* found in the cytoplasm of many plant cells, of which the green *chloroplasts* are the most common.

In order to observe the more intricate structural details of cells, one must either use certain specialized types of microscopes or else the cells must be killed and stained. Sophisticated microscopical techniques employ forms of radiation other than visible light or take advantage of special chemical and physical features of the different parts of the cell. Staining methods are based on the differential chemical nature of the various parts of the cell, which is reflected by their differential affinities for certain dyes. Figure 5-6 shows the various parts of "typical" plant and animal cells that can be observed by using a combination of microscopical and staining methods. As we have pointed out, knowledge of living systems has advanced as techniques for studying them have been developed. An excellent example, of course, is the electron microscope, which became generally available in the 1940's. With this instrument, extremely intricate details of cellular structure have been observed. Compared with the ordinary light microscope (which cannot be made to magnify clearly over about 2,000 diameters), the electron microscope is a powerful instrument indeed. It magnifies at 200,000 diameters with clarity; with special photographic methods, even greater magnification may be obtained. The source of radiation in the electron microscope is a beam of electrons that is passed through magnetic fields and through the specimen to cast an image on a photographic plate. This image, or picture, can then be viewed by the human eye. There are some disadvantages inherent in the use of the electron microscope. Not only is it an expensive and complicated instrument, but materials to be studied must be sliced ultrathin and dried thoroughly. Furthermore, since beams of electrons must travel through a vacuum, it is necessary that materials be prepared in such a way that they will not be distorted under these rigorous conditions. Needless to say, cells cannot be studied in a living state with the electron microscope. They must be killed, treated with chemicals, and sliced under the most exacting conditions.

Nevertheless, electron microscopy has yielded a wealth of information about cell structure that would not have been attainable otherwise. In Fig. 5-7, for example, we see something of the detailed structure of mitochondria, the nuclear membrane, and other inclusions that we have yet to discuss. Using a number of observations with this powerful instrument, plus certain biochemical and biophysical data, we now can conceive of the generalized or "typical" cell as shown in Fig. 5-8.

In general, the structural entities (subcellular particles) in the cytoplasm of the cell can be classified as *cytoplasmic inclusions* or *cytoplasmic organelles*. The cytoplasmic inclusions are such structures as glycogen granules, fat droplets, and yolk bodies. Most of these inclusions are rather passive entities representing stored food materials in the cell. In contrast, cytoplasmic organelles are functional entities or sites of activity in the cell. Because of their importance to living systems, we shall list and discuss the more important organelles in turn.

THE CELL MEMBRANE [8]

The electron microscope shows the cell membrane (sometimes called the plasma membrane) to be a layered structure ranging from 65 to 100 Å in thickness. Chemical analysis has shown it to be composed of lipid and protein. The lipid components are compound lipids and are primarily the phospholipids, lecithin and cephalin. The protein components belong to the fibrous protein group. Several investigators have proposed a theoretical model of molecular arrangement in the cell membrane. According to this concept (Fig. 5-9), the cell membrane is composed of a double layer of lipid molecules sandwiched between two layers of protein. This model is based on electron-microscope studies, X-ray diffraction studies, chemical analyses, and known physiological properties of the membrane.

The cell membrane serves as a boundary between the external environment and the internal environment of the cell. It thus represents a

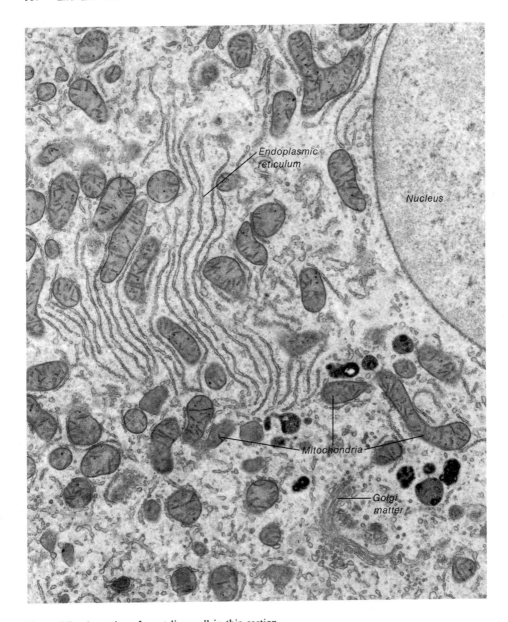

Figure 5.7. A portion of a rat liver cell in thin section,
as photographed by the electron microscope at about 38,000
magnifications. Note the internal structure of the
mitochondria. A portion of the endoplasmic reticulum is
shown; note attached ribosomes, which appear as small
dots. Several structures discussed in the text may be seen in
this view of the cell. Compare with Fig. 5.8. (Courtesy
Dr. K. R. Porter.)

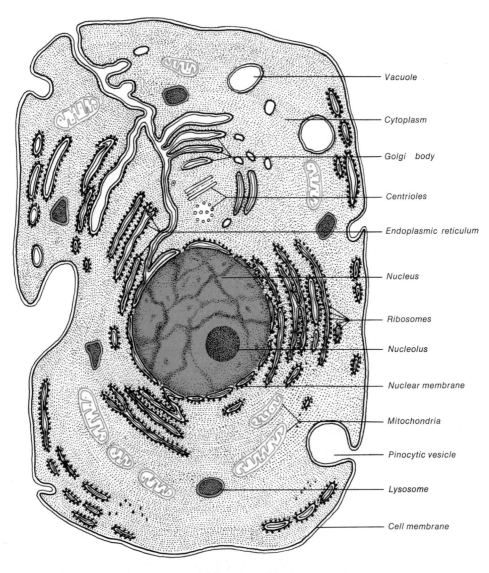

Figure 5.8. Highly diagrammatic representation of a
generalized cell, showing parts discussed in the text. This
figure is based on many lines of evidence, especially
electron-microscopic studies. The two-dimensional appearance
represents a thin slice as it might be prepared for electron
photomicrography.

barrier that all molecules must traverse in entering or leaving the cell. This
stipulation includes the molecules supplying the energy that keeps the cell

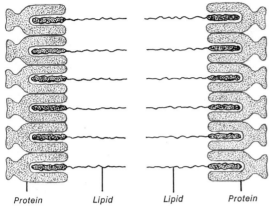

Protein   Lipid   Lipid   Protein

Figure 5.9. Theoretical model of the cell membrane in sectional view. Two layers of closely packed protein molecules enclose a double layer of less compact lipid molecules.

organized and functional, the micromolecules constituting the building blocks of the basic macromolecules, and the various by-products or waste materials resulting from the activities of the cell. Thus, the cell membrane is semipermeable; that is, it "permits" the passage of substances through it. To be more precise, the membrane is *selectively* or *differentially* permeable, since some ions or molecules pass through it while others are prohibited from doing so. Therefore, in regard to permeability, it "selects" some substances and "rejects" others. The factors involved in cell membrane permeability will be discussed later.

MITOCHONDRIA [9]

The mitochondria are filamentous or granular organelles ranging in size from about 0.2 to 0.7 μ in diameter. Their size, shape, and distribution are relatively constant in cells of the same type; however, cells of different organisms or tissues show considerable variability. Figure 5-6 shows how the mitochondria are scattered throughout the cytoplasm of typical plant and animal cells.

Although mitochondria can be seen by using the ordinary light microscope, very little detailed structure is discernible by this method. However, the electron microscope reveals a very intricate and detailed structure (Figs. 5-7, 5-8, and 5-10). The mitochondrial membrane is a double-layered structure composed of lipid and protein. The inner membrane is thrown into a series of folds forming "shelves" that extend into the matrix (liquid portion). These folds, or shelves, are known as *cristae,* and they take various forms in the mitochondria of different cell types. Figure 5-10 represents a somewhat generalized mitochondrion, and its structure may be considered representative.

Mitochondria play a very important role in living systems; the bulk

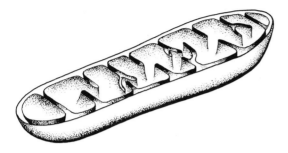

Figure 5.10. Cutaway view of a mitochondrion, drawn schematically. Note that the cristae form loosely connected compartments.

of the chemical energy of fuel molecules that enter the cell is extracted and conserved within them. Because of this role, mitochondria are often called the "powerhouses" of the cell. We shall have more to say about mitochondria in our discussion of metabolism. It is sufficient now that we recognize their important role in those energy transformations that make possible the continued organization and activity of the cells within which they are located.

The number, distribution, and structure of mitochondria relate directly to their function within living systems. They are very numerous in cells whose activities are associated with the expenditure of large amounts of energy (for example, muscle cells of the animal body). Furthermore, they are localized in particular regions of cells where energy expenditure is high. For example, they are highly concentrated in the contractile fibers of muscle cells and in regions adjacent to the cell membranes of nerve cells.

In terms of thermodynamics, mitochondria are more directly involved than any other organelles in the maintenance of the high enthalpy and low entropy characteristic of living systems. Since energy must be put into a system if it is to resist an increase in entropy, an efficient mechanism for translating this energy into a usable form is essential. It is for this particular role that mitochondria are adapted, and this role is reflected in their structure, number, and distribution within the cell.

PLASTIDS [10]

Plastids are found in at least some cells of virtually all members of the plant kingdom, except for certain of the least complex forms. They vary in size, number, shape, distribution, and chemical organization, as well as in color. On the basis of presence or absence of color, they may be classified into two major groups: the *leucoplasts* (colorless) and the *chromoplasts* (colored). This distinction is rather artificial, however, since it is known that leucoplasts may change into chromoplasts.

The most important and widespread of the plastids are the *chloro-*

plasts (Fig. 5-11), which are found in all green plants. They are particularly abundant in cells actively engaged in the process of photosynthesis, which occurs only in the presence of the green pigment chlorophyll. The

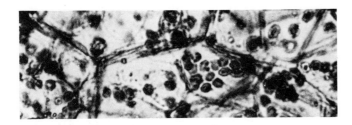

Figure 5.11.   Microscopic view of leaf cells, showing several chloropasts. They are particularly numerous in the small cell shown near the center of the photograph.

chloroplast owes its color to this pigment. Chloroplasts are typically ovoid in shape and are bounded by a double-layered membrane. Within this membrane is the matrix or *stroma,* and it contains granules called *grana.* Electron microscopy reveals that these grana consist of layers of membranes stacked on top of each other and joined together by a series of paired membranes that also extend into the stroma (Fig. 5-12). It is within the

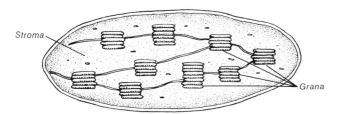

Figure 5.12.   Schematic drawing of the internal structure of a chloroplast, based on electron photomicrographs. Note the stacks of grana, which are interconnected within the stroma.

layered membranes of the grana that the chlorophyll is localized, along with certain enzymes that are functional in the photosynthetic process.

Chloroplasts, like mitochondria, are functional in the transformation of energy. The process of photosynthesis, through which the sun's energy is transformed into chemical energy, is a first step toward reversing the trend to increasing entropy. Thus, the functional role of the chloroplast is vital not only to the life of the plant cell containing it but to living systems in general, since all organisms ultimately benefit from the energy of sunlight.

THE ENDOPLASMIC RETICULUM,
RIBOSOMES, AND MICROSOMES [11]

The electron microscope has shown the cytoplasm to be traversed by a *reticulum* (network) of strands and vesicle-like bodies. This network often seems to be concentrated in the endoplasm of the cell, hence the name *endoplasmic reticulum* (Fig. 5-7). On the basis of available data, it is thought that this network is a three-dimensional continuum of cavities bounded by a membrane system. According to this view, it divides the cytoplasm into that within the network and that outside the network. The reticulum is not confined to the endoplasm, as its name might imply, but extends into the ectoplasm as well. In fact, electron micrographs indicate that the reticulum is continuous with the cell membrane at the surface of the ectoplasm and with the nuclear membrane at the outside surface of the nucleus (Fig. 5-8).

In a number of cell types (especially those that are extremely active in protein synthesis), large numbers of small granules approximately 150 Å in diameter are seen to be attached to the outer membrane of the endoplasmic reticulum. These granules are called *ribosomes*. Chemical analysis of ribosomes indicates that they are composed largely of RNA and protein. Functionally, they serve as the site where amino acids are joined together in the synthesis of protein molecules.

In this connection, another term should be presented and defined— the term *microsome*. A microsome is not a structure of the intact and living cell as such; rather, it is a term that has arisen in connection with the development of a technique for studying cells, the technique of *differential centrifugation*. In order to study subcellular particles, the biochemist breaks the cell membrane by one means or another and subjects the cell contents to high-speed centrifugation. When particles of various sizes are spun in a centrifuge, they migrate toward the bottom of the centrifuge tube at varying rates, depending on their mass. By this means, particles of different sizes can be isolated for further study. When cell contents are centrifuged at speeds equal to 40,000 to 100,000 times the force of gravity, the endoplasmic reticulum breaks up into particles of relatively small size; and these particles, the microsomes, migrate toward the bottom of the tube. Thus, a microsome is a product of differential centrifugation representing a small portion of the endoplasmic reticulum with one or more ribosomes attached, and it is capable of carrying on protein synthesis under experimental conditions. From a functional standpoint, the terms "ribosome" and "microsome" are often used synonymously—but they actually represent different physical entities.

The Golgi complex is a system of smooth membranes arranged in parallel fashion and enclosing vesicles, or cavities, of varying sizes. It is particularly conspicuous in animal cells (Fig. 5-7), especially those that are active in secretory functions. This observation, plus other evidence, has led to the belief that the Golgi complex is somehow associated with secretory processes, at least in certain cells. Other lines of evidence suggest that this organelle may have other functions as well, especially in cells that are not secretory in nature. For example, it appears to be physically involved in the formation of new cell wall material in plant cell division.

Cytologists still disagree on the identity of the Golgi complex: whether it has a separate identity from that of the endoplasmic reticulum or whether it is continuous with it. At least from a functional viewpoint, it may be best to regard the organelle as a part of the endoplasmic reticulum, since it resembles those portions of the reticulum that are devoid of ribosomes. However, electron micrographs indicate that it has structural features not characteristic of the endoplasmic reticulum proper, and some cytologists regard these features as evidence that the Golgi complex is not a part of the general membrane system within the cell.

In 1955, the cytologist C. de Duve obtained from differential centrifugation studies, a group of subcellular particles that were intermediate in size between the microsomal and mitochondrial fractions. Biochemical analysis revealed that these particles were rich in hydrolytic enzymes— that is, enzymes that catalyze the digestion of large macromolecules into micromolecules. Because of their association with digestive activity, these particles were named *lysosomes* (Greek *lysis,* loosing + *soma,* body). Apparently, the lysosomes with their hydrolytic enzymes are functional in processes of intracellular digestion. They probably account for the digestion of relatively large macromolecules taken into the cell by special transporting mechanisms. They may also function in the breakdown of cell parts whenever a cell dies. A number of electron microscope studies have confirmed the presence of these organelles in a variety of cells. Figure 5-8 shows lysosomes in relation to other parts of the cell.

In many animal cells, a clearly defined region of cytoplasm may be observed close to the nucleus. This region is termed the *centrosphere* or *centrosome*. Within the centrosphere there are a pair of small granules, the *centrioles,* which are usually rod-shaped and which may be seen with an ordinary light microscope. Thin sections of cells viewed with the electron microscope show each centriole to be a hollow cylinder 300 to 500 mμ in length and approximately 150 mμ in diameter. The centriole wall around a central cavity is composed of nine separate fibrils. The two centrioles are situated at right angles to each other, as shown in Fig. 5-8. The centrioles are apparently self-replicating organelles, and they play an important role in the division of animal cells.

5.2B The Cell as a Unit of Function

As we have emphasized, living systems can be understood to a considerable degree by studying their functional properties. Two of these properties, metabolism and self-perpetuation, are especially important because they are broad, inclusive characteristics that emerge at the cellular level. Thus, starting with the viewpoint that the cell is the basic unit within which the life phenomenon is manifested, the essence of "life" resides in the functions of metabolism and self-perpetuation. Since we have frequently alluded to these two functions, or properties, perhaps it is time we attempted to give them a working definition.

Metabolism has been defined as the sum total of the chemical activity of a living organism. However, this definition is something of a tautology, or circular definition, since we list metabolism as a basic property of a living system and then define it in terms of a "living organism." Nevertheless, these terms will have to suffice, although perhaps later on we shall have developed such a "feel" for this property that we shall no longer need a definition. In cellular terms, metabolism simply alludes to what the cell *does* in its total functioning. Within a mechanistic context, it is the operation of the structural parts that we reviewed in the preceding section.

Self-perpetuation is almost self-defining; essentially, it refers to those activities on the part of a cell that ensure the continuation of metabolism, either within a given cell or within one of its progeny. Thus, metabolism and self-perpetuation are not distinct and separate processes within a cell. As one might expect in so complex a physicochemical system as protoplasm, these two functions are inextricably interwoven. The mechanisms of self-perpetuation ensure that metabolism will continue, and metabolism makes self-perpetuation possible. Together, they are responsible for many of the activities of cells (and ultimately, of organisms) such as growth, reproduction, responsiveness, and movement. The interrelated nature of the broad properties of metabolism and self-perpetuation will become apparent as we view them in more detail.

METABOLISM [15]

From an energetic standpoint, the total chemical activity of a cell may be divided into two phases: *catabolism* and *anabolism*. Catabolism is the "tearing-down" phase of metabolism and is characterized by exergonic reactions that are chiefly decompositional in nature. Thus, such processes as digestion (the decomposition of organic macromolecules to their micromolecular units) and respiration (the decomposition of organic micromolecules to inorganic substances) are catabolic. In contrast, anabolism is the "building-up" phase of metabolism and is characterized by endergonic reactions that are chiefly synthetic in nature. For example, photosynthesis (the combination of carbon dioxide and water in the presence of chlorophyll) and the reactions that result in growth (increase in total mass) are anabolic. As an overall process, metabolism is characterized by three aspects: nutrition, respiration, and synthesis.

NUTRITION The term *nutrition* describes the means by which a cell obtains the raw materials that are essential to its maintenance. Every living system requires certain amounts and certain kinds of matter in order to maintain its structural organization through the construction, replacement, or repair of parts. It also requires energy (which it may derive from matter) in order to maintain its functional activity. Therefore, any substance taken into the cell from its environment and utilized in the cell's chemical reactions can be classified as a nutrient material. If we extend the definition to include energy as well as matter, even light would be a nutrient for cells that contain chlorophyll. For convenience, we can think of nutrients as belonging to two categories. The first category includes inorganic compounds such as water and mineral substances, as well as useful forms of energy such as light (in the case of photosynthetic cells). The second category includes the organic compounds such as carbohydrates, lipids, and proteins, which might be called *foods,* since they are sources of potential chemical energy for the cell. Perhaps it is unnecessary to say that cells vary greatly in their relative requirements for these nutrients. Generally speaking, these variations reflect major nutritional differences in the organisms of which the cells are a part. Let us digress momentarily and consider nutrition at the organismic level.

Fundamentally, animals can be distinguished from plants by virtue of the fact that animals eat and plants do not. In other words, animals take into their bodies food materials that have to be broken down into micromolecules through the process of digestion before they can be utilized. An organism that gains its nutrition chiefly or entirely by eating is called a *phagotroph* (Greek *phagos,* to eat + *trophikos,* nourishment). In contrast, plants are not phagotrophic, but they exhibit two distinct modes of nutrition. As a consequence, we are obliged to recognize two distinct groups of plants. One group consists of plants that are capable of synthesizing their own food substances from carbon dioxide and water, with sunlight usually serving as a source of energy for the process. Such plants are said to be *autotrophic* (Greek *autos,* self + *trophikos*). Other plants are dependent upon outside sources for food, as are animals, but they are obliged to receive the food in such a form that it will diffuse through cell membranes—that is, in micromolecular form. In order to utilize organic macromolecules, therefore, they are obliged to secrete digestive enzymes into their environment. These plants are said to be *heterotrophic* (Greek *heteros,* other + *trophikos*).

For the moment, let us ignore any nutritional distinctions between complex organisms and consider the requirements of cells themselves. Nutritionally speaking, we can divide cells into two basic types: those that are dependent upon their environment for organic molecules and those that manufacture their own. The latter type of cell is found only in autotrophic organisms, whereas the former type is found in all complex forms, autotrophic or otherwise. Not all cells of a multicellular green plant, for example, carry on photosynthesis; those that do not do so depend upon photosynthetic cells within the same plant for their organic nutrients. In heterotrophic plants and in animals (phagotrophs), of course, each cell must receive oxidizable organic compounds from a source external to the organism of which it forms a part.

Let us concentrate momentarily upon the organic nutrients and their role within the cell. Whether such compounds are formed within the cell that utilizes them as an energy source or whether they are transported in, they serve two major functions: They may be chemically "shattered," in which case free energy is made available to the cell, or the carbon chains may be used as building blocks in synthetic processes. The major organic nutrients are carbohydrates, lipids, and proteins. Under certain circumstances, each of these types may be utilized as energy sources; or again, each may be utilized in synthetic reactions. Generally speaking, however, the carbohydrates and lipids are "preferred" by the cell as energy-yielding compounds; protein functions chiefly in synthesis.

In actual practice, there is a rapid turnover in the cell of all organic molecules except for certain ones, such as those of DNA, that are somewhat isolated from the enzymatic machinery. This phenomenon means that in the final analysis virtually everything in the cell is a fuel substance. To draw an analogy, let us suppose that a certain lumber dealer finds it necessary, for some reason, to keep a fire going in a furnace. Under ordinary circumstances, he uses coal or oil as fuels, because they are cheap and readily available. He might use the furnace, since he has it anyway, to dispose of scrap lumber and assorted waste products, but he does not depend upon these for fuel. They are only incidentally burned. Let us assume that his supply of coal and oil is shut off. He might be forced to use whatever he can find that will burn. If maintenance of his fire is sufficiently important to him, he might even be obliged to burn his own valuable lumber. Of course, this analogy is only a rough one, since we do not ascribe consciousness and purpose to the cell as we do to a human being, but there are valid parallels. The coal and oil are analogous to carbohydrates and fats; the lumber, to proteins; and the scraps of material, to the various "used" molecules of the cell that are disposed of in the metabolic "fire."

Even though we cannot draw an exact distinction between fuel and nonfuel compounds, the original distinction is valid for all practical purposes. Carbohydrates and fats are the only materials that furnish energy to the cell in very large amounts, at least under most conditions. Proteins may or may not play a significant role in this respect, depending upon their quantity and the relative quantities of the other two fuels. Any other organic molecules that are broken down may yield some energy, but in amounts that are quite insignificant when compared with that furnished by carbohydrates, fats, and proteins.

At this point, let us consider the process of *absorption*—that is, how nutrient materials get into cells. Of necessity, these materials are present in the environment of the cell. Depending upon the particular type of cell, this environment may consist of pond water, the general atmosphere, or some form of body fluid such as blood. It may also include other cells. Regardless of the general environment, a cell is almost always surrounded by some aqueous medium, even if this medium exists only as a thin film separating closely packed cells. The aqueous medium is in direct contact with the cell membrane, even if the cell possesses a wall. (You will recall that plant cells are generally enclosed within a cellulose wall; this wall is permeable to all substances in aqueous solution.) Most of the problems associated with understanding absorption (the movement of nutrient materials into cells) involve a consideration of the structure and function of cell membranes. In addition, the nature and concentration of the nutrient substances that are absorbed must be considered.

The cell membrane has sometimes been pictured as a passive barrier containing pores that admit small particles and reject large ones. That the membrane is porous to a degree seems evident; and, in general, small molecules are absorbed more readily than large ones. However, this view of the membrane is highly misleading, because several factors govern the passage of substances across it. Apparently, the major factors involved in absorption are *osmosis, diffusion, electrical charge, solubility in lipids,* and *active transport.*

Osmosis. Osmosis may be defined as the movement of water from a region of relatively low concentration of dissolved substances into a region of relatively high concentration across a membrane that is impervious to at least some solutes. A balance of water between the cell and its environment seems to be at least partially explicable on the basis of osmosis. For example, if the concentration of dissolved substances is greater within the cell than in its surroundings, some water is absorbed into the cell by osmosis. In such a situation, the solution outside the cell is said to be *hypotonic* to the solution within the cell; and, conversely, the solution inside is said to be *hypertonic* to that outside. If the two solutions are equal to each other in concentration of dissolved particles, they are said to be *isotonic,* in which case there is no net movement of water across the membrane.

In order to demonstrate that living cells are subject to pressure changes associated with osmosis, let us consider a cell such as that of *Spirogyra* (Figs. 5-13, 5-14a), a filamentous green alga that thrives in ponds of fresh water. Although its surrounding medium is never absolutely pure water, it is nevertheless hypotonic to the protoplasmic contents of the

Figure 5.13. Diagrammatic representation of a cell of *Spirogyra.* Note the spiral chloroplast, which is imbedded within the peripheral cytoplasm surrounding a large central vacuole. Some species possess more than one chloroplast per cell, as in Fig. 5.14.

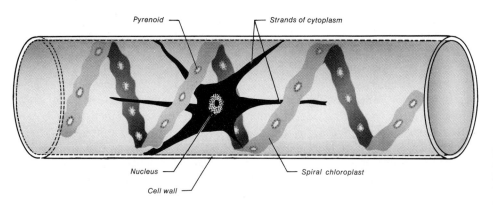

Pyrenoid —

— Strands of cytoplasm

Nucleus —

— Spiral chloroplast

Cell wall —

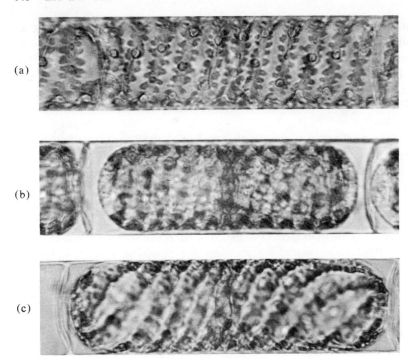

(a)

(b)

(c)

Figure 5.14. Plasmolysis in *Spirogyra*. (a) Appearance of a cell growing in pond water. (b) Appearance of the same cell about 30 seconds after it was surrounded by a 5-percent sodium chloride solution. Note that the protoplast, bounded by the plasma membrane, has pulled away from the cell wall. (c) Deplasmolysis of a cell, accomplished by surrounding a plasmolyzed cell with tap water. Note that the protoplast is returning to its normal position.

cell. There is thus a continual tendency for osmosis to occur inward. Why, it might be asked, does the cell not increase in size until it bursts? The reason lies in the rigidity of the cellulose cell wall, which is sufficient to resist bursting under these conditions. Enough pressure builds up inside the cell to establish an osmotic equilibrium. Whenever a cell exhibits an internal pressure due to osmosis, it is said to be turgid, and such pressure (resulting from osmosis) is called *turgor pressure*.

Suppose that a filament of *Spirogyra* is put into a solution prepared by dissolving 5 grams of sodium chloride in sufficient water to make the entire solution equal 100 milliliters (about ¼ pint). This solution proves to be hypertonic to the protoplasm of the cells; within a matter of seconds, sufficient water leaves a given cell to cause a shrinking of the protoplast. The cell wall, being rigid, remains in place, and the plasma membrane actually draws away from it (Fig. 5-14b). The cell's loss of turgidity due to osmosis is called *plasmolysis,* and a cell whose turgidity is less than that experienced in its normal environment is said to be *flaccid.* Unless plasmolysis has occurred to a critical degree, normal turgidity may be restored to the cells of the *Spirogyra* filament by replacing the sodium chloride solution with pond or tap water, thus reversing the direction of osmosis (Fig. 5-14c).

Many freshwater organisms that do not possess rigid cell walls manage to withstand turgor pressures by "bailing out" excess water. Many protozoa, such as *Amoeba* and *Paramecium,* have contractile vacuoles, which function as pumps in this respect (Fig. 5-15). Were it not for this mechanism, such delicate cells would soon burst. In higher animals, cells are surrounded by fluids that are isotonic to the protoplasm. The delicate red blood cells of man, for example, can be made to swell and burst if removed from their normal environment and placed in a solution that is even slightly hypotonic to them.

Although water itself is not an energy-yielding substance, it is of paramount importance to the metabolic life of cells—and hence to organisms. It serves as a solvent for and a carrier of a variety of compounds both inside and outside the cell. Furthermore, it makes possible enzymatic reactions that could not occur otherwise. In addition, its molecules actually enter into certain metabolic reactions.

Diffusion. This process is the net movement of particles (molecules, atoms, or ions) resulting from their tendency to be distributed evenly throughout a given space. In a sense, it is an exemplification of the second law of thermodynamics; that is, particles tend toward a random distribution within their particular system.

Figure 5.15. *Amoeba proteus.* Three individuals are shown with numerous cytoplasmic extensions (*pseudopodia*). Note the dark nucleus in the cell at upper right, with a light contractile vacuole near it. The cytoplasm contains numerous granules. (Courtesy Carolina Biological Supply Company.)

For example, if a vial of perfume is opened at the front of a room, its odor may be detected at the back of the room within a short time because of the passage of its molecules through the air. At least some substances dissolved in water seem to be absorbed into cells by diffusion; thus, if the concentration of dissolved materials is greater in the surrounding medium than within the cell, some of these materials may be absorbed. The exchange of such gases as oxygen and carbon dioxide between the cell and its environment is apparently due primarily to diffusion.

Note that since the movement of water into a cell (osmosis) is a function of the concentration of dissolved particles on both sides of the cell membrane, any force affecting the concentration of dissolved particles will also affect osmosis. As a consequence, diffusion and osmosis are closely related phenomena, with diffusion having a direct effect upon osmosis. This phenomenon (among other considerations) indicates that osmosis is a much more complex process than the mere differential movement of water molecules based upon their relative concentrations alone.

Electrical charge. It has been observed that charged particles enter the cell less readily than uncharged ones. As a rule, the greater the charge, the less freely a particle moves across the cell membrane. For instance, such monovalent ions as K^+ and Cl^- enter the cell more readily than divalent or multivalent ones, for example, Mg^{++} or $SO_4^=$. This phenomenon is probably best explained by the nature of the proteins present in the cell membrane. In general, protein molecules are highly charged and thus tend to repel charged particles.

Solubility in lipids. Still another factor known to be involved in absorption is the degree to which a substance is soluble in lipids. For example, the higher (more complex) alcohols are more lipid-soluble than the lower alcohols; and, in spite of their greater size and complexity, the higher alcohols penetrate the cell membrane more readily than do the lower ones. It has been postulated that since lipid materials constitute a large proportion of the cell membrane, such substances as the higher alcohols are more readily accepted by the membrane than less lipid-soluble materials.

Active transport. Of all the factors influencing the passage of nutrients through cell membranes, active transport is probably the most important and, at the same time, the least understood. As the name implies, active transport involves the passage of a substance through the cell membrane with an expenditure of energy on the part of the cell. In other words, a metabolic process is involved, and the cell is obliged to perform work in transporting many substances to its interior. There are numerous examples of ions and large molecules that exhibit low solubility in lipids being transported into the cell against an electrical and a concentration gradient. Furthermore, in such cases, if a metabolic poison is administered to the cell, transport ceases, which indicates that transport of these materials is dependent upon the processes of metabolism. For example, a cell usually maintains a high concentration of potassium (K^+) ions within the cell membrane, and a high concentration of sodium (Na^+) ions outside the membrane. The cell must work to keep such ions from establishing an equilibrium on both sides of the membrane. Although relatively little is known about the precise mechanisms involved in active transport, it appears that it is a very complex process and one that is highly important in a wide variety of absorption phenomena.

In addition to these five factors affecting nutrition, cells occasionally take in relatively large droplets of materials by a process called *pinocytosis* (Greek, *pino,* to drink + *kytos,* container). For example, many cells "drink" or "gulp" fluid materials from their environment, as a result of which certain large molecules in solution may be taken into the cell. Furthermore, cells of multicellular animals have been observed to ingest relatively large particles of organic matter (like the feeding habits of an amoeba). This phenomenon is called *phagocytosis* (Greek *phagos,* to eat + *kytos,* container). For example, certain white blood cells of the complex animal body engulf bacteria or various particles and digest them. Pinocytosis and phagocytosis may be considered special cases of active transport.

In summary, absorption is a complex phenomenon; it frequently involves chemical changes and energy transformations at the surfaces of cell membranes. It is highly important, therefore, that we conceive of the cell as an extremely active unit that maintains lines of exchange with its surrounding medium. Without these lines of exchange, it would be impossible for the cell to carry on the vital functions of respiration and synthesis.

RESPIRATION [16]   As an open system, a living cell must take in energy in order to carry on its functional activities. For the most part, this energy is obtained from organic molecules, or foods. This method is followed even by autotrophic cells, which utilize radiant energy in building their own organic molecules; the bulk of their usable energy comes from the breakdown (decomposition) of these molecules. Thus, initially, cellular energy is potential chemical energy that is "stored" in the bonds of organic molecules. Respiration is the process whereby this chemical energy of organic compounds is converted to usable energy within the cell. It is a process of oxidation, as is combustion or burning, but it does not produce the high temperatures of an actual fire, because respiration is a highly controlled form of oxidation, during which the chemical bonds of fuel molecules are broken one at a time in stepwise fashion, with a gradual release of energy. However, the total amount of energy released is equal to that which would be released if a given fuel molecule were burned in a furnace and all the chemical bonds were broken simultaneously. In the latter case, the sudden release of energy generates the high temperature that is characteristic of fire. Obviously, this kind of oxidation would be deadly to a living system. In a metaphorical sense, nature has provided an alternative: the stepwise oxidation that we call *respiration.*

In contrast to combustion, only a part of the total energy of an organic molecule is lost as heat during respiration; except for special cases, none is converted to light. Instead, a large part of the energy is transformed into a special form of chemical energy that is usable in the synthetic processes and other activities of the cell. By this means, the decompositional and other *exergonic* chemical reactions that characterize respiration are coupled to the synthetic and other *endergonic* reactions that characterize synthesis. We can illustrate this relationship, and especially the decompositional (respiratory) aspect, by means of an analogy.

You will recall that organic compounds are characterized by carbon atoms linked to each other and to atoms of certain other elements by means of energy-rich bonds. For example, the end of a long-chain fatty acid is represented as follows:

$$
\begin{array}{ccc}
\text{H} & \text{H} & \\
| & | & \\
----\text{C}—\text{C}—\text{H} & & \\
| & | & \\
\text{H} & \text{H} &
\end{array}
$$

Let us consider the carbon atom as a sort of safe with four money boxes, into which money (energy) may be put. The atom may either place lids (hydrogen atoms) on the boxes or it may attach its boxes to those of other carbon atoms, with each serving as a lid for the other (Fig. 5-16). The process of respiration begins with full money boxes, each tightly capped; and it proceeds only when keys (enzymes) to the lids are provided by the cell. Having "unlocked" the boxes, the cell is faced with two difficulties. It must dispose of the lids (hydrogen atoms), and it must convert the storage money (energy) into usable currency. We shall consider the latter process first.

Apparently, all types of cells make use of a pair of "money changers," *adenosine diphosphate* and *adenosine triphosphate,* abbreviated *ADP* and *ATP,* respectively. These compounds are identical except that ADP exhibits two phosphate groups on each of its molecules whereas ATP displays three (Fig. 5-17). It so happens that when ATP loses one of its phosphate groups and becomes ADP, energy is made available to the cell in a form that can be used. The resulting ADP molecules and phosphate groups then become recombined by utilizing energy obtained from fuel molecules and are used all over again. Hence, the "money" released from the carbon-hydrogen bonds is spent on attaching phosphate groups to ADP molecules

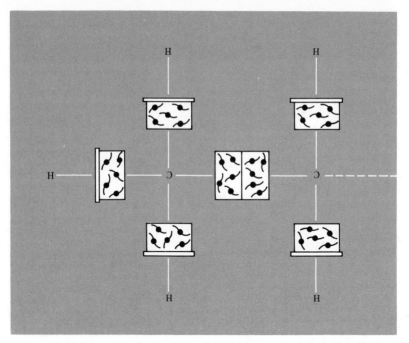

Figure 5.16. Illustration representing the storage of energy in chemical bonds. See text for a fuller exposition of this analogy.

to form ATP again, which thus becomes a source of readily available energy. This process is represented as an energy cycle in Fig. 5-18.

Of course, analogies are limited in their applicability, and they almost always present an oversimplified picture. Nevertheless, it is helpful to think of metabolic complexities in terms of familiar processes (an analogy is, itself, one kind of conceptual scheme). We shall extend this particular analogy as we proceed.

Ideally, a cell disposes of hydrogen atoms by attaching them to oxygen. As a result, water forms. Water, as we have seen, is not only nontoxic to the cell but also is highly useful. This process, however, is not as easily accomplished as might be supposed. Only by means of a complex series of enzymatic reactions does it occur; the corresponding energy release (and consequently, ATP synthesis) takes place step by step.

Let us consider the respiration of a carbohydrate such as glucose. Glucose is a hexose (six-carbon) sugar that can be absorbed into cells. In absorption, it is subjected to a series of reactions resulting in the splitting of the six-carbon molecule into two three-carbon molecules. This occurs in the hyaloplasm (general cytoplasm) of the cell. Phosphate groups become attached to each of these two molecules during the process, and each becomes *phosphoglyceraldehyde (PGAL)*. This particular transformation is endergonic, since it requires the "expenditure" of two ATP molecules

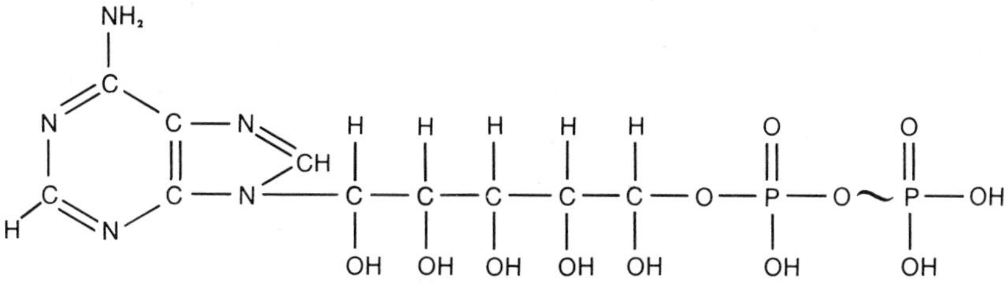

Adenosine diphosphate (ADP)

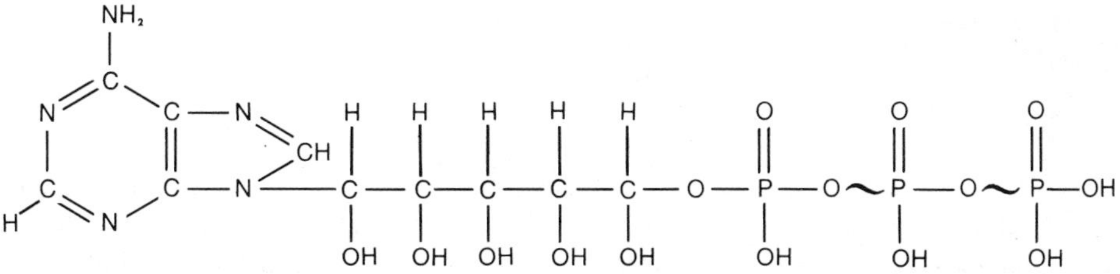

Adenosine triphosphate (ATP)

Figure 5.17. Structural formulas of adenosine diphosphate and adenosine triphosphate. The bonds (∼), of which ADP possesses one and ATP two, signify high-energy bonds. In the ordinary functioning of the ADP-ATP energy cycle, only the terminal high-energy bond of ATP is broken with a release of energy.

for the total conversion; that is, it "costs" the cell two molecules of ATP to convert a molecule of glucose to two molecules of PGAL. Each molecule of PGAL is converted next to *diphosphoglyceric acid (DPGA)* through the addition of a phosphate group and the loss of a pair of hydrogen atoms. In this case, the phosphate is inorganic, thus "costing" the cell nothing in terms of ATP energy. (The primary phosphorylations occurred at the expense of ATP, which then became ADP.) Each molecule of DPGA then proceeds to lose its two phosphate groups to ADP, forming ATP, which means that *four* molecules of ATP are formed. A hydrogen atom is lost from each molecule, and each becomes *pyruvic acid* ($C_3H_4O_3$). For each glucose atom that enters into this sequence, therefore, the end products are as follows:

$$C_6H_{12}O_6 \rightarrow 2 \text{ PGAL} \rightarrow 2 \text{ DPGA}$$
$$\rightarrow 2 C_3H_4O_3 + 2 H_2 + 2 \text{ ATP (net)}$$

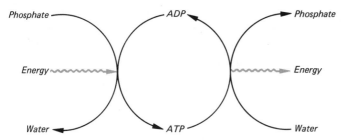

Figure 5.18. By means of the ADP-ATP cycle, energy
transformations are accomplished within cells. Ordinarily,
energy coming into the cycle is the potential chemical energy
of chemical bonds, and that shown leaving the cell is
kinetic energy as it is expended as heat, movement, the
energy utilized in synthesis, and so on.

This series of reactions from glucose (or any other suitable carbohydrate substrate) to pyruvic acid is called *glycolysis* or the *Embden-
Meyerhof* pathway. It is important to note that the net end products of
glycolysis are two molecules of pyruvic acid, two pairs of hydrogen atoms,
and two molecules of ATP. (You will recall that *four* ATP's are actually
formed, but *two* were used in the original phosphorylations, thus leaving
the cell with a net "profit" of only two.)

It should be emphasized that our presentation of glycolysis is quite
abbreviated; the entire pathway from glucose to pyruvic acid consists of
some nine distinct reactions. Perhaps it seems strange that it would take
nine reactions to divide a six-carbon compound into two three-carbon compounds, but it should be remembered that *respiration is a stepwise process*
and is highly controlled by the cellular machinery. If energy were not released gradually, it would all be lost as heat and/or light, as in combustion.
It is the "aim" of the cell to transfer a maximum of the chemical energy
available to it to the high-energy bonds of ATP, which is its usable "currency."

What happens to the two pairs of hydrogen atoms that result from
the glycolytic pathway? They are taken up by a special type of nucleotide
(*nicotinamide adenine dinucleotide,* abbreviated *NAD*) present in the
cell and are held until they can be released to gaseous oxygen. This
is the usual pathway for hydrogen released in glycolysis. The pyruvic acid
is further degraded. We shall discuss presently these other aspects of
respiration. First, however, let us see what happens in a cell if the hydrogen
produced in glycolysis cannot be given to gaseous oxygen. In most cells,
this excess hydrogen simply ties up all of the available nucleotide hydrogen acceptor with which it can combine. The damming-up of hydrogen
eventually poisons the cell, hence most organisms cannot live for very long

in the absence of gaseous oxygen. However, there are cells and even organisms that are capable of living in a total absence of oxygen. Hence, they are said to be anaerobic, which means "without oxygen."

What happens to the hydrogen atoms in anaerobic cells? They simply are transferred to pyruvic acid, forming either lactic acid or ethyl alcohol:

$$C_3H_4O_3 + 2H \rightarrow \quad C_3H_6O_3 \qquad \text{(animal cells and certain bacteria)}$$
pyruvic acid   lactic acid

$$C_3H_4O_3 + 2H \rightarrow \quad C_2H_6O + CO_2 \qquad \text{(yeast cells}$$
pyruvic acid   ethyl alcohol   and certain plant cells)

It should be pointed out that not all cells possess enzymes for making these conversions. In fact, relatively few cells can make the conversion from pyruvic acid to ethyl alcohol. If a cell does possess the capability of producing either lactic acid or ethyl alcohol under anaerobic conditions, it is said to carry on *fermentation*. If this pathway is the *only* catabolic one open to an organism, it is obliged to forego the greater part of the energy that is bound up in a carbohydrate molecule. It must make up for this energy loss by fermenting more carbohydrate if it is to carry on a degree of metabolism equivalent to that which would be possible if it were capable of utilizing oxygen. For example, when yeast cells are grown under anaerobic conditions, they consume much more carbohydrate in producing a given number of cells than is required under aerobic conditions.* To be exact, only about 5 per cent of the potential energy in a glucose molecule is made available to a cell in fermentation. For this reason, it is apparently not by accident that the great majority of organisms possess mechanisms that make oxygen utilization possible, since this ability renders a species far more capable of maintaining itself in nature where it is obliged to compete with other species. That there are relatively few anaerobic species is testimony to this principle.

In spite of the fact that the more complex organisms are dependent upon oxygen as a hydrogen acceptor, there are circumstances under which certain cells or tissues may function anaerobically. In muscle cells of man and other vertebrates, for example, energy for contraction is normally provided by the breakdown of ATP to ADP, which is, in turn, recharged to ATP by a series of steps connected with the complete breakdown of the polysaccharide *glycogen* to carbon dioxide and water. However, under

---

* Some organisms, such as yeasts, may live either aerobically (utilizing gaseous oxygen as a hydrogen acceptor) or anaerobically (utilizing its own pyruvic acid as a hydrogen acceptor). Others, such as certain bacteria, are said to be obligately anaerobic, because gaseous oxygen is actually poisonous to them. Most organisms are, of course, obligate aerobes.

conditions of great activity, the bloodstream cannot supply the muscles with oxygen at a rate sufficient to keep up with hydrogen production, and lactic acid (the end product of fermentation in this case) accumulates. In man, at least, this lactic acid is eventually carried to the liver, where it may be completely oxidized. Under these conditions, therefore, the muscle cells are obliged to function anaerobically, which greatly lowers their efficiency temporarily in terms of glycogen utilization.

As far as man is concerned, the fermentation of carbohydrates by yeasts or bacteria may be turned to his advantage. Ethyl alcohol and lactic acid products have long been valued, and the accumulation of these substances in the immediate environments of their producers is made possible through their inability to pass their waste hydrogen on to oxygen.

In summary, glycolysis is the anaerobic catabolism of carbohydrates; pyruvic acid is the end product of the process. Pyruvic acid may then go in either of two directions. If the accumulated hydrogen cannot be given to gaseous oxygen, glycolysis continues as fermentation. If gaseous oxygen is able to combine with hydrogen in the cell, then aerobic respiration of pyruvic acid occurs. These alternate pathways are illustrated in Fig. 5-19.

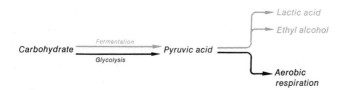

Figure 5.19. The possible fates of a carbohydrate in catabolism. Note that fermentation and glycolysis are identical processes, except that glycolysis ends with the formation of pyruvic acid and fermentation ends with the formation of either ethyl alcohol or lactic acid.

We shall now turn our attention to this second possible phase of respiration.

In the presence of molecular oxygen, which serves as the ultimate hydrogen acceptor, a series of oxidation-reduction reactions occur. The major molecules involved are nicotinamide adenine dinucleotide (NAD), flavin adenine dinucleotide (FAD), and a group of pigments called *cytochromes*. Our concern here is to emphasize the orderly sequence in which these reactions occur, the role of molecular oxygen in the process, and the energetic considerations that are important to our discussion.

We mentioned previously that the hydrogens removed from the original glucose are held by NAD, which is usually the initial hydrogen acceptor in these oxidation-reduction systems. These systems are referred to alternately as *electron-transport systems, hydrogen-transport systems,* or *cytochrome oxidase systems.* Cytochrome oxidase (cytochrome a_3) is the terminal acceptor in this chain of organic molecules. The other acceptors are FAD, cytochrome *b,* cytochrome *c,* and cytochrome *a.* Figure 5-20 depicts the sequence of this series and the points at which phosphorylation of ADP to ATP is coupled to the system. As we have shown the series, the oxidized forms of the molecules are at the bottom and the reduced forms are at the top. In the case of NAD and FAD, entire hydrogen atoms are transferred. However, ionization occurs with the oxidation of FAD·H₂ by cytochrome *b,* with the result that the cytochromes transfer only electrons. The hydrogen ions are set free within the mitochondrion. At the end of the sequence, when cytochrome a_3, is oxidized, an atom of oxygen

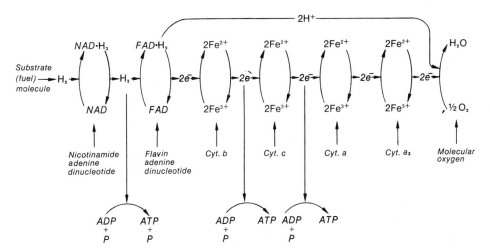

Figure 5.20. Schematic drawing of the cytochrome oxidase system. See text for amplification.

joins two electrons and two hydrogen ions, as a result of which oxygen is reduced to water. As the electrons are passed along the system, there are electron shifts in the carriers involved at the points indicated in Fig. 5-20, so that electrons pass into lower energy levels. As a result, energy is made available and is incorporated into high-energy phosphate bonds; that is, ADP is phosphorylated to ATP. Thus, a part of the energy released by the respiration of glucose is conserved, although some is dissipated as heat. As we have indicated, all or most all of the energy would be lost if a given molecule were "shattered" in a single reaction. As it is, the gradual transformation of energy into phosphate bonds by way of the sequence we have outlined constitutes a highly efficient mechanism within the cell.

Now let us consider the two pyruvic acid molecules that result from the glycolysis of a single glucose molecule. In aerobic respiration they are eventually oxidized to carbon dioxide and water. This process involves a complex series of reactions. It begins with the passage of pyruvic acid into the mitochondria. Here, a given molecule of pyruvic acid is decarboxylated, and the remainder of the molecule is joined to a molecule of a substance called *coenzyme A* (abbreviated Co-A). The resulting compound, now containing only two carbon atoms of the original pyruvic acid, is called *acetyl Co-A*. The transformation of pyruvic acid to acetyl Co-A also involves a dehydrogenation; that is, two hydrogen atoms are removed from each molecule. Thus, two more electrons are available for transfer along the cytochrome oxidase system, which means that three more molecules of ATP are formed for each molecule of pyruvic acid. This transformation, involving what is left of the original glucose molecule, may be illustrated in a highly abbreviated form as follows:

2 pyruvic acid + 2Co-A → 2 acetyl Co-A + 2CO$_2$ + 6ATP

Each molecule of acetyl Co-A now enters a complex series of reactions, which constitute a cycle. This cycle is called the *Krebs cycle* in honor of the biochemist H. A. Krebs, who worked out a major part of it, for which he was awarded the Nobel prize in physiology and medicine in 1953. It is also called the *citric acid cycle,* because citric acid is usually considered the starting point in the cycle. This cycle is a common meeting point for all organic molecules utilized by the cell as fuel. It also furnishes carbon skeletons for a number of synthetic metabolic pathways. Since the series of reactions involved form a cycle, one can only speak of a starting point in the cycle as relative to the point at which it is entered by a given compound. The end point or end product is then relative to the point just preceding the point of entry. In this context, acetyl Co-A enters the cycle by joining a four-carbon compound called *oxaloacetic acid,* which represents the end point of the cycle in this case, to form the six-carbon citric acid, which represents the starting point of the cycle. In the reaction leading to the formation of citric acid from the union of acetyl Co-A with oxaloacetic acid, the Co-A is released and may combine with more pyruvic acid coming into the cycle.

The major reactions occurring in the Krebs cycle, from our viewpoint, are decarboxylations and dehydrogenations. All of the other reactions are simply preparatory to more decarboxylation and dehydrogenation. As a result of decarboxylation, the two remaining carbon atoms of the original pyruvic acid molecule are released as carbon dioxide; as a result of dehydrogenation, the three remaining hydrogen atoms are passed along hydrogen transfer systems. This latter process, of course, leads to the generation of ATP. Since the original glucose molecule is represented by two molecules of pyruvic acid, two molecules of acetyl Co-A, and so on; then *four* atoms of carbon are released as CO_2 in the Krebs cycle, and six atoms of hydrogen are available to transfer to molecular oxygen. However, there is a net addition of three molecules of water to the Krebs cycle for each molecule of acetyl Co-A. Thus, 12 addditional hydrogens are available for every two turns of the cycle. In all, therefore, 24 electrons are delivered to the cytochrome system for each one of the glucose molecules that undergoes complete respiration.

Figure 5-21 shows the fate of pyruvic acid after it enters a mitochondrion. The major compounds of the Krebs cycle are shown, as well as the points in the cycle at which decarboxylation and dehydrogenation occur. The decarboxylations are represented in the diagram by the release of carbon dioxide, and the dehydrogenations are represented by the cytochrome oxidase system, as indicated. It should be pointed out that Fig. 5-21 is oversimplified; the reactions involved are rather complex and only an overall grasp of their significance can be gained. Furthermore, it should be noted that each reaction in the cycle must be catalyzed by a specific enzyme.

With the passage of two molecules of pyruvic acid through the Krebs cycle, the respiration of a glucose molecule is completed. The end products, as shown in our overall equation, are carbon dioxide, water, and energy (in the form of ATP):

$$C_6H_{12}O_6 + 6O_2 + 6H_2O \rightarrow 6CO_2 + 12H_2O + 38ATP$$

Thus, respiration effectively "shatters" the substrate molecule (glucose, in this case) and converts its potential energy into that of ATP. In doing so, it disposes of the original glucose atoms in the form of carbon dioxide and water. The energetic and material conversions of the entire sequence are summarized in Fig. 5-22.

A great many substances may enter the citric acid cycle by some means other than the pyruvic acid gateway. Fatty acids from fat digestion enter it as acetic acid $(C_2H_2O_4)$, which then becomes transformed to acetyl Co-A. Amino acids may enter at various places along the citric acid cycle after their nitrogen groups are removed. Since carbohydrates are the major fuels for most cells, however, the main pathway of respiration is by way of glycolysis coupled with the citric acid cycle by means of a few intermediate reactions. The energy and water are certainly necessary and usable by the cells, and the carbon dioxide presents no problem since it can readily diffuse out through the cell membrane.

How efficient is the cell in conserving the energy contained in a molecule of glucose? If one considers that a gram-molecular weight of glucose

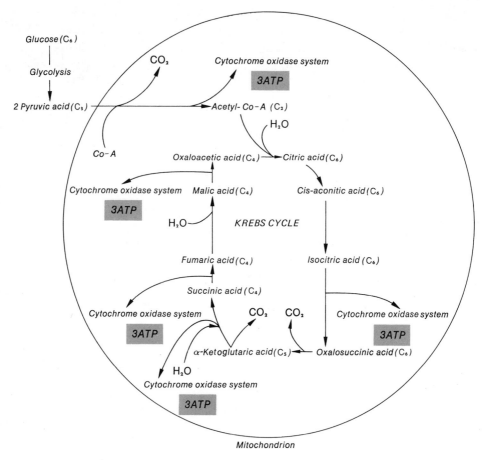

Figure 5.21. Schematic drawing showing the events occurring in the mitochondrion as a part of respiration. Most of these events are a part of the Krebs cycle. Note the points at which hydrogens are removed. ATP yields (shaded) are expressed per molecule of pyruvic acid.

contains about 690,000 calories of energy and that one high-energy phosphate bond contains about 10,000 calories, the cell has conserved about 55 per cent of the energy (380,000/690,000). Thermodynamically, this yield is very high; and the cell is thus supplied with a form of chemical energy (the high-energy terminal bond of ATP) with which to drive endergonic reactions, transport molecules across cell membranes, accomplish ciliary movement, and so on. However, as ATP is changed back to ADP with the expenditure of high-energy phosphate bonds, there is further loss

Glycolysis (4ATP—2ATP)		2ATP
$4H \xrightarrow{\text{Cytochrome system}} 2H_2O$ (from glycolysis)		6
$4H \xrightarrow{\text{Cytochrome system}} 2H_2O$ (from pyruvic acid)		6
$4H \xrightarrow{\text{Cytochrome system}} 2H_2O$ (from isocitric acid)		6
$4H \xrightarrow{\text{Cytochrome system}} 2H_2O$ (from α-ketoglutaric acid)		6
$4H \xrightarrow{\text{Cytochrome system}} 2H_2O$ (from succinic acid)		6
$4H \xrightarrow{\text{Cytochrome system}} 2H_2O$ (from malic acid)		6
Total:		38ATP

Figure 5.22. A summarization of energy yields from the complete respiration of a molecule of glucose.

in efficiency. In terms of useful activity, most cells probably realize far less than 55 per cent efficiency from their organic fuels.

SYNTHESIS [17]   To this point, we have discussed the nature of nutrient materials and how some of these materials are involved in respiration to produce the special high energy of ATP, which is the cell's "currency" that it uses to "pay" for building, replacing, and repairing its parts. However, other nutrient substances are used as the raw materials in these constructive (anabolic) processes. To draw a further analogy, they are the "bricks" or building blocks. The process by means of which the cell's building blocks (made available to it by nutrition) are fashioned into structural parts constitutes the synthetic phase of metabolism. The cell is a versatile builder. It constructs nucleic acids, structural and enzymatic proteins, lipids, carbohydrates, and a host of other types of molecules. The specific pattern of synthesis depends on quite a number of factors, such as type and relative amounts of raw material supplied by nutrition, nature of the cell's enzyme complex, total energy available that can be channeled into synthesis, the "need" of the cell for certain materials, and so on. The synthetic pattern also depends upon the specific type of cell involved. However, all types of cells synthesize the basic macromolecules that are common to all living systems, and the reactions involved are primarily synthetic and endergonic; that is, they utilize ATP as an energy source.

It is convenient to classify synthetic reactions according to the source of the energy involved. *Photosynthesis* includes those reactions occurring in cells containing chlorophyll in which an external source—sunlight—provides the energy. Such reactions combine the raw materials, carbon dioxide and water, in the formation of carbohydrates. *Chemosynthesis* involves the oxidation of certain inorganic compounds, such as H_2S and NH_3, as an energy source; and this energy is utilized in the synthesis of complex compounds from simple raw materials. Finally, *organosynthesis* includes those reactions that depend upon an internal energy source, namely, ATP derived from respiration. Of these three classes of synthetic reactions, organosynthesis is by far the most common because it is characteristic of all cells. In contrast, photosynthesis is limited to cells containing chlorophyll, and chemosynthesis is limited to the cells of certain microorganisms. We must point out that the synthetic reactions themselves are energy-consuming and that the reactions upon which we are basing our classification are energy-yielding; it is more meaningful, however, to classify synthetic reactions from the standpoint of the decompositional reactions that provide the energy for synthesis. This classification is a reflection of the intimate relation between synthesis and respiration; actually, it is difficult to discuss these two aspects of metabolism separately.

Photosynthesis.[18] With the exception of the small group of chemosynthetic bacteria mentioned above, all organisms depend ultimately upon green plants as a source of organic nutrients. For this reason, it is appropriate that we consider photosynthesis first in our discussion of synthesis. Photosynthetic cells manufacture nutrients by virtue of their possession of chlorophyll. This substance makes possible the utilization of solar energy in combining carbon dioxide and water to form glucose or other carbohydrates; oxygen is also produced in the process. Although many separate chemical reactions are involved, the overall reaction may be represented as follows:

$$\text{Solar energy} + 6CO_2 + 6H_2O \xrightarrow{\text{chlorophyll}} C_6H_{12}O_6 + 6O_2$$

Thus, for every six molecules of carbon dioxide and of water that enter the reaction, one molecule of glucose and six molecules of oxygen are produced.

Although simple carbohydrates are the immediate products of photosynthesis, the green plant does not ordinarily build up great quantities of these substances; rather, they serve as raw material for the further synthesis of organic compounds. They may be converted to more complex carbohydrates or to fats in the plant, or they may be combined with nitrogen and other elements available to the plant in its environment to form proteins. Vitamins, enzymes, and various materials essential to the well-being of the plant may finally be formed by such modification of these carbohydrates, and even more chlorophyll can be synthesized from them. It may be said metaphorically that the green plant is a very able chemist, producing a variety of substances from these fundamental materials. The actual chemistry of reactions occurring in green plants is extremely complex and is still the subject of much intense research.

There is a common notion that green plants obtain their organic nutrients from the soil or, in the case of aquatic species such as algae, from the aqueous medium. This is a mistaken idea; as we have seen, the green plant manufactures its organic nutrients from inorganic precursors. It is true that these plants depend upon their environments for essential substances such as water, carbon dioxide, and inorganic salts, but these compounds are not energy-yielding. As for plants that grow in the soil, a simple experiment will show that it is not from the soil itself that the substance of a plant is chiefly derived. A container may be filled with dirt, oven-dried, and weighed. If the seed of some plant is inserted into the soil and thoroughly watered, the seed will germinate into a plant. After the plant has grown to a considerable size, it may be pulled up and separated from the soil in which it was growing. If great care has been taken to ensure that all the original soil is still present, and if all plant parts are removed from it, a second drying and weighing will indicate that the soil has lost only an extremely small percentage of its original weight. When the plant is weighed, it will be found that it is many times heavier than the soil that has been lost. Of course, much of the weight of the plant is accounted for by the water it has absorbed. However, even its dry weight will be found to equal many times that lost by the soil.

Such experiments led early plant physiologists to a realization that the body of a land plant derives its mass from some source other than soil. As more and more carefully controlled experiments were performed, with methods being developed for the exact measurement of water and gases, the process of photosynthesis became known. Since the time of its initial discovery, biologists have probed more deeply into the complex intermediate steps involved in photosynthesis, and a great deal more is now known about it.

For many years after the photosynthetic equation was known to be quantitatively accurate, it was supposed that carbon and oxygen separated during the process; the carbon became attached to water and the oxygen was released. The plausibility of this hypothesis can readily be seen if we reduce the equation to its simplest terms:

$$CO_2 + H_2O \rightarrow CH_2O + O_2$$

It was supposed further that the unit of (CH_2O) was "multiplied" in some fashion to form sugars. Six such units, for example, might form glucose. As is so often the case in scientific matters, however, the most attractive, plausible, or even popular hypothesis does not always turn out to be the most fruitful one. In this instance, direct evidence was not forthcoming until about 1940, when scientists applied the principle of using isotopic tracers.* By incorporating "heavy" oxygen into water molecules, investigators were able to trace its fate during photosynthesis. Contrary to the earlier idea, it was found that such oxygen became the O_2 of the photosynthetic equation. Clearly, therefore, the reaction did not involve a splitting of the CO_2 molecule to liberate oxygen. Furthermore, twice as much oxygen appeared from the reaction than apparently had gone into it if all the liberated oxygen came from water, as it obviously did.

Step by step, the major features of the process became clear. It is now known that the first step in photosynthesis is *photolysis,* or the breakdown of water in the presence of chlorophyll; light energy serves to activate the reaction:

$$2H_2O \xrightarrow[\text{chlorophyll}]{\text{light}} 4H + O_2$$

The oxygen produced in this reaction may escape into the immediate environment of the plant, or some of it may be used in the plant for other reactions. As for the hydrogen, it is captured by NADP and is eventually delivered to a complex cycle of reactions that CO_2 also enters.

At this point, the second phase of photosynthesis, *CO_2 fixation,* begins. Carbon dioxide is taken up by a five-carbon compound, already present in the chloroplast, called *ribulose diphosphate (RDP).* A molecule of RDP, one of CO_2, and one of water react to produce two three-carbon molecules of phosphoglyceric acid (PGA). Each PGA molecule loses an oxygen atom (which is joined to hydrogen coming from photolysis) and becomes phosphoglyceraldehyde (PGAL). By special transformation reactions, five out of six PGAL molecules produced in this fashion are changed to three of RDP, which then go on for another "load" of CO_2. One out of six is made available to the plant.

Actually, PGAL is the end product of photosynthesis, not glucose as the overall equation would indicate. However, since PGAL *may* be converted to glucose (it may also be utilized as such by the plant or be converted to other materials), it is sufficiently accurate for purposes of representation to balance the equation as we do. One correction must be made, however. Since all the oxygen produced during photosynthesis comes

---

* As we have noted, isotopes are atoms of the same element that differ in mass. Ordinary oxygen atoms, for example, have eight protons and eight neutrons in the nucleus. The chemist refers to this kind of oxygen as $_8O^{16}$. Another kind of oxygen atom ($_8O^{18}$) has eight protons and ten neutrons. Since the number of electrons is the same in both cases, there is no difference in their chemical properties, but they differ in their physical properties. Water molecules may be prepared using $_8O^{18}$, for example, and the fate of the oxygen can be "traced" by using instruments capable of detecting it through its physical properties. Most elements consist of different isotopes, which means that tracer techniques are availibale for use in attacking a great variety of biological problems.

from water, and some water is produced during CO_2 fixation, it is more accurate to express the overall process as follows:

$$\text{Solar energy} + 6CO_2 + 12H_2O \xrightarrow{\text{chlorophyll}} C_6H_{12}O_6 + 6O_2 + 6H_2O$$

Or, to be still more specific, we might express the process of photosynthesis by means of a diagram, as shown in Fig. 5-23, which is itself an over-

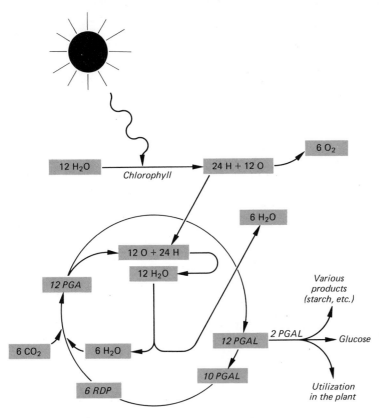

Figure 5.23. A diagrammatic representation of photosynthesis. See text for amplification.

simplification in terms of what actually happens. Nevertheless, it should be obvious that the capture of light energy and its storage in organic molecules is a process that is much more complex than our original equation might indicate.

Syntheses common to all cells. There are numerous compounds not obtained by cells as prefabricated nutrients; rather, they are synthesized within the cells themselves. These compounds are primarily the organic macromolecules (polysaccharides, lipids, proteins, and nucleic acids) that constitute the bulk of cell contents exclusive of water. As you will recall, we discussed the basic structural features of these macromolecules and the nature of their micromolecular building blocks in Chapter 4.

The synthesis of organic macromolecules from organic micromolecules derived from nutrition is called *organosynthesis,* and it is carried on by all cells. The energy required by the cell in effecting this kind of synthesis is supplied, of course, by ATP.

It is beyond the scope of this book to elaborate on the various synthetic pathways by means of which organic macromolecules are synthesized. However, later we shall consider protein synthesis within a special context and point out then that it is an example of the many organosynthetic processes common to all cells.

SELF-PERPETUATION

Having discussed cellular function, or metabolism, in terms of the processes of nutrition, respiration, and synthesis, let us summarize. It should be obvious by this time that these three processes are not independent of each other; on the contrary, they are interwoven in a highly complex fashion. Consequently, precise control must be exerted by the cell in order to maintain a harmonious relationship among *all* reactions that are occurring. Furthermore, the cell itself must adapt to a possible variety of environmental conditions; and, regardless of these conditions, it is obliged to maintain a certain degree of structural and functional integrity if it is to stay "alive." It is the capacity to maintain this "steady-state" condition that we call *self-perpetuation.* Like metabolism, it is inclusive of several complex processes; indeed, it depends to a great extent upon metabolic processes themselves, especially synthetic ones. But essentially, it ensures that metabolism is controlled and that these systems of controlled metabolism are extended. Ultimately, therefore, self-perpetuation becomes reproduction.

To state it another way, self-perpetuation contributes the dimension of *time* to metabolism. Despite environmental changes or other difficulties (unless these changes throw the cell into complete disarray), the cell continues to make more of its polyphasic self through utilization of nutrient materials. Let us be careful to note that such a process does not necessarily mean that the cell increases in its total mass. It may only be replacing wornout parts. Let us also note that self-perpetuation is, itself, dependent upon metabolism and, in a very real sense, is merely one aspect of metabolism—the *control* and *perpetuation-in-time* aspect.

Thus, metabolism is highly controlled in a living system. A protoplasmic system is in a constant state of flux: Molecules wear out; they are replaced or not, depending upon conditions; and the physicochemical complex is always changing in some degree. However, the structural pattern remains pretty much the same; the cell is in a state of *dynamic equilibrium*. This equilibrium persists if new building materials are added at approximately the same rate as old ones are degraded—that is, if synthetic (anabolic) reactions within the cell balance decompositional (catabolic) reactions. If new building materials are added more rapidly than old ones are removed—that is, if there is a preponderance of synthetic reactions over decompositional ones—growth occurs. If the converse is true—that is, if there is more decomposition than synthesis—death will ultimately be the result.

It might be said that it is the overall "aim" of a cell (or of a living system at any level) to keep its synthetic reactions at a rate *equal to* or *greater than* its decompositional reactions; the living system wages a constant battle against thermodynamic equilibrium. It never wins this fight over the long run, of course, except in a very special way. It may reproduce or extend itself in time. Reproduction is a special case of self-perpetuation and is such an important one that we shall discuss it as a separate topic.

5.2C The Cell as a Unit of Reproduction

Reproduction is at least a potential property of living systems, whether at the cellular or multicellular level. This property makes it possible for life to continue, even if catabolism overtakes anabolism in the system as a whole.

In multicellular organisms, the cell is the basic unit of reproduction, just as it is also the basic unit of structure and function. As we shall see in the next chapter, the instructions for synthesizing structural entities and for carrying out functional activities are encoded in the cellular DNA contained in the chromosomes. In the process of reproduction, these structural entities are duplicated and passed on to the next generation. Thus, in considering reproduction as a whole, one sees that it manifests itself at the molecular level of DNA, at the ultrastructural level of the chromosome, at the cellular level, and at the organismic level. However, in keeping with the Schleiden-Schwann concept, the cell is the basic unit of reproduction as well as that of structure and function. DNA, chromosomes, and multicellular organisms notwithstanding, the cell is the smallest parental unit that possesses both the genetic information and the self-regulating machinery necessary for the reproduction of the whole organism. The significance of this phenomenon is seen in all sexually reproducing organisms, which ordinarily start out as single cells, regardless of how complex they may be in terms of total num-

ber of cells. For the time being, therefore, we shall concentrate on reproduction at the cellular level.

Every species of organism, whether composed of individuals that are
unicellular or those that are multicellular, is characterized by a specific
and rather constant number of chromosomes. For example, all body cells
of the ordinary garden onion (*Allium cepa*) have 16 chromosomes; all
body cells of man (*Homo sapiens*) contain 46 chromosomes. In terms of
chromosomal constancy, there are two types of cell division. The first type,
which occurs in the growth of multicellular organisms and in asexual reproduction of unicellular forms, is called *mitosis*. In mitotic cell division,
each daughter cell possesses the same number of chromosomes as its parent
cell possessed. The second type of cell division is called *meiosis*. It produces cells whose chromosome number is one-half that of its parent cell;
the cells that result from meiotic division become involved in sexual reproduction. For example, human eggs and sperm, which are called *gametes*
or sex cells, are produced by meiotic cell division. Each sperm and each
egg possesses 23 chromosomes. The union of egg and sperm, which produces a *zygote,* or fertilized egg, creates a new cell with 46 chromosomes.
This cell will, of course, develop into a human being, all of whose body
cells will contain 46 chromosomes; this development is accomplished by
repeated mitotic division. Let us examine the processes of mitosis and
meiosis in order.

MITOSIS [19]

The first indication that a cell is about to undergo division is a visible
change in the chromatin "network" of the nucleus. Special staining and
microscopical techniques reveal that this material is not really a network
at all but that it consists of distinct and elongated threads. As the nucleus
undergoes further change, these threads gradually condense and thicken.
Because this change is the first and most obvious associated with division
of the nucleus, early cytologists settled upon the name "mitosis" (Greek
mitos, a thread) to describe the entire process of nuclear division. From
the beginning of the mitotic process to the formation of two daughter
nuclei, four progressive and interconnected stages or phases are recognized.

Prophase. This stage begins with the condensation of chromosomes
as they become distinctly visible (Fig. 5-24b). Great variation in chromosomal morphology occurs among species; there are differences both in
size and shape. Even within a species, the chromosomes can often be distinguished from one another and can be named or numbered on that basis.
In the cells of the great majority of organisms, a given chromosome is seen
to have a morphological partner; that is, the chromosomes exist in pairs,
although paired chromosomes show no tendency to associate closely in the

nucleus.* Hence, it is frequently said that an organism exhibits a certain number of chromosome pairs: the onion has 8 pairs, man has 23 pairs, and so on. As will be emphasized later, the members of these pairs are the descendants of those contributed by the individual's two parents.

If the chromosomes are closely examined as they become visible at prophase, one can see that they consist of two parallel halves, or *chromatids,* which are connected by a *centromere* (Fig. 5-24b). Hence, this stage of mitosis reveals the presence of twice as many chromatids as there are chromosomes.

At some time during prophase, the nucleoli and nuclear membrane disappear. The full significance of this disappearance is not completely understood, but one immediate result is that the nucleoplasm is no longer separated from the cytoplasm. Consequently, beginning with late prophase, a cell does not really possess a nucleus during its division, even though we speak of "nuclear division."

Metaphase. Near the end of prophase, the chromosomes become oriented in such a way that a lateral view of the cell shows that the chromatids of a given chromosome are in position to move toward opposite poles of the cell. At the point when the centromeres of all the chromosomes are so oriented as to lie in an equatorial plane (Fig. 5-24c), metaphase is said to begin. In a polar view of the cell (Fig. 5-24d), a ring or plate of chromosomes is characteristically seen; this is usually the most advantageous view for counting or studying the chromosomes. Meanwhile, a *spindle,* so called because of its shape, appears in conjunction with the orientation of chromosomes; and some of the *fibers* composing it attach to the centromeres of the chromosomes, while others simply run from pole to pole.

Perhaps the most significant event that occurs during metaphase is the division of chromosomal centromeres. As a result, each chromatid possesses a centromere. Half the original number of chromatids (now called *daughter chromosomes*) are thus prepared to move toward one pole and half toward the other, each set constituting the chromosomal complement of a daughter nucleus.

Anaphase. With the division of centromeres, which occurs simultaneously in all the chromosomes of a given nucleus in most cases, anaphase begins. There is a shortening of those spindle fibers that attach to the centromeres of daughter chromosomes, as though a pulling force were being exerted. Actually, the forces responsible for chromosomal movement in this situation are not clearly understood, but the attachment of spindle

---

* Paired chromosomes do become closely associated during meiosis, described later.

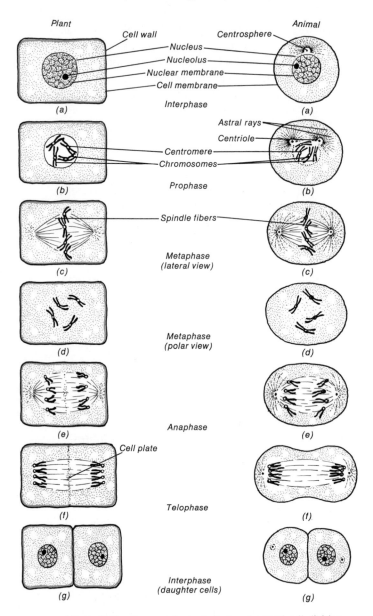

Figure 5.24. A comparison of plant and animal cell division. Each type of cell is shown as having four chromosomes.

fibers to the centromeres is suggestive of some active role by the fibers in chromosomal migration. At late anaphase, chromosomes that are moving toward opposite poles of the cell are widely separated (Fig. 5-24e).

Telophase. Telophase begins when chromosomal migration is complete, and it is somewhat the reverse of prophase (Fig. 5-24f). The chromosomes gradually lose their apparent individual identity; they collectively form the chromatin "network," or mass, typical of a nucleus that is not involved in division. Nucleoli and the nuclear membrane reappear. Telophase ends when the two daughter nuclei are identical to the original nondividing nucleus except in size (Fig. 5-24g).

A nucleus that is not undergoing mitosis is said to be in *interphase*. In actively dividing cells, interphase is a period of synthesis and growth on the part of the nucleus, which enables it to enter again into mitosis at a later time. During interphase the chromosomes lose their definite stainability, but it has been shown that their individual identity is retained. In other words, chromosomes are not dissolved and reformed at telophase and prophase respectively; they simply assume different morphological forms.

It should be recognized that the stages of mitosis are portions of a continuous division cycle and that there is no definite point between each. The phases are recognized by cytologists simply as convenient divisions for reference purposes. By observing the process closely with proper optical equipment, one can see that the nucleus moves smoothly from one phase to another.

Intimately associated with the process of mitosis in animal cells is the behavior of the centrosome and centrioles. During prophase the centrosome divides, and each half undergoes migration in such a way that the two centrioles lie opposite to each other. At metaphase a centriole is thus situated at either side of the nucleus, and each serves as a center from which the spindle fibers and *astral rays* radiate (Fig. 5-24c). Plant cells, except for those of certain lower forms, do not exhibit centrioles. Nevertheless, a spindle is generally formed, although astral rays are not.

Except for certain minor variations, mitotic cell division is a remarkably uniform process among organisms. This phenomenon is highly significant, since it lends further support to the view that living forms are fundamentally similar. Whatever the physical and chemical factors involved, mitosis is an effective means for ensuring a qualitatively and quantitatively equal distribution of certain key nuclear substances to newly synthesized cytoplasm. As we have already observed, the chromosomes are bearers of hereditary determiners (*genes*), and it is significant that each cell of an organism normally possesses exactly the same complement of these genes as any other cell. The process of mitosis makes this feature possible. Because it can produce more cells, a given multicellular organism is able to increase its own body mass, undergo histological specialization, and repair tissues through cell replacement. In the case of a unicellular organism, of course, mitotic cell division and asexual reproduction are identical processes. Since it is the case that so many phenomena are dependent upon this mechanism, mitotic cell division ranks exceedingly high as a fundamental biological process.

Inasmuch as sexual reproduction involves the union of gamete nuclei and an accompanying association of the chromosomes that come from each parent, it becomes important to understand certain phenomena involved in these processes. Let us suppose that a certain species is characterized by individuals in which all the cells, including gametes, possess 10 chromosomes. If gametes of male and female individuals unite, there are then 20 chromosomes in the zygote nucleus. It is not difficult to visualize that unless some mechanism were to reduce the number at one point or another, the chromosomal complement of these organisms would not remain numerically constant.

Such a mechanism is indeed operative in all organisms that reproduce sexually, except for a few unusual types. It involves a special type of nuclear division called *meiosis* (Greek *meioun,* to make smaller), accomplished by two successive divisions with the production of four daughter nuclei, each of whose chromosome number is exactly one-half that of the original cell nucleus. Hence, if meiosis occurs in gamete formation, as it does in animals and in a few plants, it results in eggs and sperm whose union merely restores the "double" chromosome number of the species to the zygote, and subsequent mitotic divisions ensure that all cells of the individual possess this characteristic number.

In order to understand the events that take place in the meiotic process, let us review certain details of ordinary, or mitotic, nuclear division. You recall that prophase is marked by the appearance of distinct chromosomes, each of which is composed of two chromatids connected by a centromere. The chromosomes line up independently of one another along an equatorial plate at metaphase. At anaphase, the centromeres divide; chromatids become separated; and with the subsequent events of telophase and daughter-cell formation, each new nucleus comes to possess a representative chromatid of each original chromosome. Thus, if the number of chromosomes appearing at prophase is 10, each new daughter nucleus receives 10 chromatids (daughter chromosomes), which duplicate themselves before the onset of new prophases in actively dividing cells. Because of this mechanism, chromosome numbers remain constant. In a quantitative sense, therefore, mitotic division is purely *equational.*

As is so often the case with difficult problems in biology, it must be admitted that the forces responsible for initiation of meiotic rather than mitotic division in a given cell are not entirely clear. At any rate, the nucleus of such a cell enters prophase as though it were going to divide mitotically, but the chromosomes behave quite differently than do those in a mitotic nucleus. The descendants of the parental chromosomes, brought together in the zygote that produced the individual and exactly duplicated by many mitoses, now exhibit a strong attraction for each other, and actually unite in a process called *synapsis*. In this union, *homologous* chromosomes (members of a pair) become intimately attached to each other; because the four chromotids constitute a unit, they are sometimes referred to collectively as a *tetrad* (Fig. 5-25). During synapsis, opposing chromatids of homologous chromosomes frequently become coiled and twisted about each other. They may even exchange portions, an event that has considerable genetic significance. Eventually, there is a meiotic metaphase, and the tetrads line up on a spindle. Characteristically, they separate in the plane of their original union; and the two original chromatids of a chromosome (except for any portions that may have been exchanged with homologous chromatids) move toward one pole in meiotic anaphase, while those of the homologous chromosome move toward the other (Fig. 5-25).

With regard to the number of original chromatids, this first meiotic division accomplishes precisely what a mitotic division does; that is, half of the prophase chromatids are delivered to each daughter nucleus. There is a considerable difference, however, in the distribution of these chromatids. In mitosis, one chromatid from each original chromosome becomes situated in a daughter nucleus. This is not the case in the first meiotic division. Instead, whole chromosomes go into one daughter nucleus, and a second division separates the chromatids. To state the matter differently, a mitotic daughter nucleus receives one chromatid of each *chromosome,* whereas a meiotic daughter nucleus receives one chromosome (consisting of two chromatids) of each chromosome *pair* characteristic of the species.

One would expect that after the separation of chromosomes during the first meiotic division, each nucleus would pass through telophase into interphase. Although nuclear membranes are formed, the chromosomes tend to retain their individual appearance, and interphase is thus greatly reduced. There is, of course, a great deal of individual variation among organisms and their cells in this respect. In many cells, the chromosomes remain in a prophase-like condition, with their individual identity and form being retained. Regardless of telophase-interphase details following the first meiotic division, each daughter nucleus enters the second meiotic metaphase. This time, the chromosomes line up on the spindle in such a way that centromeres divide and sister chromatids separate, as in mitosis. Since both daughter nuclei of the original cell undergo this second division, the result is four nuclei, each of which receives a chromatid representing each chromosome *pair* of the original cell. Thus, each nucleus resulting

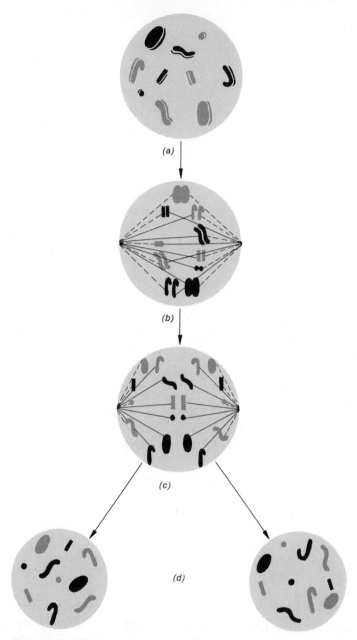

Figure 5.25. Diagrammatic representation of mitosis and meiosis in a hypothetical organism with 10 chromosomes. The gray chromosomes came from one parent of the organism, the black chromosomes from the other parent. For the sake of simplicity, only nuclei are illustrated, and nuclear membranes are not shown breaking down. On this page: (a) prophase of mitosis; (b) metaphase; (c) anaphase; (d) end of mitosis. Each daughter nucleus now possesses a representative chromatid of each original chromosome. Compare with Fig. 5.24.

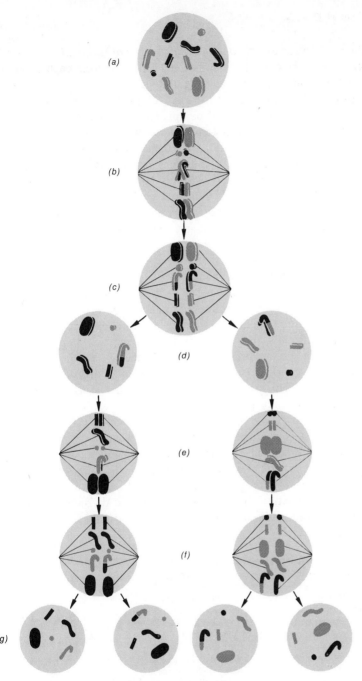

Figure 5.25. (cont.) On this page: meiotic division. In contrast to the figures shown at the left, these are flattened in order to show essential details more clearly. (a) Prophase of nucleus just before synapsis of homologous chromosomes; (b) synapsed chromosomes at metaphase *(Continued on page 178.)*

from meiotic division has *exactly one-half the number of chromatids* (which may be called chromosomes after they become separated from each other) *as the original cell had chromosomes* (Fig. 5-25).

Perhaps the full significance of meiosis will not be apparent immediately, but at least two features should be apparent at this point. First, the process of meiosis is *reductional* in terms of chromosome number, resulting in nuclei that possess only one of each original chromosome pair. This characteristic is a result of the chromosomes having divided only once whereas the original nucleus divided twice. It might be pointed out here that a cell whose nucleus exhibits homologous chromosomes is said to be *diploid* (Greek *diploos,* double), and one whose nucleus possesses only one member of each chromosome pair is said to be *haploid* (Greek *haploos,* single). It frequently becomes convenient to refer to the haploid nucleus, cell, or organism by the designation *n,* while the diploid condition is expressed as *2n.* In the formation of gametes, the reduction of the chromosome number from *2n* to *n* eliminates the difficulty that would otherwise exist in maintaining a constant chromosome number for a species. A second significant feature of meiosis is that it provides opportunity for a random mixing of chromosomes in gametes. Whereas each haploid "set" ordinarily must include a representative chromosome of each homologous pair, the distribution of original parental chromosomes seems to be entirely fortuitous (Fig. 5-25). This particular aspect of meiosis and its importance will be developed more fully in Chapter 6.

Whenever meiosis occurs in the formation of gametes, it is said to be *gametic.* This process is characteristic of animals, where eggs and sperm are normally the only haploid cells in otherwise diploid bodies. It is interesting to note that in typical gamete production in the male animal, the cell that undergoes meiosis produces four sperm cells (as we would predict); but in the production of eggs, the first meiotic division results in only one functional cell, while the other cell (called a *polar body*) receives

---

of the first meiotic division, with parental chromosomes oriented randomly. Note that portions of two nonsister chromatids of the J-shaped chromosomes have become crossed upon each other. (c) Anaphase of the first meiotic division; homologous chromosomes separate in the plane of their original union. Note that the above-mentioned portions of two nonsister chromatids of the J-shaped chromosomes have become exchanged. (d) End of first meiotic division; whole chromosomes are located in separate nuclei. (e) Metaphase of second meiotic division; chromatids of each chromosome are preparing to separate. (f) Anaphase of second meiotic division. (g) End of meiosis. Four nuclei now share the 20 original chromatids [see nucleus at (a)]. Note that each nucleus now possesses a chromosome representative of each original chromosome pair.

a very small amount of cytoplasm in the divisional process. Although the polar body eventually degenerates and thus plays no further part in the reproductive process, it may undergo the second meiotic division. The functional cell undergoes its final meiotic division with the production of a second polar body, which also degenerates. The net result of this total process, therefore, is the production of only one functional egg instead of the four that would be expected theoretically. This egg, however, has the advantage of possessing most of the cytoplasm of the original cell, a feature making for considerable biological advantage, since the egg is thus provided with a quantity of food materials that are utilized in embryonic growth following fertilization of the egg (Fig. 5-26).

Most plants exhibit *sporic* rather than gametic meiosis, with reduction of chromosome numbers occurring in the production of four haploid spores from a diploid *spore mother cell.* Pollen grains of flowering plants, for example, are such haploid spores. In the life cycle of plants whose meiotic process is sporic, a haploid, gamete-producing generation, growing from a spore, alternates with a diploid, spore-producing one, arising from a zygote. Although gametic and sporic meiosis are generally characteristic of animals and plants, respectively, certain algae and fungi display a third type, *zygotic* meiosis, where the zygote is the only diploid stage in the life cycle.* Meiosis occurs in such plants during first divisions of the zygote.

In summary, the cell is the fundamental unit of reproduction in the world of life. Regardless of how complex an organism may become (such organisms as human beings consist of several trillions of cells), its growth and reproduction are both ultimately cellular. However, the complex structures that may be produced by repeated cell divisions in the same organism are usually of such a nature that they must be considered at a higher level than that of the cell. For example, a complex animal starts its existence as a zygote whose divisional progeny become organized into progressively more complex structures. After a time, it is no longer useful to study this organism purely in terms of cellular phenomena; a different kind of conceptual scheme is required. As a result, some interesting problems arise, which we shall now discuss.

5.3 LEVELS OF ORGANIZATION AND THE PRINCIPLE OF EMERGENCE [21]

In Chapter 4, we emphasized that from a mechanistic viewpoint, "life" is a phenomenon that emerges somewhere along an organizational

---

* In addition, certain algae undergo gametic meiosis. Thus, all three types occur in the plant kingdom, although sporic meiosis is by far the most common.

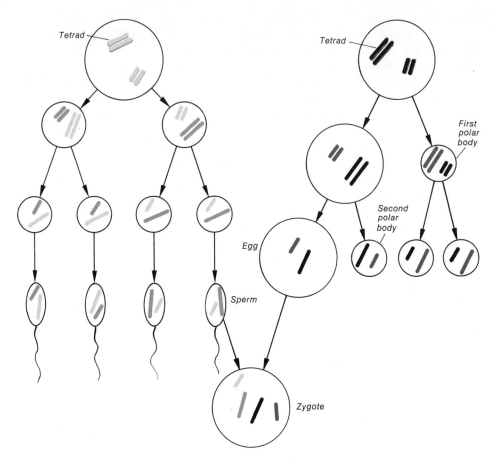

Figure 5.26. A comparison of sperm and egg development
in animals. In the interest of simplicity, only two pairs
of chromosomes are depicted, and the details of meiosis are
omitted.

continuum of matter and energy. We discussed the nature of matter in
terms of its fundamental units (atoms), the nature of energy in terms of
its capacity to do work, and some of the chemical interactions between
matter and energy. In the level of organization, molecules and compounds
were considered to be higher than atoms. As we pointed out, or at least
implied, this "levels-of-organization" concept can be followed through the
organic macromolecules. These macromolecules become organized at the
level of ultrastructure, as for example in chromosomes and membrane systems. Finally, the cell emerges as an aggregation of subcellular particles.

In this chapter, we have extended this concept of organization to the cell as a unit of structure, function, and reproduction. Each of these three aspects of cells reveals an organization of subcellular particles (nucleus, mitochondria, etc.) as well as the properties of metabolism and self-perpetuation. This is a somewhat modernized version of the Schleiden-Schwann conceptual scheme, but the implication should be clear: *The cell is a biological building-block that makes it possible for even higher levels of organization to exist and be called living systems.* Thus, cells are associated together in varying degrees of complexity and interdependence. In many circumstances, a division of labor for the intake and transformation of energy has occurred. At the highest levels of organization, such as may be found in a complex animal body, the characteristics of living systems are manifestations of highly organized and specialized cell groups.

In many of the less complex multicellular organisms, cells have become associated together in the formation of colonies with no subsequent division of labor (Fig. 5-27). In other words, each cell in the colony seems

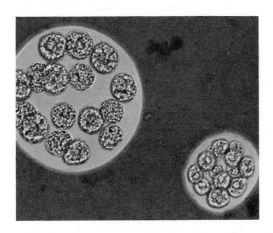

Figure 5.27. *Eudorina,* a colonial green alga: Notice that each colony consists of 16 similar cells. (Courtesy Carolina Biological Supply Company.)

to retain its separate functional identity. Such organisms are still essentially unicellular, but they represent a *colonial* level of organization. Possibly, these organisms reflect a stage in the development from solitary unicellular forms to truly multicellular organisms in which there is a division of labor. This colonial level of organization is exemplified by many of the green algae.

The next level of organization is that of a loose association of cells exhibiting a certain degree of cell specialization and division of labor (Fig. 5-28). We might call this the *associational* level. It is exemplified by the sponges, where specialized cells take over such functions as digestion and reproduction. In this case, other cells do not perform these functions; they

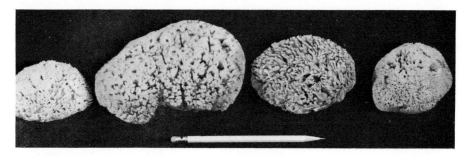

Figure 5.28. A group of bath-type sponges. Although it is not obvious in macroscopic view, a sponge represents the associational level of complexity, wherein different types of cells share a common skeletal structure. (Courtesy Carolina Biological Supply Company.)

are either very generalized, or else they exhibit specializations of their own.

At a still higher level of organization (which might be termed the *tissue* level), whole blocks or groups of cells differ from other groups both structurally and functionally (Fig. 5-29). A tissue may be defined, therefore, as a group of similar cells that are associated in the performance of a particular function. This level of organization is apparent in most multicellular organisms, where a variety of different tissues may be found in a given organism. The study of living systems at this level of organization constitutes a subfield of biology called *histology*.

Subsequent levels of organization are represented by organs, organ systems, multicellular organisms, and (in a rather special sense) groups of organisms. An *organ* may be defined as a group of tissues associated together in the performance of specific activities. Similarly, an *organ system* is a group of organs that are associated together in the performance of related activities. A complex multicellular organism, such as a human being, represents an extremely high level of organization involving integrated organ systems, which exhibit the activities characteristic of life. In a special sense, the complexity of this organization is extended to groups of organisms, where a division of labor may exist. This phenomenon is particularly obvious in an insect society such as a hive of honeybees.

Perhaps an analogy can clarify the foregoing discussion. Let us imagine a wilderness area that has just been opened to settlement. Several families move into the area, and each family builds a homestead several miles from any of the others. Any given family is virtually isolated and must grow its own food, manufacture its own clothing, and, in fact, provide for its every necessity. In time, however, other families move into the

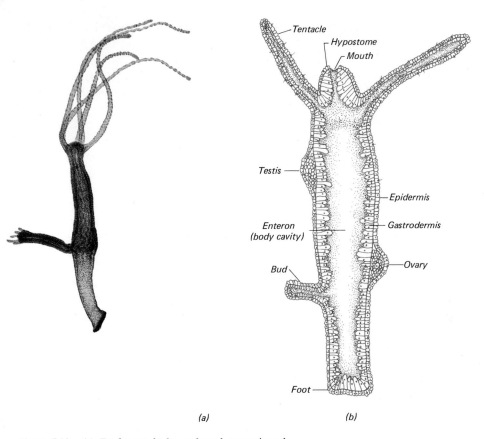

(a)   (b)

Figure 5.29.   (a) Freshwater hydra, enlarged approximately
65 times. (Courtesy Carolina Biological Supply Company.)
(b) Diagrammatic representation of a hydra as seen in
longitudinal section. Note the two tissue layers (epidermis,
gastrodermis), each of which is structurally and functionally
distinct from the other. The hydra is a relatively simple
representative of the tissue level of organization.

area, and the picture changes. Families in close proximity to each other
realize that they can get along much better if there is a division of labor.
Consequently, one man who excels at blacksmithing does this work; another raises wheat and swaps it for labor and other commodities; and so
on. Eventually, with the influx of more people, an even greater degree of
specialization is achieved. Shops and stores concentrate on particular services; clearly defined occupations and professions arise; and, in time, there
is a great division of labor.

   Within limits inherent in analogies, somewhat the same thing has apparently happened in the world of life.* At one time, evidently, all life existed in the one-celled state. Gradually, in time, the colonial and associational levels of specialization appeared and, after this, the tissue level. Eventually, multicellular organisms with organs and organ systems arose; in general, they became the most successful organisms on earth. It appears highly probable that the greater efficiency made possible by a complex division of labor played a large part in their success, especially in their adaptation to environments not accessible to the less complex organisms.

We must be careful to avoid a particularly dangerous pitfall in thinking of development (*evolution*) in these terms. It is tempting to postulate some inherent, protoplasmic drive toward specialization. While we have no absolute assurance that such an inner force does not exist in protoplasm, we have no evidence that it does. Consequently, the postulation of such a force is not a very fruitful conceptual scheme to use in explaining increased complexity and division of labor over time. In a later chapter, we shall introduce the principle of natural selection, which is a very fruitful conceptual scheme indeed. Without attempting to define natural selection at this point, perhaps we can employ it as a tentative explanation of the increase in specialization that has apparently occurred over time. It is not unreasonable to assume that under some environmental circumstances a division of labor among cells enhanced survival in a world of one-celled organisms. Following this line of thought, perhaps we can visualize how colonial, tissue-level, and more complex stages of specialization can impart certain advantages to organisms that are competing with less complex forms. An interesting question might be raised as to why these less complex forms did not disappear from the earth if natural selection explains the rise of more complex forms. As you proceed through the remainder of the book, perhaps you can supply a satisfactory answer to it.

At each level of organization from the atom to populations of organisms, properties emerge that may be unique to that level. One of the major philosophical problems in science is concerned with the reducibility of one level of organization to the theoretical constructs of lower levels; we shall examine this problem in a later chapter.

---

* It is always tempting to interpret nature anthropomorphically. For teaching purposes, scientists frequently employ analogies in which this attitude is strongly implied. It should be understood that such analogies are only meant to clarify some point, not to impute a form of intelligence to physical systems.

QUESTIONS FOR REVIEW AND DISCUSSION

1. List the contribution of the following men to the cell theory: (1) The Janssens, (2) Hooke, (3) Leeuwenhoek, (4) Dutrochet, (5) Schleiden and Schwann.

2. How does the formulation of the cell theory relate to a mechanistic outlook toward a living system?

3. In the 1940's, emphasis in cytology shifted to a great extent from the nucleus of the cell to the cytoplasm. Relate some events or developments during this period that might be correlated with this shift of emphasis.

4. Is there any such structure as a typical cell? Explain.

5. Sketch a complete cell including all the structures that a cell could contain, and briefly describe the function of each structure.

6. List and briefly explain four processes involved in the passage of substances through the cell membrane (absorption).

7. Distinguish among the terms *metabolism, anabolism,* and *catabolism.*

8. List and describe each of the three aspects of metabolism.

9. Define and exemplify phagotrophic, autotrophic, and heterotropic nutrition. Are all cells of a phagotrophic organism themselves phagotrophic? Explain.

10. Compare and contrast respiration with the actual process of fire. What is the major fuel source in respiration?

11. In what way or ways are organic molecules like money boxes? What molecules represent the "money changers" in the cell?

12. Review the glycolytic (Embden-Meyerhof) pathway. What is the end product of glycolysis?

13. Distinguish between aerobic and anaerobic respiration. How is lactic acid formed?

14. Review the sequence of events that occur in an electron-transport system. How much ATP is formed by one system for each molecule of glucose that originally entered the respiratory sequence?

15. Review and summarize the fate of one mole of glucose during its complete respiration. Account for all participants and products in this balanced reaction:

$$C_6H_{12}O_6 + 6O_2 + 6H_2O \rightarrow 6CO_2 + 12H_2O + 38\,ATP$$

16. Indicate the distinction between photosynthesis, chemosynthesis, and organosynthesis.

17. During photosynthesis, does the oxygen that is released come from the carbon dioxide or from the water? Support your answer with experimental evidence.

18. Review and explain the process of photosynthesis.
19. Explain what is meant by self-perpetuation. How does it relate to metabolism?
20. Compare in detail the processes of mitosis and meiosis. Which one of these processes is related to the phenomenon of genetic variability? In terms of chromosomal behavior, what is the basic difference in the two types of cell division, that is, what occurs in prophase of meiosis that does not occur in prophase of mitosis?
21. Distinguish between gametic, sporic, and zygotic meiosis.
22. List and briefly explain the various levels of organization in living systems.

REFERENCES

Brown, W. V. and E. M. Bertke. *Textbook of Cytology.* St. Louis: The C. V. Mosby Company, 1969. This book constitutes a rather complete and detailed treatment of cell structure and function for the student who wishes to pursue these topics in more depth.

Gabriel, M. L. and S. Fogel (eds.). *Great Experiments in Biology.* Englewood Cliffs, N. J.: Prentice-Hall, Inc., 1955. Certain experiments that are now considered classics are reviewed in this work.

Giese, A. C. *Cell Physiology.* Reference at end of Chapter 4.

Grobstein, C. *The Strategy of Life.* San Francisco: W. H. Freeman and Company, 1964. A short book presenting an overview of a living system, emphasizing levels of organization with emergent properties.

Kennedy, D. (ed.). *The Living Cell.* San Francisco: W. H. Freeman and Company, 1965. This book consists of a series of articles appearing in *Scientific American* dealing with cell structure and function.

Swanson, C. P., T. Merz, and W. J. Young. *Cytogenetics.* Englewood Cliffs, New Jersey: Prentice-Hall, Inc., 1967. This is one of the several brief books making up a series entitled "Foundation of Modern Genetics." This book will be quite helpful for those wishing to study the cell as a reproduction unit in more detail.

Wilson, G. B. and J. H. Morrison. *Cytology.* New York: Reinhold Publishing Corporation, 1966. A brief and clear presentation of the cell as a unit of structure, function, and reproduction.

SIX

Life, Cell, and Heredity

As we have seen, one of the outstanding characteristics of life is its capacity for self-perpetuation. In cellular terms, this property is reflected by the continual synthesis of macromolecules and organelles that are required by the cell in its total self-maintenance. Whenever synthesis occurs to such a degree that the cell reaches a certain critical size, it divides; that is, self-perpetuation leads eventually to reproduction. In a multicellular organism, of course, the same principle holds true: Cellular reproduction leads to organismic reproduction and growth.

Certain mechanisms within cells ensure continuity of the qualitative factors that impart to that cell and to the organism of which it is a part those distinctive characteristics causing it to be the particular kind of living system that it is. These mechanisms constitute the *hereditary* apparatus of the cell (or organism), and we have already identified them with the chromosomes. In specific terms, they are the *genes*.[1] Of course, genes are not the only physical factors involved in the hereditary process, but they do play the central role in it.

The formulation of a successful approach to a study of genes and the hereditary process constitutes one of the great conceptual schemes of modern biology. It did not begin as an outgrowth of the two conceptual schemes we have surveyed thus far, but it soon joined forces with them and thus enriched the whole of biology. More recently, the gene concept has made it possible to interpret metabolism and self-perpetuation at the subcellular level, enhancing our understanding of these processes at every biological level.

6.1 A GREAT CONCEPTUAL SCHEME: MENDELIAN GENETICS

Since the dawn of recorded history, men have been interested in variation and the "laws" of heredity. In retrospect, it seems incredible that until the middle of the 19th century, virtually nothing was known about the principles governing the hereditary process in living organisms. Even when the fundamental principles were learned, many years passed before these principles were accepted in biology. It is true that some common-sense observations had been made; among biologists there was a great deal of learned nonsense about heredity by the middle of the 19th century, but theoretical concepts were almost entirely lacking.

6.1A. The Work of Gregor Mendel

The story really began when an Austrian monk, Gregor Johann Mendel (1822–1884) (Fig. 6-1), started a series of experiments in 1856 that served as the basis for a clarification of elementary principles of heredity.[2] Mendel was not a scientist by vocation, although he did teach various sciences for many years in the *Realschule* (comparable to the American

Figure 6.1. Gregor Mendel (1822–1884). (Courtesy of the American Museum of Natural History.)

high school) of what was then Brünn, Austria. He developed a great curiosity about inheritance and conducted experiments independently in a monastery garden. Following many years of experimentation involving a variety of cultivated plants, Mendel reported his results and conclusions in 1865 and published a paper during the following year to summarize his findings. Unfortunately, the biological world was not ready for Mendel's findings and did not fully appreciate them until the year 1900, when his paper was rediscovered by three European botanists working independently. The most prominent of these was Hugo De Vries, a Dutchman. Thus, it was never known to Mendel or to his contemporaries that he had made one of the greatest scientific contributions of all time through the formulation of his elementary principles of heredity.[3]

It was common in Mendel's day to regard inheritance as the result of a blending of traits, since it was known that something of this sort occurred in the crossing of certain varieties within plant or animal species. In the four-o'clock (*Mirabilis jalapa*), for example, red-flowered plants produce nothing but more red-flowered plants when crossed only among themselves; and white-flowered plants likewise breed "true" for white flowers. However, when pollen from either a red- or a white-flowered plant is transferred to the pistil of the other type of flower, the seeds that are formed by this cross produce pink-flowered plants. Thus, a blending of traits could readily be seen. It disturbed Mendel that pink-flowered plants of this sort never bred true, as should be the case if a simple blending were responsible. This inept theory of inheritance failed entirely to explain why hybrids (offspring of parents that differ in a given trait) often revert back to parental types. For example, the offspring of two pink four-o'clocks may be white, pink, or red (Fig. 6-2). It was equally disturbing to him that this sort of reversion occurred in crosses where no blending was obvious but where a hidden trait kept cropping out.

Figure 6.2 The "blending" of traits in four-o'clocks. In this case, neither gene is dominant over the other. P, parental types; F_1, first filial generation; F_2, second filial generation, obtained by crossing $F_1 \times F_1$.

P

Red

White

Pink

F_1

F_2

For his experimental work, Mendel relied chiefly upon the garden pea (*Pisum sativum*), which he knew included several true-breeding varieties that could readily be crossed with each other. Some of these varieties were quite tall and had to be trained as vines, while others were extremely short. Other contrasting traits were seed colors (green or yellow), seed form (round or wrinkled), and flower positions (borne along the main stem or in a group at the top of the stem). In all, he worked with seven pairs of contrasting traits in this species. As it turned out, no blending of traits occurred. For example, seeds resulting from a cross between tall and short peas did not produce plants that were intermediate in height, but rather, all of them were tall. Mendel called the trait that appeared in the hybrid the "dominant" one; the one that did not appear in the hybrid he called "recessive." Hence, tallness proved to be the dominant trait in the cross just cited, and shortness was recessive.

At this point, Mendel took a very important step. He allowed hybrids for a given pair of traits to self-pollinate, and he analyzed the results of his seven separate experiments. In each case, individuals showing the recessive trait appeared and in definite numerical ratio to individuals exhibiting the dominant trait. **Without exception, in this second generation, a ratio of approximately three dominants to one recessive appeared.** For example, Mendel produced 1,064 plants in the tall-short experiment, of which 787 were tall and 277 were short. A still further extension of the general experiment revealed that in all seven groups, the individuals showing recessive traits bred true for them, one-third of the dominant individuals likewise bred true, and the remaining two-thirds of the dominants did not.*

Mendel then postulated the existence of "characters" that were associated with the gametes of parent individuals. By allowing letters of the alphabet to represent these characters, he set up his crosses on paper and manipulated them theoretically. For the sake of convenience, capital letters were made to represent dominant characters, and lower-case letters were used for recessives—a system that is still employed in genetics. Mendel came to the conclusion that only if the genetic constitution of a parent plant were represented by two characters for a given trait, with one and only one of these being transmitted to a gamete, could his results be explained.

Hence, in the crosses involving tall and short peas, where the traits of the contrasting parent plants were pure, those of the hybrids are mixed. A cross between two such hybrids, in which random combination of

---

* Since it was a simple matter to ensure that the flowers were self-pollinated, it was relatively easy for Mendel to test the genetic "purity" of any given plant.

gametes occurs, results in one individual pure for the dominant characters, one pure for the recessive ones, and two that are mixed (out of every four produced). Because of dominance, three of the four will exhibit the dominant trait (Fig. 6-3). You will recall that this agrees perfectly with Mendel's

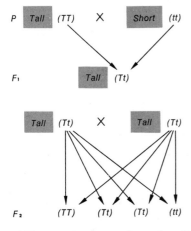

Figure 6.3. A representation of theoretical results from two generations of crossing tall and short peas. It should be borne in mind that Mendel postulated the inclusion of one and only one character (gene) of a given pair within a gamete. The parental plants can produce only one type of gamete each; hence they produce only one type of offspring when crossed. The F_1 plants, however, can produce two types of gametes each, and they produce four classes of offspring, two of which are identical in type.

experimental results. Furthermore, it explains the situation in such cases of inheritance as that of four-o'clocks, if it is assumed that neither of the characters involved is dominant over the other (Fig. 6-2). On the basis of his work with single traits, Mendel postulated a *law of segregation,* which can be paraphrased as follows: **During gamete formation, each member of a pair of characters becomes associated with a different gamete.** In other words, the vehicles of inheritance are some kind of discrete, separable "characters" that do not, themselves, show any sort of blending. They behave as separate units.

HISTORY OF THE GENE CONCEPT [4]

At this point, let us digress momentarily and consider how Mendel's work led him to formulate his law of segregation with its implication that heredity is dependent upon discontinuous, that is, separable, units. Remember, his experiments made no impact upon the biological community until 1900; and, by that time, biology was in a general state of confusion on several counts.

Seven years before Mendel's paper appeared, Charles Darwin had published his epochal book, the *Origin of Species,* setting forth a defense and explanation of organic evolution. We shall deal with this concept in Chapter 7, but it should be noted here that Darwin encountered grave difficulties that could have been solved had he known of Mendel's work. In short, he needed a particulate theory of inheritance that could be subjected to experimental analysis; in desperation, he postulated one that could *not* be. This was his so-called theory of *pangenesis,* which postulated that certain particles called "gemmules" are present in all cells of an organism and that these particles pass by way of the bloodstream (in the case of higher animals) to the gonads and become incorporated into the gametes. There were two difficulties with this hypothesis: First, it was not amenable to experimental analysis; and secondly, it assumed that acquired characteristics are inherited, which weakened Darwin's whole conceptual scheme of organic evolution.

Furthermore, certain biological developments during the latter part of the 19th century demanded a particulate explanation of heredity. Mitosis and meiosis had been elucidated during the 1870's and 1880's, and several other biological discoveries were made shortly before 1900. Mutation was one of these discoveries, made by the Dutch biologist Hugo De Vries, who attempted to modify Darwin's hypothesis of pangenesis in order to make it scientifically respectable. It was through De Vries' search for some clue in the scientific literature that he encountered Mendel's paper. The Dutch scientist was a keen investigator, and he realized immediately the significance of Mendel's work. It was chiefly through the influence of De Vries, who badly needed a particulate theory of heredity and who was aware of the number of difficulties Mendel had solved in advance of their occurrence, that Mendel's work was made known to the scientific world.

The Mendelian concept had an immediate impact upon the biological community in 1900. Although it was hotly debated for a short time, it became widely accepted as a working hypothesis within a very few years. Then between 1908 and 1910, two important developments occurred. The first of these was the publication by the Danish biologist Wilhelm Johannsen of his work concerning the theory of pure lines in bean plants. In his paper Johannsen coined certain terms that have since gained general acceptance. The characteristic of an organism he designated as its *phenotype,* and the factorial basis for the characteristic he called the *genotype.* He coined the term *gene* to describe the unit factors themselves. However, Johannsen did not use his term "gene" in any sort of precise sense (as Mendel had implied for his term "character"), basically because he was unable to account for his pure-line genotypes in precise terms. The second important development came from experiments with wheat and maize performed by H. Nilsson-Ehle of Sweden and E. M. East of the United States, respectively. They showed that quantitative inheritance (continuous variation) is dependent upon particulate genes. One of the strongest theoretical barriers to a full acceptance of the Mendelian concept of discontinuous variation had been the control by particulate and separable units (Mendel's "characters"). The work of Nilsson-Ehle and East effectively reconciled the issue of continuous variation (as seen in the sizes of beans, seed coat color in wheat and maize, and so on) and discontinuous variation (as seen in the phenotypes with which Mendel had worked in peas).

The concept of the gene as a discrete unit, or "particle," was fully established in genetic theory by the American zoologist T. H. Morgan at Columbia University. His work was performed chiefly during the first two decades of the 1900's, but his methods and viewpoints dominated genetics for a period of some 30 years (1910–1940). Morgan and his students experimented with the fruit fly, *Drosophila melanogaster*. On the basis of their research, the Morgan school formulated the *classical* theory of the gene, which holds, essentially, that a gene is a localized particle within a chromosome. It is sometimes called the "bead on a string" theory because Morgan and his students were able to show that the genes of *Drosophila melanogaster* are located at certain fixed points along the four pairs of chromosomes possessed by this organism. Among other significant accomplishments, they placed the concept of the gene as a discrete unit on a sound theoretical footing and rendered it acceptable to the scientific community.

Thus, Mendel's term "character" was replaced by the term "gene," and it was shown by the Morgan group that genes are closely associated with chromosomes, being in some fashion a part of their chemical structure. Let us note at this point that Mendel was completely unaware of the existence of chromosomes. They were not studied closely until about 1870. Mitosis was elucidated within the decade, and meiosis was described in the early 1880's. Mendel's concept of the gene (although he did not use this term) therefore preceded the discovery of chromosomes. In 1903, the American cytologist W. S. Sutton pointed out the similarities in gamete formation between Mendel's "characters" and chromosomes.[5] You recall that Mendel concluded from his experimental evidence that during gamete formation each member of a pair of characters (genes) becomes associated with a different gamete. Let us note that this process is exactly what happens to homologous chromosomes in meiosis (Figs. 5-26, 6-4).*

Since chromosomes are segregated into different gametes, it follows that whatever genes they carry are also segregated, with equal numbers of gametes being formed for each gene type when members of a gene pair are not identical. This deduction is a beautiful example of the way science grows. Mendel's genius lay in his ability to manipulate hypotheses, theories, and data in such a fashion that his conceptual scheme became exceedingly fruitful at a later time. In fact, there are very few scientists whose conceptual schemes have been more significant and far-reaching than that of

---

* When meiosis is either zygotic or sporic, as in most plants, the law of segregation still holds. In gamete formation, genes are merely segregated much earlier than is the case in gametic meiosis.

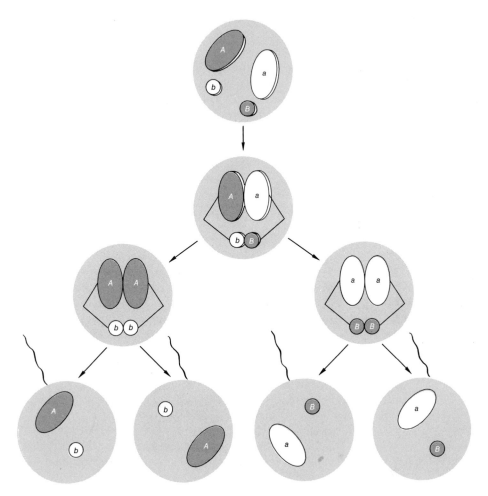

Figure 6.4.   The cytological basis for the law of segregation. Notice that genes *A* and *a* *cannot* go into the same gamete at meiosis; the same holds true for genes *B* and *b*. In this illustration, genes *A* and *b* segregate together, as do genes *a* and *B*. There is an equal chance for genes *A* and *B*, and *a* and *b* to segregate together. Compare with Figure 5.25.

Gregor Mendel, and it is ironic that he was not even regarded as a scientist by his contemporaries!

At this point, let us consider a few terms that are commonly used in genetics. In describing the genetic constitution of an organism for a given trait, one uses Johannsen's term *genotype*. Hence, the genotype for a pure-breeding tall pea is *TT,* that for a pure-breeding short one is *tt,* and the hybrid is *Tt.* The term *phenotype* is used to describe a genetic trait as it is detected by our senses. Thus, a plant from the same example whose geno- type is either *TT* or *Tt* is phenotypically tall. Whenever members of a gene pair are identical, as in the genotype *TT,* the individual is said to be *homozygous* with regard to these genes. If the members differ, as in the genotype *Tt,* it is said to be *heterozygous.* Members of the same gene pair that differ in their genetic expression, such as *T* and *t,* are called *allelic genes,* or simply *alleles.*

Let us return now to Mendel's work. His concept of the gene was essentially the same as that developed by the Morgan school more than a half-century later. However, our further understanding of the gene as a dis- crete determinant of hereditary characteristics (phenotypes) should help us greatly in appreciating the more sophisticated aspects of Mendel's work.

THE DIHYBRID CROS

On the basis of the law of segregation, let us predict what results could be expected if *two* pairs of contrasting characters (genes) were crossed. Again if we use the pea as an example, it will be recalled that Mendel found that round seed shape was dominant over a wrinkled shape and that yellow color was dominant over green. If a pure-breeding plant that bears round, yellow seeds were crossed with one bearing wrinkled, green seeds, the situation might be symbolized as follows: *RRYY* × *rryy.*

Because of genic segregation, the hybrid seeds should be *pheno- typically* identical to those of the parent that was characterized by round, yellow seeds, but *genotypically* the seeds should be heterozygous for both gene pairs, as is shown in Fig. 6-5.

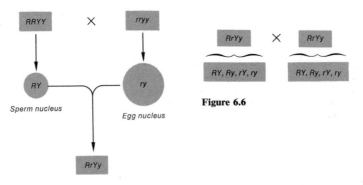

Figure 6.6

Figure 6.5

When two plants produced by such hybrid seeds are crossed (or one plant is allowed to self-pollinate), with regard to genotype, four types of sperm nuclei should be formed, as well as four types of egg nuclei, as is shown in Fig. 6-6. We illustrate in Fig. 6-7 the possible combinations that may occur when this cross is made.

Genotypically, several combinations would occur, but let us notice the theoretical *phenotypic* results. Of every 16 seeds formed, we should observe on the average the distribution shown in Fig. 6-8.

Sperm nuclei	Egg nuclei			
	RY	Ry	rY	ry
RY	RRYY	RRYy	RrYY	RrYy
Ry	RRYy	RRyy	RrYy	Rryy
rY	RrYY	RrYy	rrYY	rrYy
ry	RrYy	Rryy	rrYy	rryy

Figure 6.7

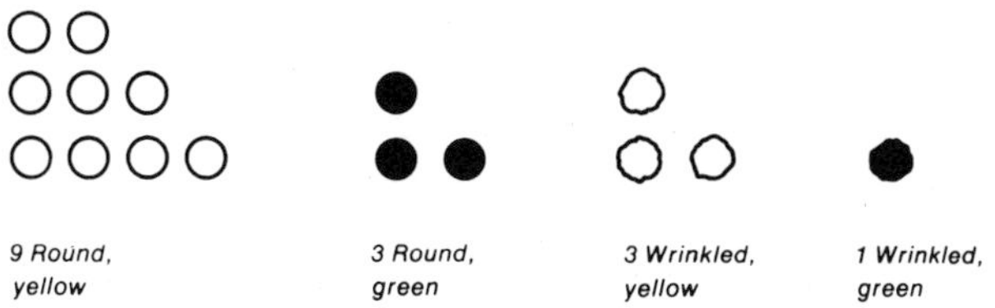

9 Round, yellow   3 Round, green   3 Wrinkled, yellow   1 Wrinkled, green

Figure 6.8

Mendel performed this very cross and produced 556 F$_2$ seeds, as follows:

315 round, yellow
108 round, green
101 wrinkled, yellow
 32 wrinkled, green

Since this result is a 9:3:3:1 ratio, allowing for some chance variation, it provided Mendel with very good evidence that his law of segregation was valid. Furthermore, he carried the experiment further by testing the F$_2$ seeds for genotype, which was accomplished by planting them and allowing the resulting plants to self-pollinate. His results substantiated, in general, the theoretical expectation.

From these and other experiments, Mendel was able to formulate a second important generalization, the *law of independent assortment,* which applies to genes of unlike pairs in their association within the same genotype. It should be obvious from the experiment just discussed that neither gene pair influences the other in any way. Taken separately, each produces a 3:1 phenotypic ratio in the F$_2$ generation, even though the experiment involves both pairs. Stated more precisely, **the law of independent assortment holds that a given gene pair segregates independently of any other gene pair in the formation of gametes.** When one traces out the possible fates of genes and their chromosomes during meiosis, one readily sees why this "law" is operative (Fig. 6-4). It should be remembered, however, that Mendel arrived at both his first and second laws through experimentation and statistical analysis and that it was many years before the cytological basis for their validity was known.

6.1B Historical Retrospect

One might well ask why Mendel's work was not given serious consideration at the time it was published (1866). Several possible factors have occurred to historians of biology, but one apparent reason for this neglect can be identified with the tenor and thrust of biology at that time. Charles Darwin had published his highly influential book, the *Origin of Species,* just seven years before Mendel reported his own work, and the whole of biology was preoccupied during the 1860's with the subject of organic evolution. As we shall see in the next chapter, where we deal with evolution as a great conceptual scheme in its own right, Darwin emphasized variation as a key to understanding evolution. However, like virtually everyone else in the 19th century, Darwin thought of variation in *continuous* terms (which it is in the case of many traits—for example, variations in height among human beings), and it was only natural to think of inheritance in the same way. Almost universally, the accepted conceptual scheme was the analogy of a paint-pot, wherein various colors might be blended to effect a mixture. In the same way, it was thought, hereditary factors (whatever they are) become blended in an individual. It was this paint-pot concept that was challenged by Mendel's work. But it was so deeply ingrained in 19th-century biological thought that more than one lonely voice was required to upset it.

Even so, Mendel might have brought it off had biology been ready for his findings. But such was not the case. Even when the processes of mitosis and meiosis became known in the 1870's and 1880's, the connection was not apparent immediately. Remember too that Mendel was an obscure monk, and his work was accomplished as a hobby. In the light of human nature, it is understandable that the giants of mid-19th-century biology would not have been impressed with Mendel, even if most of them had known of his work. We do know that one prominent botanist in Germany, Karl Nägeli, corresponded with Mendel throughout the course of his experimental work. It is almost infuriating now to read Nägeli's condescending letters to Mendel; they reveal no understanding of his work whatsoever. In fact, in the year of Mendel's death, 1884, Nägeli published a book on heredity consisting of what biologist Garrett Hardin calls "822 dispensable pages [within which] he did not once refer to the work of the priest at Brünn." It is small wonder that Mendel himself lost heart and eventually destroyed every vestige of his personal effects that referred in any way to his work in heredity.

6.2 FURTHER CONCEPTUAL DEVELOPMENTS IN GENETICS

As you will recall from our previous discussion, a number of biologists extended the work of Mendel following the rediscovery of his paper in 1900. Chief among these was the Morgan school, which did an incredible amount of work roughly between the years 1910 and 1940.[6] To review even the highlights of this work is beyond the scope of this book; however, let us examine some of the concepts that are most significant to later topics in this chapter.

6.2A Intergenic Linkage

By definition, the law of independent assortment can apply only when gene pairs are located on different chromosomes. Let us compare the inheritance of two hypothetical genes, *A* and *B,* when they are independent (located on different chromosome pairs) and when they are linked (located on the same chromosome pair). It can be shown by diagram that genes located on the same chromosome are obliged to become associated *together* in a gamete and that there is no independent assortment (Fig. 6-9). In fact, if one assumes that no interchange occurs between the chromosomes, it would appear that only one pair of genes is involved, since a 3:1 ratio is obtained.

The species of pea with which Mendel worked is characterized by seven pairs of homologous chromosomes; and he studied seven different traits, all of which showed independent assortment. Had he considered an eighth trait, it would necessarily have segregated with one of the other seven. Thus, he would have observed an exception to his typical 9:3:3:1 ratio in the dihybrid cross, which would have necessitated a further qualification of the law of independent assortment. For example, a trait that Mendel did not study is the presence or absence of tendrils (modified leaves that serve as holdfasts). The gene controlling the presence of tendrils is dominant over that which is related to their absence. Let us consider a cross between a pea plant with tendrils, bearing round seeds, and a plant without tendrils that bears wrinkled seeds (Fig. 6-10). Obviously, the typical 9:3:3:1 ratio characteristic of independent assortment does not appear in this cross, and there are far more parental types than recombinants among the F_2. Thus, we might conclude tentatively that these genes are linked. However, it is evident that intergenic linkage is not complete, since the two recombinant types (round with no tendrils and wrinkled with

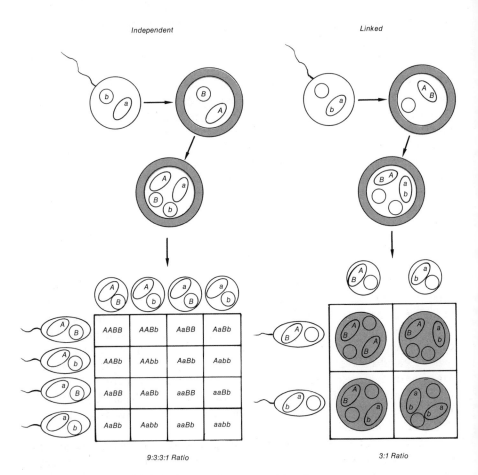

Independent

Linked

9:3:3:1 Ratio

3:1 Ratio

Figure 6.9. A comparison of independent assortment and linkage. In an actual cross, would you expect a 3:1 ratio in the F_2 if the two genes involved were linked? Explain.

tendrils) appear in small numbers. If one compares the number of round with the number of wrinkled individuals, it is apparent that there is an approximate 3:1 ratio (323:126) as expected. The same is true of the ratio between plants with tendrils and those without tendrils (321:127). Thus, the alleles of each pair of genes apparently segregated from each other, with dominant and recessive genes appearing in a 3:1 ratio. However, the two sets of alleles did not segregate independently of one another, nor did they segregate in a completely dependent manner. Therefore, if these two allelic sets are linked, the linkage is not complete.

From the purely genetic evidence of this cross, there appears to have been some interchange of material between homologous chromosomes giving rise to a few gametes containing recombinations of linked genes.

P	Round, tendrils RRTT	X		Wrinkled, no tendrils rrtt

F₁ → Round, tendrils — RrTt

F₁ X F₁	Round, tendrils RrTt	X		Round, tendrils RrTt

F₂

Round, tendrils	319
Round, no tendrils	4
Wrinkled, tendrils	3
Wrinkled, no tendrils	123

Figure 6.10. A cross involving two pairs of linked genes. In this case, linkage is not complete (that is, crossing over occurs). Compare with Fig. 6.9. As an exercise, diagram this cross in the fashion of Fig. 6.9.

Other explanations could be made for these data, but when all possibilities are considered, this one emerges as the simplest and the most logical. In fact, cytological evidence supports this explanation. You will recall that in our discussion of meiosis (Section 5.2C), we pointed out that during synapsis an exchange of parts may occur between chromatids of different homologous chromosomes (Fig. 5-25). Thus, such an exchange as we have postulated on the basis of genetic evidence does indeed occur. Cytological examination of synapsing chromosomes reveals that exchanges involving any particular point on a chromosome do not occur in every meiotic event, but only in some. This phenomenon accounts partly for the relatively small number of recombinant gametes that combine and produce recombinant offspring. In fact, the percentage of exchange (crossing-over) is relatively constant when two particular traits are considered, and the location of genes within chromosomes may actually be mapped with fair precision.[7]

It should be apparent from this discussion that crossing-over of genes from one member of a pair of homologous chromosomes to the other during meiosis contributes to variability in gametes and offspring. Just the random distribution of chromosomes in the formation of gametes (Fig. 5-25) provides almost unlimited opportunity for variation from parental types. When the two sources of variability are added together, the significance of meiosis and sexual reproduction becomes impressive indeed. In Chapter 7, we shall consider how genetic variability originates and how it plays an important role in the process of evolution.

6.2B Sex Determination and Sex Linkage

Since Mendel's time, it has been found that, in many plants and animals, the sex of offspring is determined by the inheritance of a certain chromosomal complement. For example, there are normally 23 pairs of chromosomes in the body cells of the human being, 22 of which consist of morphologically identical members. In the female, the other pair also consists of like chromosomes; in the male, however, the two members of this pair are both morphologically and genetically dissimilar. For purposes of distinction, biologists refer to members of the 22 pairs as *autosomes* and to members of the 23rd pair as *sex chromosomes*. The male, of course, possesses one sex chromosome that females do not carry; it is arbitrarily called the *Y chromosome*. Its partner sex chromosome in the male is called an *X chromosome*. The female possesses a pair of X chromosomes.

At the time of sperm formation in the testes of the male, both the sex chromosomes and autosomes undergo segregation. Thus, it is a matter of chance as to whether the X chromosome or the Y chromosome go into a particular sperm, but both cannot be carried to the egg by a single sperm. The inheritance of sex depends upon whether an X-bearing sperm or a Y-bearing one fertilizes the egg. The problem of sex determination actually is a complex one involving many factors; the initial step in the process, however, is the combination in the zygote of either two X chromosomes (resulting in female sex) or of an X and a Y (resulting in male sex).

Let us postulate that since the X and Y chromosomes differ morphologically, they might be expected to bear genes that are not homologous. As a matter of fact, the Y chromosome bears few genes, whereas the X chromosome is known to carry a large number. Because genes located within the X chromosome of a male do not have alleles, the inheritance pattern of these genes is greatly affected. For example, it has been discovered that a gene controlling normal color vision resides in the X chromosome of the human being. Its recessive allele, when effective, interferes with the ability, characteristic of most people, to distinguish between certain colors. Possible genotypes and phenotypes of persons having these genes can be listed. The letter Y represents the absence of any gene at all, because the Y chromosome carries none for this trait.

CC normal (homozygous) female
Cc normal (heterozygous) female
cc color-blind female
CY normal male
cY color-blind male

Since the production of a color-blind female depends upon each parent contributing a recessive gene, females exhibiting the abnormality are somewhat rare. On the other hand, color-blind sons can be produced by a normal man and a heterozygous woman, as shown in Fig. 6-11. For this reason, it is generally men who exhibit recessive traits dependent upon *sex-linked* genes (located on a sex chromosome). Perhaps by a manipula-

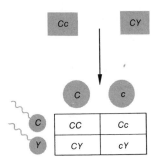

	C	c
C	CC	Cc
Y	CY	cY

CC   *normal (homozygous) female*
Cc   *normal (heterozygous) female*
CY   *normal male*
cY   *color-blind male*   **Figure 6.11**

tion of genotypes, you will be able to determine why such traits appear to skip characteristically from maternal grandfather to grandson.

In addition to their significance in sex determination and sex-linked inheritance, sex chromosomes are of interest to biologists in another respect. They provide strong support for the theory that genes are associated with chromosomes, since alternate hypotheses purporting to explain inheritance are difficult to reconcile with the observations and experiments involving sex-linkage and sex determination. This phenomenon may not be readily apparent, because we have taken a gene-chromosome theory for granted throughout most of our discussion. In the early days of genetical research, however, the sex chromosomes were of tremendous theoretical significance. Although there are other lines of evidence indicating the gene-chromosome relationship in organisms, perhaps the data from experiments involving sex chromosomes are the most conclusive of all. In other words, the hypothesis that genes are localized within chromosomes receives strong confirmation from the data regarding sex determination and the inheritance pattern of such genes as those associated with color-blindness. The gene-chromosome theory, therefore, is a fruitful conceptual scheme, allowing unlimited expansion of theoretical constructs.

It would be difficult to overemphasize the importance of genetic developments that have occurred within the conceptual framework of the classical gene. This framework is an extension by the Morgan group of Mendelian genetics. Essentially, the gene is viewed as a discrete unit located within a chromosome. As such, a given gene is capable of segregating from an allelic gene on a homologous chromosome during meiosis; recombining with a new allele in gamete fertilization; reassorting during crossing-over; or mutating to a different form. This concept of the gene as a discrete biological unit has been frutiful in a variety of directions. Not only has genetics itself made great progress around this concept, with many practical implications for medicine and agriculture, but it has unified several fields of biology whose basic viewpoints seemed in irreconcilable conflict.

As we have mentioned previously, before 1900, Darwinian evolution ran into serious trouble for want of a mechanism whereby variation could be explained. After 1900, it was not apparent immediately that Mendelian genetics provided this mechanism. In fact, it appeared at first that the gene concept only compounded the problem. But gradually, and especially as the Morgan school elucidated new genetic concepts, the pieces of the evolutionary puzzle began to fall into place. The last major problem was solved in the 1930's when genetic theory and evolutionary theory were brought together under the single roof of biometry (statistical analysis of biological systems).

Furthermore, by this time, a number of fields that had previously been largely isolated from each other—for example, physiology, cytology and embryology—found a common base in the gene concept. Eventually, beginning largely in the 1940's, this concept united the fields of biochemistry, biophysics, and microbiology and introduced a new level of emphasis to the study of living organisms, namely, molecular biology.

6.3 GENE ACTION: BIOCHEMICAL GENETICS [8]

Between the years 1902 and 1908, an English physician-biochemist, Sir Archibald Garrod, attempted to relate the newly discovered Mendelian genetics to biochemistry. He had observed that albinism, a condition that is marked by a lack of pigmentation, behaved as a Mendelian recessive when analyzed in the light of breeding experiments in animals. He noted further that a number of metabolic defects (including albinism) in the human seemed to be present from birth. Garrod termed these abnormalities "inborn errors of metabolism." A number of these "errors" were physiological defects that were detectable primarily through urinalysis. Notable among them was a condition called *alkaptonuria,* which causes its victims little injury other than possible embarrassment—their urine turns black upon exposure to air. Garrod began examining the marriage records of families having children with this disorder, and he found that it occurred with significantly greater frequency in first-cousin marriages than in the general population. On the basis of his total analysis, he suggested that alkaptonuria, like albinism, was inherited as a Mendelian recessive. He was able to show further that the immediate cause of the condition was biochemical: The victim was unable to metabolize the benzene ring portion of the amino acids tyrosine and phenylalanine (Fig. 6-12). Going one step

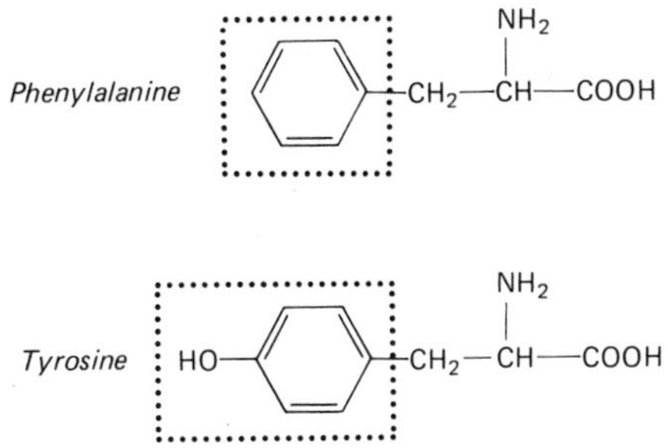

Phenylalanine

Tyrosine

Figure 6.12. Structural formulas of phenylalanine and tyrosine. The benzene ring portion of each formula is indicated by dotted lines.

further, he postulated that individuals with alkaptonuria lack a particular enzyme that, in the normal individual, is responsible for the breakdown of the benzene ring.

Garrod attempted in 1908 to popularize his theory of inborn errors of metabolism through a series of lectures to the Royal Society, and he later published a book by this title. However, like Mendel before him, Garrod was ahead of his time; he failed to bring off the union of genetics and biochemistry. One finds only an occasional reference to Garrod's work in the technical biological literature extending into the 1940's. Perhaps it is merely coincidental that both he and Mendel were some 35 years premature in their concepts.

6.3A The One Gene–One Enzyme Hypothesis [9]

Modern biochemical genetics came into being in 1937 when George W. Beadle, an American geneticist, joined forces with Boris Ephrussi, an Italian geneticist, in the study of eye color pigments in *Drosophila*. The results of their work with these pigments led them to conclude that each gene responsible for a particular step in pigment formation had one primary action. Stated more simply, it appeared that, in chemical terms, a given gene did one thing and one thing only; they suspected rather strongly that the action in each case was enzymatic. Garrod, of course, had suggested this very thing several years before. However, by 1937, it was more widely appreciated that enzymes are essential for biological reactions. Beadle and Ephrussi had shown many instances where gene action seemed to correspond very closely with enzymatic activity. However, their work was handicapped because very little was known about the biochemical pathways involved in the traits that they were studying in *Drosophila*. This work had paid rich dividends in new insights, but it became apparent that further success in identifying gene action with specific biochemical reactions in this organism would come only with great difficulty.

At this point, Beadle joined E. L. Tatum, an English biochemist, and they decided to reverse the former strategy.[10] Instead of working from known genes to unknown reactions, they would attempt to go from known reactions to unknown genes and use a simpler organism than *Drosophila*. They chose to work with a bread mold, *Neurospora,* since it seemed to be well suited to genetic studies, and certain biochemical pathways had already been worked out for it. They also took advantage of the fact that X rays induce mutations in genes. They subjected their cultures of *Neurospora* to this type of irradiation in the hope that they might obtain mutant genes that could be identified with specific biochemical reactions. It so happens that *Neurospora* requires for its heterotrophic nutrition a variety of inorganic salts, water, an organic carbon source such as glucose, and a single vitamin, biotin. This combination of substances is called a *minimal medium.* *Neurospora* is capable of synthesizing all of its other nutrient requirements, such as amino acids, nucleotides, and vitamins (with the single exception of biotin).

At the outset, the two scientists knew the biochemical pathway leading to the formation of vitamin B_1 (thiamin). For our purposes, we shall simplify this pathway symbolically, using the letters X and Y to represent precursor substances that combine to form thiamin. It is not necessary to understand the prior synthetic pathways of X and Y; these pathways are represented below as dotted lines. The important thing to note is that substances X and Y are joined through the action of a *single enzyme* to form thiamin:

$$\cdots \cdots X \searrow \quad \overset{\text{enzyme}}{\underset{\cdots \cdots Y \nearrow}{\Big\rangle} \longrightarrow} \text{thiamin}$$

Spores are asexual reproductive bodies consisting of a single cell. If spores of *Neurospora* are irradiated and placed on a minimal medium to which thiamin has been added, any spore carrying a mutation of the gene responsible for thiamin synthesis will grow as well as those that have not so mutated—that is, spores that are "normal" in their ability to synthesize thiamin. Any mutations in genes that control the synthesis of other vitamins, amino acids, and so on, will cause the spores that bear them to die on this thiamin-enriched minimal medium.

The spores that *do* survive under these conditions are allowed to grow sufficiently so that some of the mycelium, or filamentous mass, produced by each spore is transferred to a minimal medium *to which X and*

Y have been added. Those cultures that fail to grow on this medium obviously lack the enzyme that catalyzes the synthesis of thiamin. By numbering the test tubes appropriately, the investigator can then identify the source of his enzyme-less (thiamin-deficient) strain and can use it for genetic studies. This entire procedure is shown in Fig. 6-13.

A similar strategy was pursued by Beadle and Tatum in studying the genetic basis of a great variety of enzyme deficiencies in *Neurospora.* On the basis of all their studies, they advanced a conceptual scheme in 1941 that they termed the *one gene-one enzyme hypothesis.* Although this hypothesis was modified later to account for additional data, it constitutes a landmark in the development of genetic concepts. Essentially, Beadle and Tatum showed that genes are not mysterious little particles that must be regarded in semivitalistic terms; in contrast, genes work through biochemical pathways that can often be charted and identified. Once this phenomenon was realized and once it became known that gene action could be studied at the biochemical level, great strides were made in extending this concept to organisms that are more complex than *Neurospora,* including man. Thus, the decade of the 1940's saw a great synthesis of interest and methodology among such biological areas as genetics, developmental biology, and biochemistry. Quite deservedly, Beadle and Tatum were awarded the Nobel prize for Physiology and Medicine in 1958 for this highly significant work they had accomplished immediately before and after 1940.

In summary, Garrod's viewpoint has been vindicated by modern genetical and biochemical research. Basically, he postulated that genes are responsible for the production of enzymes; yet, he formulated this concept in the days when genetics and biochemistry were both infant sciences.

This example of scientific prophecy on the part of Garrod and its ingenious fulfillment by Beadle and Tatum is certainly an example of science at its best; it is only a pity that the insights of such men as Garrod and Mendel reach fruition too late for them to receive their just recognition.

6.3B Chemical Nature of the Gene

From the very inception of Mendelian genetics and the birth of the gene concept—that is, shortly after 1900—there was a great deal of speculation concerning the physical nature of the basic unit. Mendel himself did not seem to have been caught up in this speculation. In fact, there was some confusion as to whether Mendel's "character" should be made to represent the actual phenotypic trait under consideration or whether it was some sort of transmission unit that somehow caused the trait to develop.

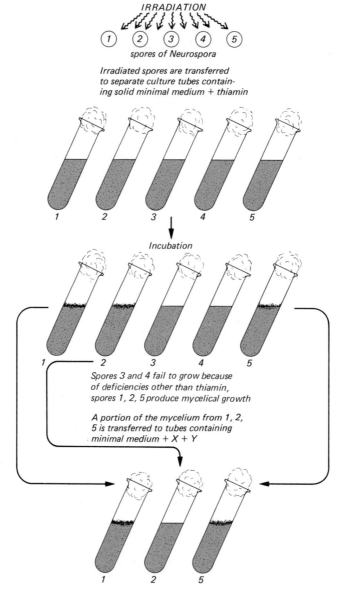

IRRADIATION

spores of Neurospora

Irradiated spores are transferred
to separate culture tubes containing solid minimal medium + thiamin

Incubation

Spores 3 and 4 fail to grow because
of deficiencies other than thiamin,
spores 1, 2, 5 produce mycelial growth

A portion of the mycelium from 1, 2,
5 is transferred to tubes containing
minimal medium + X + Y

Tubes 1 and 5 grow; 2 fails to grow.
Hence, the original culture 2 lacks
the capacity to produce the enzyme that
synthesizes thiamin from substances X and Y.

Figure 6.13. Diagram showing Beadle and Tatum's technique
in producing and identifying genetically controlled
biochemical deficiencies in the mold *Neurospora*.

This controversy explains Johannsen's wise reluctance to relate his term "gene" to a definite operational unit. Genetic knowledge was not sufficiently advanced in 1911, when he proposed the term, to allow him to make a firm commitment on the nature of the gene.

During the years when Morgan was working, relatively little effort was made to find out what a gene "really" was. Geneticists were generally content to use the term operationally, much as chemists were content to use the term "atom" for a long time. In each case, the concept was fruitful before much was known about its nature as a physical entity. However, in the case of the gene, the rise of biochemical genetics made the question of the nature of the gene somewhat more urgent. Was it an enzyme or some entity that *produced* an enzyme? If the latter, what could its chemical and physical nature possibly be?

To a great extent, the problem of the gene's nature is still unsolved, despite the great amount of progress that has been made toward understanding it. The term "gene" is still an operational one, although geneticists have preferred to coin a number of other terms that are more precisely descriptive. Thus, a "gene" may be viewed as a unit of recombination (*recon*), a unit of mutation (*muton*), or a unit of biochemical activity or function (*cistron*), and each term must be understood in the context within which it is used. We shall make no attempt to follow the lines of research that have made these new terms necessary, but it will be helpful to identify the *kind* of substance that composes genes.

Before the turn of the century, biochemistry had advanced sufficiently so that the existence of the large macromolecules in living systems was known. In fact, it was suspected even before 1900 that the type of substance that we presently call *nucleoprotein* (which is composed of protein molecules attached to nucleic acids) was somehow associated with inheritance. Among other lines of evidence, it had been determined that animal sperm, as well as chromosomes, are almost pure nucleoprotein. By the 1940's, when the question of the nature of the gene became an urgent one, the organic chemistry of the nucleic acids had been worked out rather thoroughly.

It is beyond our scope here to attempt a survey of the developments that led to the identification of DNA as the genetic material of living systems. Suffice it to say that by 1940 the evidence was quite strong. For one thing, the localization of DNA in the nucleus, and specifically within the chromosomes, was a good indication that it is involved in the transmission of genetic information. Techniques had been devised for quantifying the amount of DNA in a given cell and correlating it with genomes, or "sets," of chromosomes. This line of work, among others, provided strong circumstantial evidence that DNA is the functional chemical substance of the gene.

One of the most compelling lines of evidence for this viewpoint came from a group of singularly beautiful experiments involving the bacterium

Diplococcus pneumoniae (pneumococcus), which is the causative agent of one type of pneumonia in the higher animal body.[11] This work was reported in 1944 by the American bacteriologist O. T. Avery and his co-workers. They utilized two varieties, or types, of pneumococci. One type, a *virulent* form, was capable of inducing pneumonia in mice; the other, an *avirulent* form, was incapable of causing the disease. These two different bacterial forms, or strains, are readily distinguishable on solid-culture media because of certain discernible differences in their growth characteristics.

Actually, this line of work had begun in the 1920's when a British microbiologist, Frederick Griffith, had injected *living* avirulent cells together with *dead* virulent cells into mice and had found this mixture to be lethal to these animals. Furthermore, he was able to recover *living virulent* cells from the bodies of the dead mice. This phenomenon was very puzzling to Griffith. At best, it looked like a case of the inheritance of acquired characteristics; and at worst, it looked like magic. No immediate rational explanation could be given for this strange phenomenon; for years, it was known simply as the "Griffith effect" (Fig. 6-14).

By 1944, the Avery group was able to show that the substance involved in the Griffith effect was DNA.[12] Pneumococci, among certain other types of bacteria, are capable of transferring small amounts of DNA from one cell to another by way of the culture medium. This transfer can occur even from dead cells to living cells. In fact, Avery and his co-workers were able to isolate a highly purified form of DNA from virulent pneumococci, and they found that they could transform avirulent cells to virulent ones merely by exposing these cells to the DNA in solution. This series of experiments is highly conclusive evidence that DNA is the genetic material of bacterial cells. With this evidence as a clue, other experiments were devised that also indicated conclusively that DNA is the genetic substance of all organisms. However, certain viruses (if these are to be considered organisms) do use RNA as their genetic substance.

At the same time, scientists became involved in learning about the chemical nature of DNA. By 1950, the quantitative relationship among the four nitrogenous bases became known (see Sec. 4.2), and it was realized that the DNA molecule is constructed according to some balance of its component micromolecules: pentose sugars, phosphate groups, and nitrogenous bases. It was in 1953 that our present conceptual model of DNA was presented as a joint proposal by an American biologist, J. D. Watson, and an English biochemist, F. H. C. Crick.* Since 1953, this model has

---

* In 1968, Watson authored a popular account of their work that possesses the gripping qualities of a detective story. This book, entitled *The Double Helix*, became a best seller on the popular market. Published originally by McClelland and Stewart Ltd., it has since been issued as a paperback by New American Library, Inc. (Signet).

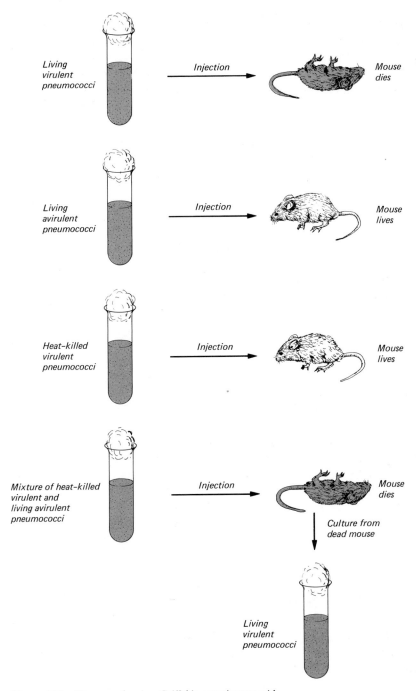

Figure 6.14. Diagram showing Griffith's experiments with pneumococci and mice.

stimulated a vast amount of research in biology, and its elucidation is one of the greatest conceptual triumphs in the history of science.[13]

What, then, is a gene? Is it a molecule of DNA, a *portion* of such a molecule, or can we identify it at all? Let us explore these questions further by considering the mode by which genes operate in living systems.

6.4 THE GENETIC MACHINERY OF LIFE [14]

So far in our discussion of heredity, we have made little reference to cells. This omission could imply that the mechanisms of heredity are somehow operative only at higher levels of organization in complex organisms. Such an implication would be unfortunate, because like most biological phenomena, genetic mechanisms operate first of all at the cellular level. Let us examine the cell as a self-perpetuating unit—that is, as an entity whose metabolism is controlled and regulated. As we shall see, this control and regulation is largely a reflection of gene action.

Metabolism, you will recall, is the sum total of the chemical activities that occur in a living system. These chemical activities are virtually all catalyzed by highly specific enzymes, and enzymes are protein substances. Thus, any structural or functional features exhibited by an organism are, to a great extent at least, a reflection of the proteins that are synthesized within that organism. Since the genetic material (DNA) of the organism is also influential in the development of its structural and functional features, it would appear logical to seek a functional connection between DNA and protein. Actually, this approach to the study of metabolism and self-perpetuation has been employed widely in biology, with the result that we now have a fairly clear understanding of the relationship between DNA and protein. In functional terms, a gene is a unit of DNA that specifies the synthesis of specific protein or polypeptide chains under conditions of precise control and regulation. Let us see how this synthesis actually works in a cell.

6.4A The Gene as a Unit of Control: Protein Synthesis

The DNA molecule is both autocatalytic and heterocatalytic; that is, it can both replicate itself and specify the exact structure of other large macromolecules.[15] According to the Watson-Crick model of DNA (Fig. 4-29), this substance consists of two helical strands of sugar-phosphate molecules, between which four kinds of nitrogenous bases are linked together in pairs. Apparently, a DNA molecule is replicated (reproduced) whenever the weak hydrogen bonds between linked base pairs break; then the two complementary strands unwind, and a new strand is built up on each original strand from micromolecular components present in the nucleus (Fig. 6-15). Each new double-stranded molecule then assumes the characteristic helical form. On occasion, however, one (but apparently not both) of the two DNA strands may "template" a complementary strand of RNA, not DNA. Whenever this action occurs, the base *uracil* is used as a "sub-

Figure 6.15. Replication of DNA according to the theory proposed by Watson and Crick. The two complementary strands of a DNA molecule (black) unwind, and a new complementary strand (shaded) is built upon each original strand. The end result is two molecules of DNA identical with the original.

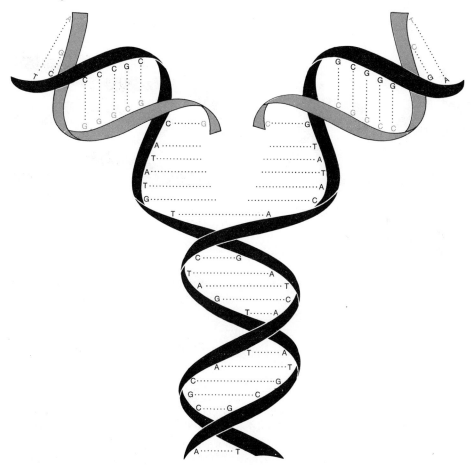

stitute" for the base *thymine*. In other words (as we noted in Section 4.2), the four nitrogenous bases found in RNA are adenine, cytosine, guanine, and uracil.

Let us consider that the DNA molecule has information coded into its structure by means of a four-letter alphabet with the letters arranged in meaningful sequences up and down the chain. As the RNA is being synthesized, or "templated," on the DNA strand, the information is being passed from one four-letter alphabet to another that is only slightly different. This process is called *transcription*. When transcription takes place, the RNA strand does not remain joined to its complementary DNA strand; rather, it moves away. The DNA strand may serve as a code, or template, for the assembly of another strand of RNA, or it may replicate itself. By using the first letters of the five different bases involved in DNA replication and RNA synthesis, one can compare these processes in a short segment of a hypothetical DNA molecule (Fig. 6-16). You will note that DNA and RNA are

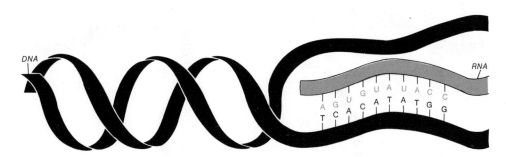

Figure 6.16. RNA synthesis on one strand of a DNA molecule, greatly simplified. Notice that uracil, not thymine, is coded by adenine.

differentiated by a different design in this illustration, and we shall follow this pattern as we present subsequent diagrams. Note that the synthesized RNA molecule is single-stranded, in contrast to the double nature of the DNA molecule. Furthermore, it appears that RNA molecules are produced in shorter segments than the entire DNA strand from which they are templated. However, they are ordinarily much longer than the segment shown in Fig. 6-16, which we have simplified for illustrative purposes.

What happens to the RNA molecules thus formed? Apparently, they pass out of the nucleus into the cytoplasm, where they eventually carry the coded information to the ribosomes. For this reason, this particular kind of RNA is called *messenger* RNA (abbreviated mRNA). The RNA that composes ribosomes is called *ribosomal* RNA (rRNA), and it is thought to be templated from a specific region associated with a nucleolus in chromosomes. Thus, all the rRNA found in ribosomes is quite similar; the mRNA, which in contrast may carry many different coded messages, is much more diverse.

Upon reaching a ribosome, a given mRNA molecule attaches in some manner to its surface or to the surface of an aggregate of ribosomes. Apparently, the rRNA provides points of nonspecific attachment for the mRNA (Fig. 6-17). The mRNA is connected to the ribosomes in such a way that

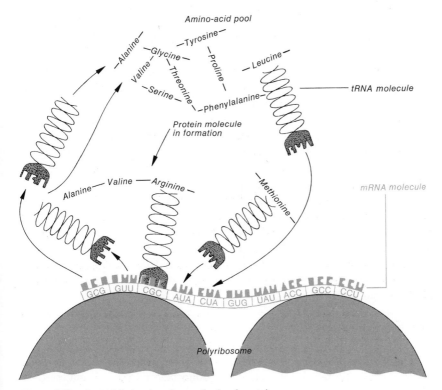

Figure 6.17. A model showing the synthesis of protein. Specific tRNA molecules pass successively along the mRNA molecule, and each contributes its amino acid molecule to the developing protein molecule. The tRNA molecules then return to an amino acid pool for another "load." Notice that a triplet of mRNA nucleotides codes a single amino acid.

the sequences of bases are exposed for interactions with another type of RNA that enters the picture at this point. This RNA is called *transfer* RNA (abbreviated tRNA, or sometimes sRNA, for *soluble*), and its individual molecules are much smaller than either those of mRNA or ribosomal RNA. In each molecule of tRNA, a chain of about 70 nucleotides is folded so that it resembles a short DNA molecule—that is, it appears to be a double-stranded helix. Apparently, the region of the "bend" of the tRNA molecule is specific as a point of attachment to mRNA, and one of the open ends of the helical strand is specific as a point of attachment to an amino acid. For example, a certain type of tRNA will attach itself only to the coded "alanine site" on a given mRNA molecule (Fig. 6-17). It appears that tRNA molecules are the same in all kinds of cells; thus, one can visualize 20 different kinds of tRNA molecules to correspond with the 20 different amino acids ordinarily involved in protein synthesis. These tRNA molecules are also thought to be templated by the DNA in the nucleus.

Attachment of an amino acid to a given tRNA molecule is accomplished enzymatically and is accompanied by the expenditure of energy on the part of the cell. Therefore, the process requires ATP as an energy source and also some 20 different enzymes that activate amino acids. These enzymes are also responsible for ensuring that each amino acid is attached to its correct tRNA molecule. This entire process, which takes place in connection with ribosomes, is called *translation;* it involves the transfer of the encoded information from the 4-letter alphabet of the mRNA to a 20-letter alphabet of the protein.

Let us attempt to visualize how the mRNA code might work. If we assumed that one nucleotide would code for one amino acid, we could only code four different amino acids (4^1). Again, if we assumed that a specific sequence of two bases coded for one amino acid, we could code for only 16 amino acids (4^2). However, if we considered that a specific sequence of three bases might code for one amino acid, we could code for more than all 20 amino acids, 64 in all(4^3).

Many lines of evidence indicate that this last possibility is correct—that three mRNA nucleotides are required to code an amino acid. Thus, if a molecule of mRNA consists of 30 nucleotides, as we have shown in our accompanying drawings, 10 molecules of tRNA can be accommodated. Each of these 10 molecules carries an amino acid to the messenger RNA-ribosomal complex (remember, our numbers are greatly reduced for purposes of illustration). Eventually, the specified kinds of tRNA, each with an amino acid in tow, attach themselves at specific sites on the mRNA molecule. These amino acids are joined enzymatically by peptide linkages, and a protein molecule is thus formed (Fig. 6-17). The protein molecule breaks away and becomes functional as an enzyme or as a structural protein, and the 10 molecules of tRNA are released from the mRNA molecule. At this point, they return to the general cytoplasm for another load. In contrast, there is a very rapid turnover rate of mRNA molecules, at least in bacterial cells, where it appears that a given molecule of mRNA may code only a single protein. Afterwards, it is broken up and replaced by another mRNA molecule. However, it is probable that, in some protoplasmic systems, mRNA molecules are used more than once.

Perhaps an analogy will serve to clarify the DNA-RNA-protein synthesis sequence we have outlined above. Let us suppose that a certain library possesses a copy of a rare old book, perhaps a Gutenberg Bible. Certainly, the library is not going to lend this book, inasmuch as it might easily be lost or damaged. However, the library might allow the book to be photographed page by page so that facsimile copies could be made. These copies might then be used in private studies for the preparation of scholarly papers, which in turn stimulate learned activity. DNA is something like the rare book. It never leaves the nucleus; instead, copies in the form of mRNA are released to the cytoplasm. Finally, proteins are formed, and they become directly involved in cellular activity.

The genetic code, which is a triplet code for the 20 different amino acids that are incorporated into protein molecules, was worked out (and is still being worked out) by using techniques that enable investigators to determine just which triplet combinations of mRNA nucleotides code for which amino acids. Much of this work has been accomplished by *in vitro* (outside the living system) studies. By structuring RNA chains according to known base sequences and then using them to effect protein synthesis, one can determine just what triplets may be responsible for coding each of the amino acids. For example, a synthetic RNA composed entirely of uracil nucleotides will produce a peptide chain containing only phenylalanine. This phenomenon leads to the conclusion that the triplet U-U-U codes for phenylalanine. Since the number of possible combinations of nucleotide triplets is 64, it is not surprising that the code is redundant; that is, some amino acids are coded by any of several different triplet combinations. It appears that some triplets also serve as "punctuation" marks for a given sequence, telling the whole procedure to "stop" or "start" at certain points.

Let us review the significance of the DNA-RNA-protein synthesis mechanism for the process of mutation. If DNA makes a "mistake" in its replication, so that a "wrong" nucleotide is incorporated into a newly replicated strand, the triplet of which it is a part is changed. Thus, the DNA triplet will code for a different mRNA triplet, and consequently for a different amino acid; for this reason, such a substitution on the DNA strand is called a *missense* mutation. For example, let us consider the production of the protein hemoglobin, the pigment in red blood cells. This protein is composed of four polypeptide chains of two different kinds (called *alpha* and *beta* chains, respectively). In the human, normal adult hemoglobin has a specific amino acid sequence in these two different types of chain; the sequence in each case is determined by the encoded information of DNA that is responsible for hemoglobin production. It is known that the *alpha* and *beta* chains of hemoglobin are under the control of two different genes.

A mutant form of hemoglobin is known in which one amino acid (glutamic acid) in the *beta* chain of normal hemoglobin is replaced by the amino acid valine. This one substitution in each of the two *beta* chains of a hemoglobin molecule leads to a hereditary disease known as *sickle-cell anemia,* and the genetic pattern is that of a Mendelian recessive. The red blood cells of a person homozygous for this mutant gene often assume a "sickle" shape (Fig. 6-18), and their ability to carry oxygen is greatly

Figure 6.18.   The effect upon human red blood cells of a gene that influences the production of sickle-cell hemoglobin. (a) A normal red blood cell in "face" view; (b) normal red blood cell in edge view. The depression in the center of the cell is caused by early extrusion of the nucleus. (c) Typical sickle red blood cells as they may be seen in the blood of a victim of sickle-cell anemia.

impaired. This is an example of a missense mutation where a triplet that would ordinarily code for one amino acid is changed to one that codes for a different amino acid (in this case, the change is from glutamic acid to valine), thus altering the polypeptide chain. This altered chain, in turn, affects the oxygen-carrying properties of the red blood cell and has an adverse effect upon the individual who possesses this gene in the homozygous condition (in fact, such individuals usually die in childhood). Other abnormal hemoglobins are known to depend upon this same type of missense mutation.

What would happen if a mutation resulted in a triplet that does not code for *any* amino acid? Not all of the 64 triplet combinations are involved in genetic coding, and so it is entirely conceivable that such a mutation could occur. This type of mutation does occur, as a matter of fact; and such a nonfunctional triplet is called a *nonsense* mutation. Not as much is known about nonsense mutations as has been learned about missense mutations, but it is quite likely that such a drastic impairment of a protein molecule or a polypeptide chain might well cause it to be totally functionless as an enzyme. In fact, nonsense mutation may well account for the nature of most recessive genes. If such a gene codes for a "nonsense" (nonfunctional) enzyme, then a pair of such genes in a living system would mean that some "normal" reaction would not be catalyzed at all. However, if such a gene were present in combination with one "normal" gene (the heterozygous condition), a functional enzyme would be produced, and probably in sufficient quantity to catalyze all of the necessary reactions normally controlled by that particular enzyme system. This explanation would account very nicely for "dominance" and "recessiveness" in functional terms.

Operationally, therefore, we can think of a gene as being a certain region of a DNA molecule (*how much* of a region would depend upon a great many factors) that encodes a specific polypeptide sequence. However, geneticists do not attempt to use this vague term in a very precise sense but instead have developed a great many other terms (such as muton, recon, and cistron).

From recent knowledge of the genetic code, it has become possible to construct nucleotide sequences that can be made to act like genes outside of living systems. This exciting line of work has far-reaching implications. For example, it may be possible some day to construct specific nucleotide sequences and use them to replace such genes as those that are responsible for sickle-cell anemia, albinism, or alkaptonuria. If geneticists ever achieve this ability, it may be possible to prevent those diseases that are dependent upon what Garrod called inborn errors of metabolism. It might also be possible in this type of genetic work to alter the genotypes of individual organisms, including man, in a variety of directions. Whether this achievement would be a blessing or a curse remains to be seen, but it is probably not an immediate problem. So many technological handicaps must be overcome before such "genetic engineering" becomes possible that few biologists consider it more than a remote possibility, at least for many more years.

6.4B The Gene as a Unit of Regulation [16]

Living cells are highly efficient systems, carrying on their metabolic processes with a minimal loss of free energy. One can interpret their efficiency as a reflection of the processes of evolution. During the millions of years that were required by cells to evolve, it seems logical to assume that they would develop mechanisms whereby maximum efficiency is achieved. In other words, natural selection has favored the survival of the most efficient cell types.

A system as complex as a living cell requires very intricate and precise mechanisms of regulation, at least if it is to use its available energy in the most economical way. The evidence now available in biology indicates that such mechanisms exist at a variety of levels in the control system of the cell.

In normal cells few metabolic products accumulate to any great extent. As we noted in Chapter 4, individual chemical reactions in a living system do not reach an equilibrium; rather, the products of a reaction are usually carried on into some other reaction in a specific metabolic pathway. This characteristic, within itself, suggests a highly regulated system in which substances are produced as they are "needed."

Since enzymes catalyze or regulate almost all reactions within cells, the concept of metabolic regulation actually refers, for the most part, to the regulation of enzymes. This regulation might conceivably affect both enzyme activity and enzyme synthesis. Enzyme activity is dependent upon a number of factors, such as the specific tertiary structure of the enzyme, the number of polypeptide chains the enzyme contains and how these chains are linked, and the susceptibility of the enzyme to its own end products, which might well cause inhibition or inactivation of the enzyme. Let us illustrate this last possibility with an example. Suppose a certain product Y is formed by a series of reactions, each of which requires an enzyme, as illustrated in Fig. 6-19. When the end product Y reaches a certain concen-

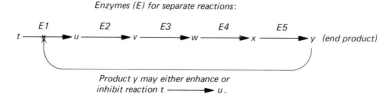

Figure 6.19. Diagram illustrating a possible mechanism for positive and negative feedback operating at the level of enzyme activity.

tration, it may inhibit the activity of enzyme (1) in this illustration, thus effectively limiting its own production. This action is termed *negative feedback,* since product Y "feeds back" to enzyme (1) and negates or stops its action. On the other hand, suppose the increased concentration of Y *enhances* rather than *inhibits* the action of enzyme (1). This action would be *positive feedback.* Such regulatory mechanisms as these do not directly involve gene action. They are very rapid and efficient processes; and, apparently, they are quite common in cells.

Those regulatory mechanisms that affect enzyme synthesis are related to the genetic processes that we discussed in Section 6.3. However, one must realize that genes do not continuously produce mRNA, and thus protein. Apparently, a great many cells (of the human body, for example) possess genes for the production of enzymes, but these enzymes are never produced. In other words, the synthesis of enzymes may be either *induced* or *repressed.* The actual process of induction or repression may occur at any one of several points along the protein synthesis pathway. For example, it might involve some mechanism for controlling the concentration of a particular mRNA.

At the risk of oversimplifying a complex situation, let us consider two models of regulation in the living cell. One of these illustrates the phenomenon of enzyme induction; the other, enzyme repression.

When cells of *Escherichia coli,* a species of bacteria, are placed in a medium where the only nutrient source is the sugar lactose, they are unable to utilize it immediately, even though it enters the cells. This inability arises because these cells lack an enzyme, *β-galactosidase,* which is necessary for the breakdown of lactose (a disaccharide) into its two component monosaccharide sugars, glucose and galactose. However, after only a short period of time, β-galactosidase is formed inside the cell; lactose has *induced* the production of β-galactosidase. If the cells are removed from the lactose medium and placed in a glucose medium, they cease producing β-galactosidase. If they are placed in a lactose medium once more, they start again to produce β-galactosidase.

It has also been determined that still another enzyme, *permease,* must be produced by cells of *E. coli* in order for lactose to enter the bacterial cell. Thus, at least two enzymes are necessary for the initial utilization of glucose by this organism: the permease enzyme, which is necessary for the entrance of lactose into the cell, and β-galactosidase, which breaks lactose down to its monosaccharide components. These two enzymes are produced by two separate genes, which are called *structural genes* since they are directly responsible for the structure of the two enzymes.

On the basis of this development and similar work, the French biologists François Jacob and Jacques Monod have proposed a model of enzyme induction (Fig. 6-20). This model assumes a kind of hierarchy of genes. Jacob and Monod proposed a unit of genes called an *operon.* According to the Jacob-Monod model, two other kinds of genes exist, at least functionally, in addition to the structural genes just mentioned. These are known as *regulator* and *operator* genes. It appears that these two types of genes do not govern the ultimate formation of metabolic enzymes, as structural genes do; rather, they code for substances (probably proteins) that exert their effects within the operon system.

Let us assume that the operon consists of three genes: the operator gene and two structural genes, A and B (Fig. 6-20). Gene A represents the

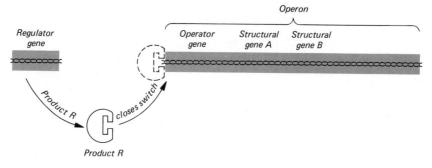

Lactose molecules absent: structural genes are inactive

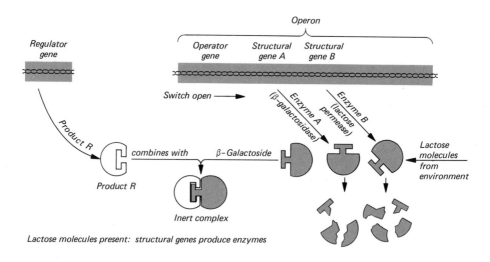

Lactose molecules present: structural genes produce enzymes

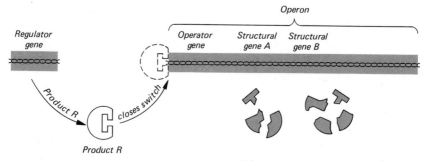

Lactose molecules broken down: structural genes cease activity

Figure 6.20. A model of enzyme induction according to the operon concept of Jacob and Monod. The regulator gene controls the action of the operator gene as long as no substrate is present, thus inhibiting the production of structural enzymes *A* and *B*. When a substrate is present, it ties up product *R*, thus allowing the operator gene to "switch on" the structural genes under its control.

DNA segment responsible for the production of β-galactosidase, and B represents the gene that codes for the permease enzyme. The operator gene acts as a switch: When it is open, the structural genes are active; when it is closed, the structural genes are inhibited. The operator remains inoperative (closed) as long as a repressor substance, produced by the regulator gene, is present. Whenever lactose is present in the environment, however, it reacts with the repressor substance and "binds" it so that it is no longer capable of repressing the operator gene. At this point, the operator switches on, and the structural genes under its influence commence to code their characteristic mRNA. Thus, β-galactosidase and the permease enzyme (in our model) are produced, and lactose is attacked. With the disappearance of the substrate, the system returns to its former operation; that is, the repressor substance turns off the operator, and enzyme production by the structural genes ceases. Thus, both of the structural genes are inducible. Different mutant strains of *E. coli* can exist for the various genes involved, including the regulator and operator genes. A variety of experiments involving different mutant strains of *E. coli* have been carried out, and the resulting data are accounted for by the Jacob-Monod model.

In another set of experiments involving a mutant strain of *E. coli,* Monod found that the synthesis of the amino acid tryptophane is terminated in the cell by the addition of tryptophane to the medium. He was able to demonstrate that this phenomenon was not merely a case of negative feedback, which would operate at the level of enzyme activity; rather, ʹin this case, the enzyme *tryptophane demolase,* which is essential to the synthesis of tryptophane, was missing. This discovery indicated that he was working with a regulatory mechanism at the level of enzyme synthesis. When this type of regulation is compared with the induction system represented by the operon model, it can be seen that the *substrate* in the induction system induces the formation of the enzymes; whereas, in the repression system, the *end product* inhibits the formation of the enzymes. Jacob and Monod also postulated for the repression system a model that is very similar to the one for induction (Fig. 6-21). The same hierarchy of genes exists; however, the regulator gene produces an incomplete repressor that is unable to switch off the operator. Thus, the operator turns on the structural genes, the number of which is variable depending upon how many enzymes may be involved in the particular synthesis. The structural genes, in turn, produce the enzymes, and tryptophane is formed. However, if tryptophane is formed in excess of that utilized in protein synthesis or other metabolic pathways, it combines with the incomplete repressor, making a *complete* or *active* repressor. The complete repressor then shuts off the operator gene, which, in turn, shuts off the structural genes, resulting in no enzyme being formed. Thus, the production of tryptophane is stopped under these circumstances.

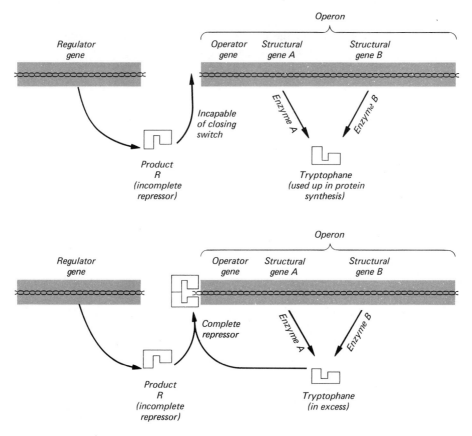

Figure 6.21. A model of enzyme repression according to
the operon concept of Jacob and Monod. The regulator
gene in this case produces an incomplete repressor which is
incapable of "switching off" the operator gene and thus
allowing the operator gene to "switch on" the structural genes
which are responsible for making the enzymes necessary
for the synthesis of tryptophane. When tryptophane is
produced in excess of that being utilized in protein synthesis,
it complexes with the incomplete repressor which now
"switches off" the operator gene, thus causing the structural
genes to be "switched off." As a result, tryptophane is not
synthesized when it is not required in metabolism.

In summary, these models account for the ability of the cell to synthesize enzymes according to the requirement for or availability of nutrients
in its environment. By the use of repressor and inducer systems, the cell is
thus able to utilize nutrients for which it has no need to store enzymes—
they can be made "on order." Furthermore, it need not waste energy in
producing enzymes that it may not have to use. One can, therefore, visualize

how cells that developed such regulatory systems over evolutionary time have come to possess great survival potential in competition with less efficient cells.

QUESTIONS FOR REVIEW AND DISCUSSION

1. What observation led to Mendel's dissatisfaction with the blending theory of inheritance?
2. Who was chiefly responsible for making Mendel's work known to the scientific world? What set of circumstances led to his discovery of Mendel's paper and why did this person accept Mendel's theories so readily?
3. Who was responsible for coining the terms *gene, genotype,* and *phenotype?* Distinguish among these three terms.
4. Relate the importance of the work of T. H. Morgan and his students to the concept of the gene as a discrete unit.
5. Cite some parallels between the behavior of genes and the behavior of chromosomes in inheritance.
6. Define homozygous, heterozygous, and allele.
7. Explain what is meant by Mendel's law of independent assortment. Is this law universally valid? Explain.
8. Cite several factors that might have accounted for the general apathy that greeted Mendel's work when it was first published.
9. Cite and briefly explain two phenomena which contribute to variability in gametes and offspring.
10. Distinguish between autosome, sex chromosome, X chromosome, and Y-chromosome. Which chromosome is sex-determining in man?
11. Summarize the contribution of each of the following persons to the present concept of gene action: Garrod, Beadle, Ephrussi, Tatum.
12. Explain what is meant by the "one gene-one enzyme" hypothesis. Outline the strategy that was pursued in formulating this hypothesis.
13. Distinguish between the terms "recon," "muton," "cistron," and "gene."
14. Review and summarize the work of O. T. Avery and his co-workers.
15. Outline and explain the process of protein synthesis. What is meant by the term transcription? Translation? Distinguish among m-RNA, r-RNA, and t-RNA. What is a codon? What is a polyribosome?
16. What is a mutation? Give an example of a "mistake" in protein synthesis.
17. Distinguish between the regulation of enzymes at the level of enzyme action and at the level of enzyme synthesis.

18. What is meant by negative feedback, enzyme induction, and enzyme repression? Give examples of each phenomenon.

19. Of what adaptive value are the systems of regulation mentioned above?

20. Normal human pigmentation (*A*) is dominant over albinism (*a*). What genotypic and phenotypic results would be expected from the following matings? *AA* × *aa*; *Aa* × *aa*; *Aa* × *Aa*; *aa* × *aa*.

21. A man with normal pigmentation, whose father was an albino, marries an albino. What is the probability that their first child will be an albino?

22. A man with normal pigmentation marries a woman with normal pigmentation. They have an albino child. What are the genotypes of all three individuals?

23. In chickens, rose comb (*R*) is dominant over single comb (*r*). A rose-combed male is mated to a rose-combed female. Of the 18 chicks produced, 10 are rose-combed, and 8 are single-combed. What are the genotypes of the parents?

24. In guinea pigs, black coat color (*B*) is dominant over white (*b*), and rough coat (*R*) is dominant over smooth (*r*). What are the expected genotypic and phenotypic results of the following crosses? *BBRR* × *bbrr*; *BBrr* × *bbRR*; *Bbrr* × *bbRr*; *BBRr* × *BbRr*; *BbRr* × *BbRr*.

25. A black, rough male guinea pig is mated to a black, rough female. Out of several litters totaling 21 individuals, 10 are black and rough, 4 are black and smooth, 5 are white and rough, and 2 are white and smooth. What are the genotypes of the parents?

26. In cattle, the polled condition (*H*) is dominant over the horned condition (*h*). A cross between an individual with red coat (*R*) and one with white coat (*r*) results in roan (*Rr*). A polled, red bull is mated to three cows. With cow A, which is horned and white, a horned roan calf is produced. With cow B, which is horned and roan, a horned red calf is produced. With cow C, which is polled and red, a horned red calf is produced. What are the genotypes of all individuals?

27. What would be the genotypic and phenotypic results of the following crosses? Roan × roan; Red × roan.

28. Why would it not be possible to establish a true-breeding herd of roan cattle?

29. In rabbits, black fur is dominant over brown, and long hair is dominant over short hair. A male is mated to several brown, short-haired females. These matings result in the following offspring: 11 brown, long-haired; 16 black, long-haired; 12 brown, short-haired; 15 black, short-haired. Express the genotype and phenotype of the male.

30. In man, the determination of sex depends on whether the male sperm carries an X chromosome (resulting in a female) or a Y chromosome (resulting in a male). In other words, body cells of females carry two X chromosomes, and those of males carry one X and one Y. During meiotic division, the egg of the female must of necessity carry one

X, whereas segregation of the X and Y in spermatogenesis results in some sperm that are Y-bearing and others that are X-bearing. One human abnormality, called red-green color blindness, is the result of a recessive gene carried on the X chromosome. It has no allele on the Y. Consequently, the genotypes CC, Cc, and cc are possible in females, but a male must be either CY or cY. Working theoretically, answer the following questions: (a) Is it possible for a female to be color blind? (b) Can two persons with normal vision produce a color-blind daughter? (c) Can two persons with normal vision produce a color-blind son? (d) Can two color-blind parents produce a child with normal vision? (e) Let us suppose that a woman with normal vision, whose father was color-blind, married a color-blind man. What proportion of their sons may be expected to be color blind? What proportion of their daughters may be expected to be color blind? Can any of their daughters be "carriers" (heterozygous)? If one of their sons whose vision is normal marries a woman of the genotype CC, can they have any color-blind children? Can the trait "crop out" later as a result of the son's family background?

31. In *Drosophila,* the fruit fly, sex determination is the same as human sex determination. Normal flies have bright red eyes; a certain recessive, sex-linked gene is responsible for white eyes. From a pure-breeding strain of red-eyed flies, let us select a female and breed her to a male from a pure-breeding strain of white-eyed flies. (a) Will all their offspring have eyes of the same color? (b) What will be the color of the eyes of male flies? (c) What will be the color of the eyes of female flies? (d) Now suppose that we let the male and female offspring of this original pair mate at random and we collect exactly 100 of their offspring, 50 males and 50 females. How many of the females should have white eyes? (e) How many of the males should have white eyes? (f) How many of the males should have red eyes? (g) How many of the females should have red eyes?

32. In man, there is a type of blindness known as aniridia, which is due to a dominant gene. Hemophilia, a disease in which the blood does not clot properly, results from a sex-linked recessive gene. A non-hemophilic man who is blind from aniridia but whose mother was not blind marries a nonhemophilic woman who is not blind but whose father was afflicted with hemophilia. If four sons are born to this union, what different combinations of traits might they exhibit in regard to aniridia and hemophilia?

REFERENCES

Bonner, D. M., and S. E. Mills. *Heredity.* Englewood Cliffs, New Jersey: Prentice-Hall, Inc., 1964. This is one of the brief textbooks in the "Foundations of Modern Biology" series. It presents a rather clear and concise treatment of the area of heredity.

Burns, G. W. *The Science of Genetics* (2nd ed.). New York: The Macmillan Company, 1972. An introductory textbook in genetics, written in a concise and lucid style.

Carlson, E. A. *The Gene: A Critical History.* Philadelphia: W. B. Saunders Company, 1966. The development of the gene concept from the re-discovery of Mendel to present-day investigation is presented in this work.

Peters, J. A. (ed.). *Classic Papers in Genetics.* Englewood Cliffs, New Jersey: Prentice-Hall, Inc., 1959. A series of classic papers in the field of genetics from Mendel through 1955 are presented in this work.

Swanson, C. P., T. Merz, and W. J. Young. *Cytogenetics.* Reference at end of Chapter 5.

SEVEN

Life, Cell, Heredity and Evolution

Before entering into a discussion of our fourth conceptual scheme, let us recapitulate briefly. We have discussed three great conceptual schemes and their implications for modern biology: biogenesis, the cell theory, and Mendelian genetics. In other words, we have attempted to explore the nature of life, the physical units by means of which life manifests itself, the manner in which life maintains its steady-state nature within these units, and the mechanisms by which life is perpetuated to subsequent living systems.

Because gene replication is such a precise and generally accurate process, living systems are perpetuated generation after generation with remarkable similarity. This phenomenon is particularly evident in cell division, where succeeding generations of cells are usually genetically identical. However, in organismic reproduction as a whole, two major factors operate to upset the status quo of perpetuation: *mutation,* which may become a factor of change in any form of reproduction, whether it be sexual or asexual; and *recombination,* which is the genetic shuffling process operative only in sexual reproduction.

The stability of living systems is such that short-term changes in perpetuation result in mere phenotypic novelty. Everyone knows that no two people look exactly alike (unless they came from the same fertilized egg); but, regardless of differences, they are still *people.* Are there, however, accumulated changes over long periods of time? Is it possible for so many differences to occur that changes of great magnitude (such as the separation of one species into two species) might occur? There is no *direct* way to answer this question, of course, since this kind of process might very well take a long period of time. But given the mechanics of self-perpetuation that we have studied thus far, it is definitely a logical implication.

However, in historical terms, this is getting the cart before the horse. The question occurred to biologists and other scientists long before such concepts as steady state and self-perpetuation were a part of biological thought—but for reasons that were entirely different from those we have set forth. Let us explore the problem in the light of history before we pursue it in terms of modern biological concepts.

7.1 A GREAT CONCEPTUAL SCHEME: ORGANIC EVOLUTION

The concept that living systems are subject to profound biological change is termed *organic evolution.* More specifically, and in organismic terms, it is the concept that species of organisms undergo significant changes over long periods of time. Charles Darwin described the concept succinctly by calling it "descent with modification." It has emerged in biological thought only after the most intensive struggle; and it is probably safe to say that even now, the concept is accepted by only a minority of people in the Western world (for reasons that are set forth in Chapter 9.) [1]

7.1A The History of Evolutionary Thought

There have probably been evolutionists ever since man first contemplated nature, but certain of the ancient Greeks were the first to express the idea that some forms of life may have sprung from other forms. As was characteristic of much of their thinking about natural phenomena, the good and the bad were so interwoven that most of it must be put down as hopeless and fruitless speculation. Some of Aristotle's writings indicate that he toyed with the idea of organic change, but his total thought-system assumed the immutability of "forms" in nature. This idea coincided nicely with the medieval view of the fixity of species, based upon a literal interpretation of the biblical account in Genesis. Consequently, Aristotle was highly regarded by the religious authorities of that period.

We have noted how the biblical account of creation was accepted throughout the Middle Ages as the full and final explanation for animal and plant diversity. This situation changed very little during the Renaissance, especially since Protestant authorities were even more fervent than those of the Roman Church in their insistence upon biblical literalism. Most students of nature living during this period (and indeed for some time after the Renaissance) were loyal churchmen, who were quite content to accept the traditional doctrine of the fixity of species. After all, they were chiefly concerned with descriptive studies; and the conceptual scheme of divine, instantaneous creation was adequate for their needs. Furthermore, no compelling evidence was developed during most of that time to create doubt in their minds.

However, this picture began to change dramatically in the 18th century. Numerous voyagers told about strange organisms found in distant lands. Observers puzzled over the remains of marine animals found high on the tops of mountains. Still other remains that were discovered could not be correlated with any known living organisms, causing men to wonder if extinction could be a reality. More important, geologists learned how to interpret rock stratifications and came to the conclusion that the earth was much older than traditionalists held it to be. All of these discoveries could be reconciled with the biblical account in one way or another by the formulation of what philosophers call *ad hoc* hypotheses.* At least for some students of nature, however, the combined evidence became so overwhelming that it could not be ignored or explained away. Evolution was

---

* The Latin expression *ad hoc* literally means "for this." An *ad hoc* hypothesis is one that must be added to a major hypothesis in order to account for conflicting data.

staring the entire scientific community in the face by the end of the 18th century, but there were few who had eyes to see it.

THE EARLY EVOLUTIONISTS

By the latter part of the 18th century, a number of scientists had begun to doubt the general doctrine of the fixity of species, but the time was still not ripe for a full-blown evolutionary scheme. However, one important naturalist, the Frenchman Georges Louis Leclerc, comte de Buffon (1707–1788), included the subject in his immense *Natural History*. He made no outright proposal of an evolutionary concept, but a modern reader of Buffon can see quite readily that he was thinking rather clearly in evolutionary terms. Somewhat later in the 18th century, one of his contemporaries, an Englishman named Erasmus Darwin (1731–1802), expressed a general evolutionary view in some of his writings. Neither Buffon nor Darwin advanced the case for evolution to any great extent, but they did help to popularize the idea. By the year 1800, the notion that organisms are subject to change was being entertained widely in the scientific community.

Perhaps the most important of the early evolutionists, the Frenchman Jean Baptiste, chevalier de Lamarck (1744–1829), was more definite in his expression of an evolutionary hypothesis. His major ideas were set forth in his *Zoological Philosophy,* published in 1809. Essentially, Lamarck's theory of evolution rested on the assumption that organisms undergo an unconscious striving toward some adaptive goal because of an innate tendency toward progression. This inner force is responsible for physical change through the use or disuse of bodily organs. Thus, the continual use of a structure by an organism would strengthen and perhaps enlarge the structure, and this modification would then be inherited. For instance (and this example is the most frequently cited), Lamarck speculated that giraffes originally had short necks; but through stretching to reach higher leaves, their necks became longer. This process would explain such adaptations as the long ears of rabbits, the wings of birds, and the claws of tigers. Known today as *the theory of inheritance of acquired characteristics,* Lamarck's hypothesis is unacceptable to modern biologists. However, it must be remembered that it was almost a century after Lamarck that genes and their role in inheritance were known, and it is worthy of note that any biologist of that period would express a belief in evolution and attempt an explanation of the forces involved. Although his was an inadequate explanation, Lamarck did much to focus the attention of other biologists upon the problem.

There were at least two reasons, however, why Buffon, Erasmus Darwin, and Lamarck made no really profound impact upon evolutionary thought during the times they lived. First of all, the time was not ripe for a general concept of evolution. Secondly, none of the men provided a really effective explanation of organic change. Buffon did not try to do so; Erasmus Darwin veiled his speculations in the language of poetry; and Lamarck was unable to supply evidence for his theory. Theirs were merely halting steps toward a much fuller expression of evolutionary thought.[2]

In the meantime, geology and biology continued to make spectacular gains. A few men here and there began to talk and write in terms of evolution; but for the most part, the prevailing socio-theological atmosphere of Western Europe and America discouraged open expression on the subject. In the scientific community, it was realized that Lamarck had done the cause of evolutionary thought little service by advancing his inept theory, and no one cared to attempt a generalized statement on this difficult subject. Among lay persons, there existed an almost total suspicion of any biological concept that might disagree with the biblical account of creation.

CHARLES DARWIN [3]

It was within this intellectual framework that Charles Robert Darwin (1809–1882) (Fig. 7-1), grandson of Erasmus Darwin, developed his theory of evolution. Darwin was a member of a well-to-do English family. He studied at the universities of Edinburgh and Cambridge, taking a degree at the latter institution in 1831. His education was not a scientific one; indeed, education in the sciences as we know it today was not available in universities at that time. Darwin took what we would call a "liberal arts" degree. However, he had come under the influence of a Cambridge naturalist, J. S. Henslow, who recommended him for the nonpaying position of naturalist on a five-year voyage of an exploring vessel, H.M.S. *Beagle*. It was on this voyage that Darwin, largely through his own efforts, received his education in biology and geology.

Long before the voyage ended, Darwin became convinced that species are not immutable (unchanging), as the prevailing tradition held. But he was very cautious in his statements and even in his thoughts. A retiring person by nature, and one who shrank from unpleasantness and criticism, he kept his ideas on evolution mostly to himself. After the voyage had ended in 1836, Darwin married and retired with his wife to a secluded country village not far from London where he remained occupied with biological pursuits and with his thoughts. For the better part of two decades, he wrote sketches of a developing evolutionary hypothesis, discussed the subject with a few close friends, and eventually came to a rather firm conclusion: Evolution has occurred in nature; the evidences for it are overwhelming to the open and informed mind. But how? What are the forces that bring it about? By studying the artificially selective practices of animal

Figure 7.1.   Charles Darwin (1809–1882). This photograph was taken in 1881. (Courtesy of the American Museum of Natural History.)

breeders, by reflecting upon the ideas of those who had studied trends in human populations, and by drawing upon his own wide experience as a naturalist, Darwin finally came to the conclusion that evolution proceeds according to a process of *natural selection*. In essence, he meant by this expression that because of intense competition among organisms, nature "selects" those that are superior and that these superior organisms win out in the struggle for existence. As a result, over long periods of time, Darwin reasoned, this process has allowed the extinction of some forms of life and has ensured the continued success of others.

For many years after Darwin had the essentials of his theory well in mind, he still declined to publish it. He contemplated the eventual publication of an exhaustive treatise on the subject, but there is reason to believe that his fear of the criticism that he knew quite well to be forthcoming caused him to postpone the project year after year. In the meantime, other observers were thinking about evolution. Finally, in 1858, Darwin received a manuscript setting forth the essentials of his own theory from a naturalist in the Far East. This man was Alfred Russel Wallace (1823–1913), an Englishman who had been pondering the question of evolution for a much shorter period of time than Darwin had studied it, but who had struck through to much the same general conclusion. Since he was on the other side of the world, Wallace hoped that Darwin might see fit to sponsor the publication of his paper in a learned journal. Receipt of this manuscript forced Darwin's hand. He wrote to Wallace and explained his own position, that he had come to these same conclusions many years before, and Wallace agreed to the joint publication of a paper setting forth the essentials of evolution by natural selection.

The incident with Wallace made Darwin realize that if he wished to claim original credit for a theory of evolution, he had best publish a book on the subject as quickly as possible. He therefore abandoned his plans for an exhaustive treatise, sublimated his fears, and within a few months' time delivered to the publisher a manuscript bearing the title *On the Origin of Species by Means of Natural Selection, Or the Preservation of Favoured Races in the Struggle for Life* (in Victorian England, book titles often rivaled the books themselves in length). It was offered to the public on November 24, 1859.

As Darwin had expected, a storm of controversy broke when the *Origin of Species* appeared. The strongest opposition came from the clergy, but there was also a violent reaction from the pious laity, and not a few scientists added their voices to the outcry. Despite his labored writing style and a tendency toward obscurity of meaning, Darwin left few readers in doubt about the awful implications of his book: species are not immutable; the biblical account is scientifically deficient; instead of God, the prime mover in nature is a process; man himself is an animal, a part of nature. Wherever possible, Darwin avoided any direct confrontation with the cherished ideas of a conservative society whose roots still drew nourishment from both the Protestant Reformation and medieval Scholasticism.

We shall defer until Chapter 9 any discussion of the social and religious implications of the Darwinian revolution. What of the biological implications? What did Darwin, the biologist, say to other biologists, and what was he trying to accomplish?

THE ORIGIN OF SPECIES   In essence, Darwin sets forth two great concepts in the *Origin of Species:* (1) Living forms have an evolutionary origin, and (2) The major factor in evolution is natural selection. Unfortunately for clarity of understanding, he did not keep these ideas separated; however, each is developed exhaustively. At least on the first of these themes, the main thrust of his argument is clear enough. During the twenty-odd years that Darwin had been thinking about evolution, he had amassed a formidable array of evidence. Even his chapter headings reveal how very impressive this evidence was: "On the Geological Succession of Organic Beings," "Geographical Distribution," "Mutual Affinities of Organic Beings: Morphology: Embryology: Rudimentary Organs." These representative titles indicate that a very great deal was known about evolution, but no one had put it all together up to this time. Suddenly, a great number of scientists and nonscientists alike realized that the evidence for the occurrence of evolution was overwhelming; this point was never in serious question after the *Origin of Species.*

Darwin's second concept is considerably less clear, which is understandable, since it deals with the problem of *process* and is thus a far more difficult theme than the first. In general, his argument on the process of evolution can be summarized as follows:

1. He presents the observable evidence that, in its totality, supports the following:
   a. *Variation* exists within species; that is, no two individuals in a population are exactly alike.
   b. *Overproduction* of offspring is the rule in nature.
2. He draws what would appear to be two logical conclusions from these observable phenomena:
   a. *Selection* of the more fit of the several competing organisms occurs, since there must necessarily be a struggle for existence—hence, the expression "natural selection." In a metaphorical sense, nature sees to it that a survival of the fittest occurs.
   b. *Inheritance* of traits that are favorable to survival bestows a competitive advantage upon the offspring of "fit" organisms.

Of these two latter conclusions, the first was by far the easier to approach. Darwin emphasized it very strongly, presenting quantities of data indicating its general validity. The second conclusion was never verified by Darwin (remember, the science of genetics had not yet developed), and his attempts to explain it eventually led him into difficulties. As a matter of fact, the genetic hypothesis that he finally developed was essentially Lamarckian; that is, it assumed an influence by ordinary body cells upon those involved in sexual reproduction.

Another difficulty inherent in natural selection as Darwin expressed it was that it seemed to operate as a limiting factor, determining in what direction evolution could or could not go, but failing to explain the origin of such phenotypes as natural selection might influence. Darwin used such expressions as "struggle for existence" and "survival of the fittest," which implied that natural selection is chiefly a process that operates to eliminate the unfit. His critics pointed out, with some justification, that natural selection was simply a negative factor in evolution: Unless organisms can compete successfully, they do not survive. As we shall see, this negative aspect of natural selection is indeed only a part of the story. The concept also required genetic insights in order to become more than a rule governing the elimination of the unfit.

In summary, Darwin made two outstanding contributions to evolutionary thought. First, he established (on a valid historical basis) that organic evolution actually occurs in nature. Evidence that has been found since his time has only strengthened Darwin's case, but Darwin himself was able to present enough data to convince all but the most skeptical that evolution is a reality. His second contribution was the identification of natural selection as an important factor in the adaptation and the origin of species. Darwin lacked the genetic insights necessary to a clear exposition of natural selection—and there were other difficulties as well—but it is a tribute to his genius that his concept of the processes of evolution was essentially a clear one. Whatever the difficulties of his theory, he made evolution scientifically plausible and conceivable, which is the major reason that he convinced the vast majority of the scientific community of his day.

DARWIN'S IMPACT ON BIOLOGY   As was well illustrated by Gregor Mendel, a discoverer may be so many years ahead of his contemporaries that the rest of science has to catch up with his insights before the value of his conceptual scheme can be appreciated.[4] Almost the opposite was true in Darwin's case; biology had literally been waiting for an evolutionary conceptual scheme. When the idea of organic evolution was finally conceptualized, almost every aspect of biology seized upon it. It was especially important to taxonomy and to geographical distribution (which is a part of what we presently call ecology), where masses of factual data that had accumulated for decades were finally made intelligible. But other important areas—notably, anatomy, embryology, and paleontology—were thoroughly revolutionized by the idea. Thus, Darwin achieved what is almost a rarity in the history of ideas: He was paid great honor by his fellow scientists and by other leaders of thought within his own lifetime.

EVOLUTION AFTER DARWIN

The period between 1859 and 1900 was a time of rapid development in biology. Mendel's work was published in 1866; chromosomes and their behavior in mitosis and meiosis were described between 1866 and 1885; and progress was evident in virtually every area of biology. Nevertheless, the fundamental principles of genetics had not been clarified. (Mendel, you will recall, had made no impact on the scientific world.) In 1900, Mendel's work was rediscovered by three biologists working independently, which is an indication that the time was ripe for its understanding and appreciation.

Strangely enough, the new science of genetics appeared at first to be devastating to Darwin's theory of natural selection. This result was partly a reflection of the human tendency to view a new piece of knowledge as the whole truth and partly a misunderstanding of the raw materials of both genetics and natural selection. Specifically, the conflict arose when the process of mutation was discovered shortly after Mendel's paper was found. Today, we define mutation as a change in a gene (or, biochemically speaking, an alteration of nucleotide sequence in a specific region of a DNA molecule). It was first considered, however, as an almost mystical force that could effect profound changes in hereditary materials. Because scientists made certain observations involving gross chromosomal abnormalities that appeared to create new species in great and sudden jumps, an alternative hypothesis to natural selection was put forth. Called the *mutation theory,* it soon claimed large numbers of leading biologists among its adherents. It was not until the 1930's that mutation and natural selection were reconciled; in the meantime, Darwin's views were generally regarded as badly outmoded.

As it turned out, the mutation hypothesis revealed itself as one of those half-truths that look better at first inspection than they do after they have been subjected to experimental analysis. Mutation is indeed a major factor in evolution, as we shall emphasize presently, but not in the sense conceived by early champions of the mutation hypothesis. They visualized mutation as a process resulting in sudden and drastic improvements in organisms; to them, natural selection was merely a negative factor that eliminated the unfit. It was subsequently shown that the vast majority of mutations do not produce drastic changes in organisms—and when they do, the affected organisms are almost always unable to compete with the standard types from which they mutated. A better understanding of how mutation worked as a process did not come for several years.

Shortly before and during the 1930's, the major factors of evolution began gradually to fall into place. By this time, both mutation and natural selection had been subjected to considerable study; furthermore, other factors appeared to be involved in evolution besides these two. One of the most important developments was the introduction of statistical methods into genetics. Once large numbers of organisms could be analyzed to determine how evolution actually worked, it became much easier to fit the pieces of the puzzle together. Since that time, the *synthetic theory* of evolution has replaced the older hypotheses. Most modern biologists feel that no additional basic factors of evolution remain to be discovered. This does not mean that everything is known about evolution as a process; it simply means that, for several decades, no data have been forthcoming that cannot be accommodated by the synthetic theory and that it has attained an exceedingly high degree of reliability in prediction.

7.1B The Modern Synthesis

We call the modern theory of evolution a *synthesis,* because it incorporates and unifies the several factors that are known to be operative in effecting changes among organisms. Factors included are natural selection and mutation, which, as we have seen, were each championed at one time as being self-sufficient to explain the process of evolution. Not only are other factors now recognized, but also each factor is related to the others in such a way that the total picture is meaningful. We shall devote some attention to these factors as they relate to the whole of evolution.

The synthetic theory of evolution recognizes four basic processes. Two of these, mutation and genetic recombination, are the sources of evolutionary variability. The other two, natural selection and reproductive isolation, act upon the sources of variability in determining adaptation.

MUTATION

Since Darwin's time, the phenomenon of mutation has been discovered and studied extensively. A mutation is a change in a gene. Although genes are highly stable, usually duplicating themselves with fine exactness, every now and then a mutation does occur. In other words, genes are not completely stable; and, when a gene mutates, its new form is duplicated in cell division as was the old one.

If a mutation occurs in an organism without affecting its reproductive cells or its reproductive potential, there is neither genetic nor evolutionary significance to the event. Any resulting changes spread no farther than such cells as may be produced from this cell. Effects are thus localized; the mutation, whether potentially advantageous or detrimental to the organism, is of necessity lost to the species when its bearer dies. However, if a mutation occurs in a reproductive cell that becomes involved in the formation of a new individual, there is a chance that it may produce significant effects in the species. We have already pointed out that most mutations are harmful ones. A mutant gene may change the smooth balance of factors concerned with development so radically, for example, that the bearer does not even survive until birth. In other instances, mutant genes may be responsible for structural or functional abnormalities in the

fully formed individual.* It should not be difficult to see why most mutations are harmful; after all, the thousands of genes that contribute to the
genetic makeup of a complex organism must be highly coordinated. Over
long periods of time, the species of which it is a member has adjusted to
its environment and is obviously successful to some degree, or it would be
extinct. The chances are considerably greater that a random mutation will
upset this genetic balance rather than improve upon it. To draw an analogy,
it is possible that one might improve the operation of a highly organized
machine by throwing a heavy wrench into its gears, but the chances are
much greater that such action will only succeed in tearing up the machine.

Nevertheless, an advantageous mutation does sometimes appear in
species. When this mutation occurs, there is a chance that it may become a
part of the stable genotype through the process of natural selection. Thus,
over long periods of time, species may change for the better in terms of
ecological success through the accumulation of advantageous mutations.

Mutation is the *primary* source of genetic variability; that is, it supplies the raw material with which the other factors have to work. Apparently, it is the only mechanism by which new hereditary material is
incorporated into genetic systems.

GENETIC RECOMBINATION

In sexual reproduction, different gene combinations may be brought
together in the formation of a new genotype. Any differences in allelic
genes depend ultimately upon mutation, of course; but, for the new organism, its gene pattern is a result of the new combinations brought about
through sexual reproduction. We call this phenomenon *recombination,* and
it may be defined as the production of new genotypes from genes that
already exist. By its nature, therefore, recombination is a *secondary* source
of genetic variability.

Recombination occurs in three different ways: (1) When a set of
chromosomes from one parent becomes associated with a set from the
other parent in sexual reproduction, many new combinations of alleles are
made possible in the diploid zygote. Ultimately, these combinations may be
expressed in the total genotype of the organism. (2) During meiosis, the

---

* Of course, if the "new" gene were recessive to its normal allele, as most mutant
genes apparently are, it would be carried in the heterozygous condition and would
not appear until a combination of two such genes occurred. (See the following discussion of recombination.) Because there is a good chance that any given human
gamete may carry a harmful recessive mutation, laws forbidding the marriage of
two persons who are closely related are genetically sound. Such a marriage would
provide a better opportunity for two recessives originating in a common ancestor
to come together in the homozygous condition.

formation of chiasmata between chromatids of homologous chromosomes may result in a new combination of genes for each chromatid involved. (3) Also during meiosis, chromosome "sets" may become changed in number, or individual chromosomes may undergo changes.

These methods of recombination seem oriented toward diploid organisms, which raises an interesting point. You are aware, of course, that the vast majority of species *are* characterized by diploidy, and you will probably have no difficulty in seeing how recombination operates when chromosomes exist in pairs. Actually, haploid organisms that reproduce sexually at least some of the time (this characteristic includes most haploids) may also experience changed genotypes through recombination, because new combinations of chromosomes may be incorporated into new individuals (somewhat like shuffling cards in a new deal) or because chiasma formation may be responsible for new combinations with a given chromosome. Nevertheless, evolution has definitely "favored" the diploid condition (Fig. 7-2). Perhaps you can understand why after you have reflected a little on the circumstances.

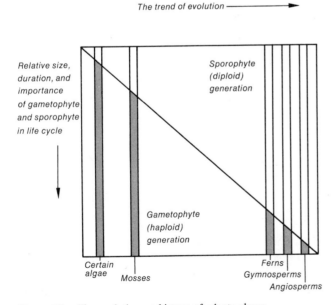

Figure 7.2. The evolutionary history of plants shows particularly clearly how the emphasis has shifted in the life cycle from gametophyte to sporophyte (haploid to diploid). This, among other lines of evidence, suggests that diploid organisms or phases of life cycles have certain evolutionary advantages over haploid organisms or phases of life cycles.

You will recall our statement that most mutations are harmful to the organism and that most mutations are apparently recessive. In a diploid organism, any new mutant gene involved in recombination is "covered" by its dominant allele on the homologous chromosome. Consequently, several generations of inbreeding might be required before recombination produced a homozygous genotype for any particular recessive mutant. For this reason, diploid organisms have built-in protection against harmful mutations. They may even carry numerous genes that would reduce their vitality or even kill them if they were expressed in the homozygous condition. As a matter of fact, it has been estimated that most complex organisms, which carry perhaps 10,000 genes or more in their total genotype, probably have a number of such potentially harmful genes. Haploid organisms obviously have no such advantage. To draw an analogy, any mutant haploid organisms are obliged to pay cash for their "mistakes" (mutations), whereas diploid organisms are able to pay on the installment plan.

Apparently it is not by accident that the majority of organisms in nature are diploid, since the diploid condition gives an organism quite an advantage in absorbing potentially harmful mutant genes. You may wonder, therefore, why haploid organisms have not disappeared completely. There is a possible explanation, but it would take us beyond the scope of this book. Suffice it to say that diploidy is characteristic of most species at the present time, and it is within diploid genetic systems that recombination works most effectively as an evolutionary factor.

The third type of recombination, changes in chromosomes, is a very important secondary source of genetic variability. We observed in Chapter 6 that the number and individual form of chromosomes in body cells is the same for all members of a given species. Called the *chromosome number law* when formulated around the turn of the century, this principle appeared at first to be an argument against the very occurrence of evolution. However, subsequent investigation revealed that violations of this law are not infrequent in nature; indeed, that they constitute a very important source of genetic variability.

Chromosomes may lose entire pieces of chromatin, and any gametes carrying such a deficient chromosome may exert profound and far-reaching effects upon the species involved. Moreover, chromosomes sometimes pick up extra pieces of chromatin lost by other chromosomes, with similar potentially far-reaching effects. Still another type of chromosomal change occurs when a portion of the chromosome becomes inverted or switched from its original position. Sometimes, nonhomologous chromosomes become entangled and exchange pieces of chromatin. All of these chromosomal changes cause rearrangements in genic materials, with the result that variability is produced. Detailed studies of chromosomal morphology in a variety of organisms indicate that such chromosomal changes as we have listed are very much involved as a source of genetic variability in evolution.

In addition to those changes affecting individual chromosomes, there may be variations in the chromosome *number* of individuals within a species. Again, this change is initiated when a chromosome is lost or gained during a divisional process. If a gamete that receives an abnormal set of chromosomes becomes involved in fertilization, the event may have evolutionary significance. However, changes in number of chromosomes are apparently not so important in evolution as the changes in form.

NATURAL SELECTION

Given all these sources of variability, we must see how they concern organisms and species as they actually exist in nature. We mentioned earlier that two factors—natural selection and reproductive isolation—influence the adaptations of organisms, and we shall attempt to clarify these processes.

Darwin conceived of natural selection as an essentially negative force in evolution, serving to eliminate those organisms and species that could not compete successfully with other organisms and species. It would be unfair to imply that Darwin's outlook was entirely negative. As he saw natural selection, it allowed superior organisms and species to succeed when those that were less fit perished. Furthermore, it would be grossly unfair to imply that since Darwin could not explain heredity, he could not be trusted to explain anything else. This attitude was prevalent among the early adherents of the mutation theory, and a trace of it remains in biology even today. That Darwin was a genius should be clear to anyone who has read the *Origin of Species,* and his theory of natural selection was the first attempt to explain evolution that really made sense. It still makes a great deal of sense, and subsequent developments have generally served to clarify and expand Darwin's theory, not invalidate it. As a consequence, we mean the same thing today that Darwin meant when he used the term "natural selection," but we mean some additional things as well.

Perhaps the most direct way to define natural selection in the modern sense is to say that it is *differential reproduction of genetic types.* In other words, organisms with inferior traits leave, on the average, fewer offspring than do those with superior traits. "Inferior" and "superior" are defined by the environment. By its very nature, natural selection does not initiate these traits; initiation is the role of mutation and recombination. Furthermore, environment plays only a limiting role in natural selection—and it is here that the modern definition differs most from the Darwinian definition. It plays no part in producing variations, but it serves as the ultimate test for the "fitness" of variations. Those organisms that survive reproduce, and their genes are passed on to their offspring. Those organisms that perish do not reproduce at all, or else they produce fewer offspring. Adaptations are established in a population, therefore, whenever they bestow some advantage upon their possessors against which less fortunate organisms are unable to compete, *within the stated environment.*

As it actually occurs, natural selection is a very complex affair, and it requires special techniques and statistical tools for its analysis. Those studies that have substantiated natural selection as a process in evolution are exceedingly intricate, and we shall not attempt to review them at this point. However, in a later section, we shall look at some examples of evolution in which natural selection has played an obvious part. Perhaps its role will be somewhat clearer when it is viewed in relation to other factors.

REPRODUCTIVE ISOLATION

Every student of nature is well aware that species are not distinct and readily identifiable entities. Complex interactions of organisms, including the tendency of animals to move about, result in a heterogeneous mixture of individuals belonging to a variety of species. There are very few environments where only one species is found.

A close analysis of any given species reveals that it is usually composed of different *races*—that is, types differing from each other in various ways but still interbreeding rather freely with the production of fertile offspring. For example, close to a hundred different races of the grizzly bear, *Ursus horribilis,* are presently recognized, and each race generally occupies a different geographical area. Theoretically, whenever two races become geographically isolated to the extent that they interbreed only within an overlapping area, they are called *subspecies.* In turn, if a subspecies becomes absolutely isolated from other subspecies in a reproductive sense, it is called a *species.* In practice, it is very difficult to recognize whether or not a population of organisms constitutes a race, a subspecies, or a species. Nevertheless, these distinctions are quite valid, and we can discuss the problem of species formation within the framework of the definitions given.

On the basis of much valid research, it appears that new species originate by small steps whenever isolated populations become races, whenever the races become subspecies, and whenever the subspecies become species (Fig. 7-3). By using the expression "isolated," we are speaking in terms of any condition wherein any two groups within a species are prevented from interbreeding.

In geographic isolation, populations may be separated by water or land barriers and thus go their separate evolutionary ways. Mutation and recombination occur differently in each group; and natural selection acts,

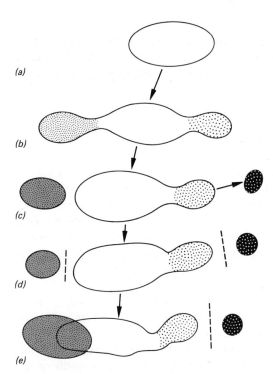

(a)

(b)

(c)

(d)

(e)

Figure 7.3. Diagram showing the sequence of events leading to the production of different races, subspecies, and species, starting with a homogeneous, genetically similar group of populations. (a) A single population in a homogeneous environment. (b) Environmental differentiation and migration to new environments produce racial differentiation of races and subspecies (indicated by different shadings). (c) Further differentiation and migration produce geographic isolation of some races and subspecies. (d) Some isolated subspecies differentiate with respect to genic and chromosomal changes controlling reproductive isolating mechanisms. (e) Environmental changes permit once-isolated populations to exist in the same region, now remaining distinct because of the reproductive isolating barriers that separate them; they can be recognized as good species. [From G.L. Stebbins, *Processes of Organic Evolution* (Englewood Cliffs, N.J.: Prentice-Hall, Inc., 1966).]

in each case, on whatever is produced through variability. If the environments are similar, there may be no actual reproductive isolation, even though the populations are separated for long periods of time (millions of years, apparently, in some cases). Frequently, however, chance mutations and recombinations acted upon by natural selection create differences of such magnitude that the populations will not interbreed if they are brought back together.

Organisms may be genetically isolated through variability within a population. For example, many animals exhibit highly intricate courtship patterns that depend upon precise stimulus-response mechanisms; even a single mutation may alter this pattern sufficiently in a given organism that it will be less likely to participate in reproduction. In many cases, this event would simply mean that natural selection "discriminates" against this set of genes to the extent that it soon disappears. It is possible, however, for such a mutant gene to become fixed in the population sufficiently that it gives rise to a new race. Different modes of sexual reproduction and different expressions of the environment make possible the existence of a great variety of such isolating mechanisms.

It should be noted that reproductive isolation resulting in the rise of a race (incipient genetic isolation), then a subspecies (partial genetic isolation), and then a species (complete genetic isolation) may take a tremendously long time. It has been estimated that, on the average, establishment of a new species in nature by this route takes something like a million years. It is small wonder that many people fail to grasp or to appreciate the process of evolution.[5]

7.1C Evolution in Action

At this point, it would be logical to present a thorough case history of evolution in order to show just how mutation, recombination, natural selection, and reproductive isolation work together. However, such a procedure is impossible. Excellent examples of each factor can be cited, and we have presented a few of these, but we cannot show conclusively that the evolution of any specific group of organisms has come about as a result of the interaction of these factors. Our evidence is only circumstantial—strongly so, but circumstantial, nevertheless.

Let us take a different approach to the problem. In science, as in all areas of human endeavor where alternative conceptual schemes are available for consideration, the proper question to ask is, "How well does the evidence support the favored conceptual scheme, both in explanation and in predictability, as compared with its alternatives?" In other words, given the conceptual scheme of organic evolution, how well does it work deductively as compared with any conceivable alternate explanation? Darwin himself recognized the logic of this approach:

> From looking at species as only strongly-marked and well-defined varieties,* I was led to anticipate that the species of the larger genera in each country would oftener present varieties, than the species of the smaller genera; for wherever many closely related species (i.e., species of the same genus) have been formed, many varieties or incipient species ought, as a general rule, to be now forming. Where many large trees grow, we expect to find saplings. Where many species of a genus have been formed through variation, circumstances have been favourable for variation; and hence we might expect that the circumstances would generally be still favourable to variation. *On the other hand, if we look at each species as a special act of creation, there is no apparent reason why more varieties should occur in a group having many species, than in one having few.*†

---

* Darwin's term "variety" may be considered an equivalent to our term "race" or possibly even "subspecies."

† Italics added.

Note the comparison of alternatives. Now Darwin proceeds with the deductive, or "if . . . then," reasoning in testing this evolutionary sub-hypothesis:

> To test the truth of this anticipation I have arranged the plants of twelve countries, and the coleopterous insects of two districts, into two nearly equal masses, the species of the larger genera on one side, and those of the smaller genera on the other side, and it has invariably proved to be the case that a larger proportion of the species on the side of the larger genera presented varieties, than on the side of the smaller genera. Moreover, the species of the larger genera which present any varieties, invariably present a larger average number of varieties than do the species of the small genera. . . . All that we want to show is, that, when many species of a genus have been formed, on an average many are still forming; and this certainly holds good.[6]

Actually, it was this very line of reasoning that had led biologists and geologists of the 18th and 19th centuries to evolution. For example, Darwin had observed on the Galápagos islands, where he spent some time while on his long voyage, that each of the several islands had its own distinct finch species. What possible sense did this phenomenon make, he reasoned, according to a concept of special creation? In like manner, geologists had puzzled over the evident succession of fossil organisms in rock strata; and anatomists had wondered about vestigial structures in animals, both embryonic and adult.* In every case, it became obvious that creationism was a scientific dead end. In the same manner, new evidence, such as similarities and dissimilarities in body proteins, the radioactive dating of fossils, comparisons of number and shape of chromosomes, is subject to rational interpretation only if viewed in the light of the conceptual scheme of organic evolution. Hence, as we said earlier, evidence found since Darwin's time has only strengthened his case. If the circumstantial evidence was overwhelming in his day, it is little short of conclusive in our own.

Since the ultimate test of a scientific conceptual scheme is how well it functions in producing workable and testable theories, let us review one instance of the applicability of the conceptual scheme of organic evolution.

Beginning shortly after 1900, a tremendous amount of genetic research was accomplished using the fruit fly, *Drosophila melanogaster* (Fig.

---

* For example, all vertebrate animals develop pouches in the region of the pharynx at an early stage of embryogeny. In the fishes and amphibians, these pouches perforate in the formation of gills; but, in the land vertebrates (reptiles, birds, and mammals), they only *start* to do so and then become modified into structures other than gill openings.

7-4). As a result, more was probably known by the 1930's about the genetics of this organism than about that of any other. In the meanwhile,

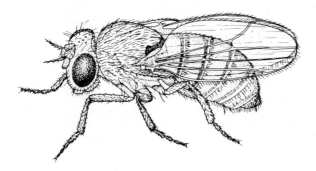

Figure 7.4. *Drosophila melanogaster* (female), the fruit fly, greatly enlarged. This insect has been utilized widely in the study of genetics and evolution.

statistical methods were developed whereby the evolution of populations could be studied meaningfully. Attention was soon focused on the entire genus *Drosophila,* whose species number in the hundreds. At the beginning of these studies, the line of reasoning went something like this: If evolution has produced these several species from a common ancestral stock, then we should be able to go into the field, survey the geographical areas inhabited by each species, find subspecies and races, observe where their geographical areas overlap, do chromosomal studies and find evidences for genetic kinship, and, finally, be enabled to describe an overall pattern of evolution in this genus.

As a result of the studies that have been carried out within the framework of this broad hypothesis, the evolution of the genus *Drosophila* is now well understood. Although not every problem concerning evolution was solved, the point remains: Investigators did find the patterns they anticipated, which means that the basic conceptual scheme is a fruitful one. The data make no sense on any other basis and, indeed, would never have been sought without it.

Let us consider still another case. Darwin called attention in the *Origin of Species* to the large number of wingless insects on the island of Madeira, where strong winds sweep over the terrain almost constantly. He reasoned that natural selection has favored the wingless condition here, since the presence of wings would put an insect at some disadvantage— upon rising in the air, the insect would quite probably be blown out to sea.

Thus, natural selection had created a kind of "either-or" situation: Insects either had very strong wings or no wings at all.[7]

Within recent years, it occurred to a group of investigators to test Darwin's hypothesis under special conditions. They reared large numbers of normal *Drosophila,* whose wings are rather delicate, and they also reared large numbers of flies that had been rendered wingless by a single recessive mutant gene in the homozygous condition. They released equal numbers of both strains of flies on Madeira and made periodic collections. Within a very short time, only wingless flies remained. Just as Darwin would have predicted through his assumption, natural selection had "discriminated" against the winged forms. A comparable experiment performed as a control in a relatively windless environment produced the very opposite result: Wingless forms were unable to compete with their winged relatives and disappeared from the population.[8]

Examples of this kind of experimentation are legion, and even though some puzzling and apparently inexplicable cases remain, the total implication is clear. Organic evolution is a reality in nature, and the synthetic theory is admirably vindicated as a satisfactory explanation of its mechanisms.

7.2 ORGANIC EVOLUTION: A CRITIQUE

Beginning about 1940, biology took on something of a new complexion. Some of the reasons for this change are now obvious: the coming of age of biochemistry and biophysics, the advances just prior to this time in genetic and evolutionary thought, the introduction into biological research of radioisotopic "tracer" techniques, the invention of the electron microscope. These and other developments changed the outlook in biology profoundly. For the first time, it became possible to study living phenomena in terms of their macromolecules, and there was a significant shift of emphasis toward this level of organization. This particular approach to the study of living systems has been termed *molecular biology.*

If the viewpoints of molecular biology had been available to students of evolution before the gross evidences (for example, those from comparative morphology, geographic distribution and paleontology), biologists might have begun studying evolution in terms of mutation and cytogenetics. Even now, it is logical to ask: How do modern cellular and molecular insights fit into the conceptual scheme of evolution—do these insights strengthen the concept, or do they weaken it? The answer to this question is unequivocal: Molecular biology has strengthened the concept immeasurably.

The identification in the early 1950's of DNA as the fundamental genetic material of living systems and the subsequent studies of mutation in terms of DNA alteration have provided very important explanations of evolutionary mechanisms. Thus, such studies as that involving sickle-cell anemia (described in the preceding chapter), are very important to the overall consideration of evolution as a process. They indicate that genes operate through physiological channels and that evolution is explicable in naturalistic terms at every level.

We can visualize, therefore, how the accumulation of many adaptive mutational changes might eventually result in speciation among all groups of organisms. Granted, long periods of time are required; therefore, we cannot expect to demonstrate the transformation of one species into another. But it now appears that this accumulation is the chief mode of the evolutionary process. *External* variation (expressed in diverse phenotypes) is a result of *internal* variation (alteration of DNA by some molecular process). The evolutionary significance of any such variation, or mutation, is a function of recombination and natural selection within a given environment.

But, it may be asked (and often is), has evolution been *proved?* Again, at the risk of being overly repetitive, let us emphasize a cardinal principle of scientific endeavor: **Great conceptual schemes are not subject to final proof.** Their validity depends upon how well the evidence converges around them in comparison with their alternatives. From the standpoint of history, it seems fair to say that as a process over time, evolution is as well substantiated as any process or event could be that is not subject to direct human observation. More important, however, it is a conceptual scheme that continues to be exceedingly fruitful in the generation of theories that can be tested. So very many of these theories have proved to be reliable in explanation and predictability that there can be no serious question of the validity of organic evolution as a conceptual scheme.

What of the modern synthetic theory? Is it the ultimate explanation of the processes of evolution? If the history of scientific theories is any guide, we can predict that it is not the ultimate. At the present time, it seems inconceivable that any of its major factors—mutation, recombination, natural selection, and reproductive isolation—would ever be shown to be inoperative, but there may be other factors that are as yet undiscovered. Many biologists feel that the synthetic theory is a bit too glib and that it fails to account for the existence of a great many adaptations in a variety of organisms. Future research may even reveal the operation of Lamarckian factors in evolution; at this point, it would be dogmatic to rule them out entirely. Evolutionary theory, and especially the modern synthesis, developed during a period when there was widespread suspicion of teleological thinking in biology. There is a present tendency to reopen the entire question of purposiveness, which could have some very interesting implications for evolutionary theory. In the spirit of scientific open-mindedness, we shall simply have to wait and see.

QUESTIONS FOR REVIEW AND DISCUSSION

1. Summarize the historical developments that culminated in an atmosphere that was receptive to a general theory of evolution.
2. Summarize the viewpoints of Buffon, Erasmus Darwin, and Lamarck regarding evolution. Why did these men have limited influence as compared with Charles Darwin?
3. Is the term "Darwinism" synonymous with the term "evolution"? Explain.
4. What two concepts did Darwin attempt to validate in the *Origin of Species?* Summarize his argument on the *process* of evolution.
5. How do you account for the fact that Darwin received acclaim during his lifetime, whereas Mendel was completely ignored?
6. Outline and define the major features of the synthetic theory of evolution.
7. If most mutations are harmful, how can it be held that mutation provides the raw material for evolution?
8. Why do we say that evolution has "favored" the diploid condition?
9. How does the modern definition of natural selection differ from the Darwinian definition?
10. Distinguish between the terms "race," "subspecies," and "species." Why is it difficult to make a clear distinction in nature among these taxa?
11. An account is given in this chapter of an experiment involving winged and wingless fruit flies. What was the point of this experiment?
12. In what ways has modern molecular biology influenced evolutionary thought?

REFERENCES

Darwin, C. R. *On the Origin of Species by Means of Natural Selection, Or the Preservation of Favoured Races in the Struggle for Life* (6th ed.). New York: The New American Library of World Literature, Inc. (Mentor), 1958. The great classic on evolution, the first edition of which was published in 1859.

Eiseley, L. *Darwin's Century.* Garden City, N. Y.: Doubleday and Company, Inc., 1958. An excellent account of the development of evolution as a conceptual scheme.

Huxley, J. S. *Evolution: The Modern Synthesis.* New York: Harper and Row, Publishers, 1943. A classic in evolutionary thought.

Ross, H. H. *Understanding Evolution.* Englewood Cliffs, N.J.: Prentice-Hall, Inc., 1965. This book surveys the field of evolution from the formation of stars to the development of complex organisms.

Simpson, G. G. *The Meaning of Evolution. New Haven:* Yale University Press, 1949. This outstanding book, although several years old, is still one of the best sources for achieving an understanding of evolution.

Stebbins, G. L. *Processes of Organic Evolution* (2nd ed.). Englewood Cliffs, N.J.: Prentice-Hall, Inc., 1971. Although brief, this work by a distinguished evolutionist is an excellent study of evolution as a process.

Wallace, B., and A. M. Srb. *Adaptation* (2nd ed.). Englewood Cliffs, N.J.: Prentice-Hall, Inc., 1964. This book is recommended in its entirety for this chapter.

3

THE FALL OUT

All problems of [human] life ultimately are biological
ones, and the facts with which the student of organisms
deals should be explored not for themselves alone
but for the suggestions they may offer for the
more complex phenomena of life.

—EDMUND W. SINNOTT

Introduction

The explosion of a thermonuclear device such as a hydrogen bomb sets in motion a chain of events that extends far beyond the initial blast. For months and even years, radioactive elements and compounds hover in the atmosphere and accumulate on the surface of the earth, where they may find their way into the tissues of living organisms. This secondary process is called a *fallout,* because it constitutes a veritable rain of radioactive materials. In its overall effects, the fallout of a thermonuclear explosion may prove to be far more important to man's welfare than the blast itself.

In a completely metaphorical sense, something similar happens in the realm of ideas. A conceptual scheme may exert a profound influence upon the scientific community and mankind in general at the time it is set forth, but if the scheme is far-reaching in its implications, the initial impact is minor in comparison with its long-range effects. To a certain extent, we have seen the fallout from those conceptual schemes that we have examined closely: biogenesis, the cell theory, Mendelian genetics, and organic evolution.

In general, however, we have dealt with the implications of our conceptual schemes for biology itself. What about the impact of these ideas on other areas of human activity than biology? What are some of the logical implications for other fields, and for biology itself, in cases where the fallout has hardly even begun? How does biological science impinge upon man's practical affairs? His social needs? His spiritual well-being? These are urgent questions; and their answers are important, even critical, to man's very survival as a species.

This section, therefore, constitutes the "practical" aspect of our subject. True, we shall introduce certain principles and pursue a number of theoretical problems, but these principles and problems are mainly extensions of the four conceptual schemes discussed in Part II.

EIGHT

The Human Scene

Of the several far-reaching implications that attended Charles Darwin's evolutionary scheme, none is more profound than the concept that man is a part of nature. Man's relationship to the rest of the living world had been realized by an individual here and there, and perhaps dimly by mankind in general, but it took a bold statement of evolutionary principle to bring the issue into focus. *Man is an animal,* said Darwin, *and however unique his position in the world of life, he is a part of that world.* Innocuous as this notion may sound today, it shook Western civilization of the mid-19th century to its very roots. Before Darwin, there had been a strong tendency to regard *Homo sapiens* as a species far removed from the rest of his world. *But all life is one,* Darwin argued, *and we might as well make the best of it.*

Unfortunately, man has not always made the best of his situation, even with the advantages bestowed upon him by Darwin's insights. He has destroyed his forests, exhausted his land, polluted his waters, and filled his atmosphere with poisons that neither he nor his fellow organisms can tolerate indefinitely. He has invented insecticides and herbicides so powerful and so indestructible that their widespread use poses a threat to all of nature. He overpopulates his world to the extent that he invites mass claustrophobia and then proceeds to expose the human gene pool to the hazards of radiation by experimenting with more powerful weapons wherewith to destroy himself. All of this is done in the name of progress and civilization—these catchwords seem to justify almost any action whatsoever.

Of course, man has improved his living conditions, reduced the occurrence of disease, and increased his control over the environment, all of which are to the good. Biological advances have had a great effect upon man and his world, and many of these advances have greatly improved our cultural standards. But it may be that man, the crowning glory of 3 billion years of organic evolution and the product of a million years of cultural evolution, is on the verge of outsmarting himself. Without doubt, he is in a technological predicament of his own making. Furthermore, the situation is not getting better; instead, it is rapidly getting worse.

To really understand just how serious man's predicament is coming to be, it is necessary to turn one's eyes away from the superficial prosperity of our age (at least in places where it exists) and learn some basic principles of organismic relationships. This particular biological viewpoint, called *ecology,* is absolutely essential to an understanding of the present situation between man and nature. Perhaps it is safe to say that it is only through the rigorous application of sound ecological principles that mankind will be able to avoid disaster. Ecology, therefore, will be our starting point in examining the human scene.

8.1 SOME BASIC PRINCIPLES OF ECOLOGY

All of nature is a complex, interwoven pattern of relationships. Each organism affects and is affected by every natural factor in its environment, including other organisms. Any change in a given environment, no matter how small, causes a chain of reactions that produce reverberations throughout that environment. Such a chain of events may be relatively insignificant and short-lived in its overall effects, as in the case of a rain shower or a dust storm; or it may result in profound changes throughout a given environment, as might be the case if a new animal or plant species suddenly invaded the area. The point we wish to make is that, in some way or ways, every organism is interrelated to everything in its environment. It is the consideration of these relationships that we call ecology.

Perhaps the simplest way to approach the study of ecology is by selecting an *ecosystem*—that is, a limited environmental area such as a pond, a small desert, or the upper reaches of a mountain (Fig. 8-1). By

Figure 8.1. Comparison of the gross structure of a terrestrial ecosystem (a grassland) and an open-water ecosystem (either freshwater or marine). Necessary units for function are the following: (I) abiotic substances (basic inorganic and organic compounds); (II) producers (vegetation on land, phytoplankton in water); (III) macro-consumers or animals: (A) direct or grazing herbivores (grasshoppers, meadow mice, etc., on land, zooplankton, etc., in water), (B) indirect or detritus-feeding consumers or saprovores (soil invertebrates on land, bottom invertebrates in water), (C) the "top" carnivores (hawks and large fish); (IV) decomposers, bacteria and fungi of decay. [Adapted by permission from E. P. Odum, *Ecology* (New York: Holt, Rinehart & Winston, Inc., 1963).]

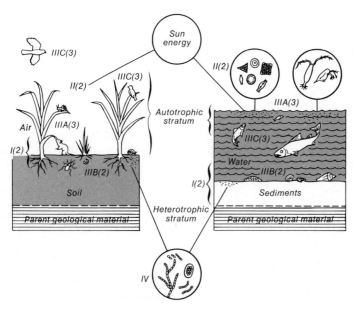

definition, the ecosystem is the fundamental unit of consideration to the ecologist, because it is within such a situation that he can attack problems of relationship most simply and directly. For our purposes, let us consider (theoretically, to be sure) a delimited portion of nature from the ecological viewpoint.

8.1A A Freshwater Pond as an Ecosystem

Imagine a well-isolated pond of some 12 acres in surface area located in the Midwestern United States. You approach this pond in mid-June armed with a boat, field glasses, a variety of seining nets, sampling equipment, bottles, and a compound microscope. We assume that your background training enables you to identify the birds, fishes, arthropods, flowering plants, algae, and protozoa that you encounter in your observations. You make a list of such organisms according to species and more general groupings. Furthermore, you collect samples both of pond water and of mud from the bottom of the pond, which you analyze later for chemical content and for the presence of both living and dead (or decaying) organisms, including such microorganisms as bacteria. After you have completed your total analysis, you might group your findings in the following manner:

ABIOTIC COMPONENTS

These substances are the nonliving materials present in the ecosystem. They include the several chemical elements and compounds found in the mud, in the atmosphere above the pond, in the water, and include, indeed, the water itself. Strictly speaking, sunlight and temperature must also be considered abiotic components, because they figure prominently in the total picture of life as it occurs in this pond.

Although it would be too much to expect that a single investigator could demonstrate their total involvement, abiotic components of an ecosystem serve the requirements of the numerous organisms that are present. In this case, the photosynthetic plants (including both rooted flowering plants and algae) utilize carbon dioxide from the atmosphere and water from the pond in photosynthesis. They also take up inorganic, or "mineral," substances from the water and the soil. These substances are then incorporated into their organic syntheses. Sunlight, of course, is essential to the photosynthetic process. Both animals and plants are dependent upon oxygen from the atmosphere to serve their respiratory needs. Obviously, an account of abiotic involvement in the ecology of this pond could go on and on, but it should be evident that such factors as we have described are essential to the several living forms occupying this particular ecosystem.

PRODUCERS

In essence, all the energy available to our planet originates in the sun and is transferred through space as the radiant energy of sunlight. Green plants on earth apprehend and "capture" only a small fraction of 1 per cent of this available energy, but this amount is sufficient to drive every reaction in every living system on earth. Those organisms in which energy-rich compounds are synthesized and in which this kinetic radiant energy is transformed to potential chemical energy are termed *producers*. In other words, they are those organisms that possess chlorophyll.

The most important of the producers in a freshwater pond are the photosynthetic algae, although rooted flowering plants at the shallow margins of the pond may play a significant role also. If we consider the pond as a whole, it is only in cells of producer organisms that total energy content increases; and it is this energy that ultimately sustains all life in the ecosystem.

CONSUMERS

This group of organisms includes all the animal life that may be associated with the pond in any way. For an energy source, they are dependent either directly or indirectly upon the producers. For example, a variety of microcrustaceans (arthropods) and small fish consume algae, thus increasing their own total body mass or the numerical strength of their population,* with a corresponding increase in total energy content. Those animals that subsist directly upon producers are called *primary consumers*. Animals that eat primary consumers are called *secondary consumers;* these in turn become prey for *tertiary consumers;* and so on.

Even within a small pond, the trophic, or nutrient, interrelations become fantastically complex. Seldom, if ever, does the pattern follow a straight chain arrangement. For example, some fish consume both algae and microcrustaceans, and perhaps frog eggs as well. A large fish might feed on crayfish, frogs, and other fish, all of which conceivably represent a variety of trophic levels. For this reason, it is an oversimplification to speak of a *food chain* except in highly restricted cases. Instead, we think of trophic relationships in terms of a *food web* (Fig. 8-2).

Ultimately, the bodies of those organisms that die in the pond are

---

* Ecologically, a population is a group of individuals belonging to the same species that occupy some definite environmental area—in this case, the pond ecosystem.

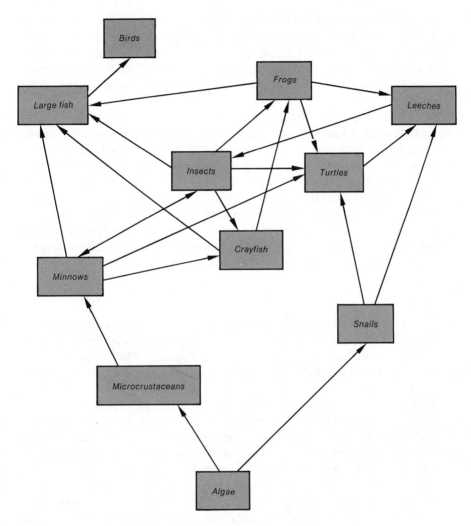

Figure 8.2. A schematic representation of a food web as
it exists in a freshwater pond. It is deliberately simplified
for purposes of presentation; for example, the sources of food
for insects are incomplete since they involve the aerial
and terrestrial environments. Notice that food chains (for
example, from algae to birds) may exist as a part of a
food web.

DECOMPOSERS

decomposed into micromolecular units that are useful to the producers.
Wastes expelled from the bodies of consumer organisms are also decom-

posed. This process of breakdown is accomplished by *fungi,* chief among which are the bacteria. Thus, just as the producers are all photosynthetic plants and the consumers are all animals, so are the decomposers all fungi.*
These plants are heterotrophic organisms; that is, they receive their organic, energy-rich molecules from a source outside their own bodies and in micromolecular form.

The chemical activities of decomposers are many and varied; but essentially, they move enzymes across their cell membranes into the general environment and then absorb many of the resultant products into their bodies. By this means, their own populations are built up and maintained. Eventually, they become subject to decomposition themselves. In the final analysis, the end products of decomposition are capable of supporting only autotrophic growth in the ecosystem. In other words, biotic factors are decomposed to abiotic components. For the most part, this process involves the decomposition of organic macromolecules to their micromolecular components, which are, themselves, oxidized to inorganic substances.

THE CARBON CYCLE

In summarizing the respective roles of these groups of organisms, let us single out for consideration the cycle undergone by a single element, carbon, as it is involved in our pond-ecosystem. This cycle is shown schematically in Fig. 8-3. Note that the *matter* under consideration, carbon, is theoretically cyclic but that the *energy* driving the carbon cycle is not. It enters the total process as radiant energy; after many transformations as chemical energy, much of it eventually leaves the system as heat. Thus, the second law of thermodynamics is operative within the ecosystem. In considering the carbon of the system, one should understand that it may or may not stay in the ecosystem. For example, any given carbon atom may appear in a molecule of carbon dioxide and be carried away from the pond by the wind; or a bird might consume a carbon-containing molecule and then migrate and eventually die in a geographical area far removed from the pond. Hence, we only say that matter is *theoretically* cyclic in an ecosystem.

Let us carry our consideration of these events one step further. Imagine that we could mark a particular carbon atom in some fashion whereby we might be able to keep up with it at all times. Imagine also that

---

* For purposes of simplification, we are regarding all organisms as either plants or animals, in the classical sense. Within this framework, the fungi are those plants that do not possess chlorophyll. Actually, some animals are decomposers also, inasmuch as they feed upon decaying organic matter. Thus, in a forest ecosystem, some beetles feed upon dead wood; and, in a pond, a variety of animal life subsists primarily upon dead plant and animal materials.

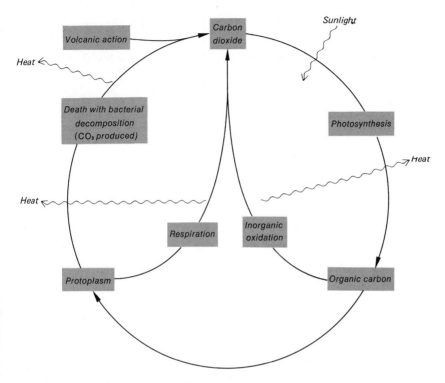

Figure 8.3. A schematic representation of the carbon cycle in nature. Notice that the *matter* involved is cyclic, but the *energy* involved is a one-way process.

it stays in the ecosystem for as long a time as we care to trace its various adventures.

To begin with, suppose our carbon atom is situated in a molecule of carbon dioxide that is located in the atmosphere over the pond. By a quirk of fate, this molecule becomes caught in a downdraft and is immersed in the water. After undergoing two or three processes of chemical reactivity with water molecules, it diffuses through the cell wall and cell membrane of a green algal cell. It is taken up quickly by the machinery of a chloroplast, spun about in the several chemical reactions of photosynthesis, and incorporated into a molecule of glucose. This molecule is combined with several other glucose molecules to form a long chain of starch, which is stored within the cell.

Although many algal cells in the area are consumed by small water animals, this particular one happens to belong to a species that is eaten only when these animals can locate no other food. As a consequence, our carbon atom remains inside its starchy prison throughout a great part of the summer. However, a heat wave during August raises the water temperature past the point of tolerance for this algal species, and the organism dies. It is only a matter of hours until the cell wall has decomposed sufficiently that bacteria start to work on the cell membrane; indeed, enzymes located within the cell have already started to decompose it from the inside out. The cellular starch consists of tiny granules, each containing thousands of starch molecules; and these granules pour out of the cell through a gaping hole in the wall.

Ordinarily, starch granules of this type might retain their composite structure for some time. Eventually, however, mechanical stresses within the water tend to separate the component molecules from each other. This process renders each molecule susceptible to the action of starch-digesting enzymes produced by bacteria that are literally everywhere in the pond. However, the particular starch granule occupied by our carbon atom is swept up by a tiny protozoan, *Paramecium,* and is taken into the cell (it has only one—in protozoa, the cell *is* the organism). Enzymes produced inside the cell quickly chop the starch molecules into single, micromolecular units of glucose, most of which are "shattered" by glycolysis and the Krebs cycle. The energy thus realized is then used to drive the paramecium's locomotor structures, the cilia, and to serve its cellular machinery in a thousand other ways. But the particular glucose molecule within which our carbon atom is situated undergoes no such fate; rather, it is rearranged by a series of enzymatic reactions and is converted to a fatty material that is stored within the cell.

One day, during a period of rapid wave action at the surface of the pond, the paramecium is carried to the very bottom. Quite by chance, it is swept into the digestive system of a clam, or mussel, and is strained out along with other items. The clam wastes no time in digesting everything it has taken in. However, the clam does not digest fatty materials quite as readily as carbohydrates; instead, with only a few chemical modifications, it stores the molecule within its own tissues. Our carbon atom stays inside the clam until that animal dies.

It does not take long for a clam's soft body to become exposed, once the strong shell muscles relax. At this point, a large crayfish moves in and consumes the better part of the dead clam. It is within this crayfish that the digestive processes begin once more on the fatty tissues of which our carbon atom is a part. But, as luck would have it, a large bass spies the crayfish and gulps it down only minutes after it has eaten the clam, and the digestive processes of the crayfish are halted momentarily. They begin again when the enzymes of the bass attack the soft parts of the crayfish, stomach contents and all. The carbon atom soon finds itself employed as one of the many carbon atoms making up the structure of a fatty acid. This molecule is then fed into the metabolic processes of a liver cell, where it is torn apart, atom by atom. Afterwards, our carbon atom is cushioned on either side by an atom of oxygen and is thus expelled, by way of the bloodstream, into the water from the gills of the fish. Hence, it becomes available once more to some producer, or it may escape into the atmosphere and wander about for many years before it is involved again with living systems.

Obviously, this travelogue of a carbon atom could go on and on. It should be equally obvious that our account is greatly simplified. In actual practice, it is highly likely that a given carbon atom might be, sequentially, a part of dozens of organisms within an ecosystem. Nevertheless, this example shows the cyclic nature of matter as it becomes involved in living systems. A similar process could be traced for each of the several chemical elements that play a vital role. The carbon cycle shown in Fig. 8-3 is representative of the manner in which these elements are shuffled back and forth among the organisms and are interchanged, in many cases, with the atmosphere above the pond and the mud constituting its floor.

8.1B Food Chains, Food Webs, and Pyramids of Numbers

Hypothetically, the fundamental trophic relationship in nature is the *food chain*. For example, let us imagine a microcrustacean that subsists exclusively upon algae; a secondary consumer (small fish) whose sole diet is this microcrustacean; a tertiary consumer (large fish) that is restricted in its nutritive habits to this one species of small fish; and a fourth consumer (bird) that eats nothing but this large fish. Obviously, this sequence of organisms constitutes a chain extending from the producers (algae) through the fourth consumers (birds).

It is not without reason that we call such a food chain a hypothetical one, because it does not actually work this way in nature. There are indeed primary consumers that subsist primarily upon algae; even at this level, however, organisms are seldom so discriminating that they do not consume protozoa or other small animals as well. As for the larger consumers, such as fish, no known species is restricted in its diet to a single trophic level. Thus, our concept of a *food web* (Fig. 8-2) is much more realistic than the idea of a *food chain*.

Nevertheless, food chains of sorts do exist, and they can be used to analyze trophic and energetic relationships within ecosystems. At the very least, an ecologist can work with trophic levels in his computations of energy transfers and thus come to some general understanding of nutritive relationships. Because of the complexities involved, good examples based on actual data are hard to come by, but a few precise analyses have been made. For example, ecologist Howard T. Odum studied the productivity of

Silver Springs, in Florida, and measured the yield at different trophic levels.[1] While this study is not strictly analogous to our example of a freshwater pond, there is every reason to believe that the same thing occurs, in principle, within every ecosystem.

Odum's study of Silver Springs involved the measurement of energy losses through respiration, decomposition, and nonutilization; and his statement of results is, of necessity, rather technical. However, for our purposes, his study can be simplified by a single graph illustrating net productivity at the various levels that he analyzed (Fig. 8-4). Note that the yield at each

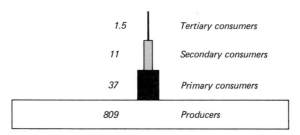

1.5   Tertiary consumers

11   Secondary consumers

37   Primary consumers

809   Producers

Figure 8.4. A pyramid of productivity according to successive trophic levels in a freshwater ecosystem, Silver Springs, Florida, as measured by H. T. Odum. The figures represent grams of dry weight of organism per square meter.

level in actual available energy for the next level diminishes greatly as one ascends the scale. This loss is what we would expect if the second law of thermodynamics is applicable to living systems. Although usually stated differently, one implication of this law is that some energy is lost in every energy transformation. In other words, 100 per cent energy conversion is as impossible in living systems as it is in mechanical systems.

A close examination of Fig. 8-4 reveals a great disparity in efficiency between various trophic levels. This disparity is a reflection of a great many complex factors.* Obviously, it is difficult to generalize on energy losses; nevertheless, one thing is clear: **The longer the chain, the less there is to show for the energy captured by the producers.** This principle is reflected by the ecological expression *pyramid of numbers* (Fig. 8-5), which represents one of the most fruitful conceptual schemes of modern biology.

The implications of these trophic relationships should be obvious.

---

* For example, can you suggest a possible explanation for the vastly different efficiencies between the producer-primary consumer and primary consumer-secondary consumer levels?

Figure 8.5. A graphic illustration of the principle of the
food chain or pyramid of numbers. For purposes of presentation, it is assumed that there is a 10-percent rate of
energy retention at each trophic level (compare with the
data shown in Figure 8.4). At (a) a 10-percent yield from
the producer results in 100 pounds of consumer weight.
The same is true at (b) of the primary consumer, but the
ultimate consumer in this chain realizes only a 0.1-pound,
or a 0.01-percent, yield from the producer.

Man is a consumer—and a complex one, inasmuch as he subsists on organisms that represent every conceivable trophic level. Thus far in his experience, man has been able to afford a degree of carelessness in his dealings
with nature. But the food web-pyramid of numbers principle is rapidly
becoming more than a matter of academic concern to ecologists. As the
numbers of human beings multiply, and as they convert productive areas
into living space, it may well be asked whether our species is not attacking
itself at its very base. However, let us consider some additional important
principles before examining the basic question of the human implications
of ecology.

8.1C The Balance of Nature

The expression "balance of nature" is somewhat ambiguous. It implies
a static condition among species and populations that is not borne out by
close examination. Even a highly restricted ecosystem is in a constant state
of flux; indeed, the history of life as a whole on our planet has been marked
by constant change. In this sense, there has never been a "balance of
nature," and it is highly unlikely that such a state will ever exist. Thus, the
expression should be used only with certain qualifications.

However, within these certain defined restrictions, it is useful to think
in terms of balance. For example, let us suppose that a city grows up on
the banks of a river. At the first, this river is a balanced ecosystem with

producers, various levels of consumers, and decomposers. As the city grows, it constructs sewerage pipes that empty directly into the river. If the stream is relatively large, deep, and fast-flowing, and if the volume of sewage is not great, the bacteria and other decomposers may well be able to handle the extra load of organic materials. In time, the city will probably build complex facilities for decomposing its wastes with the ultimate goal of rendering the sewage materials incapable of supporting heterotrophic growth. However, this goal is seldom realized. At least in the United States, growth of a city usually runs so far ahead of adequate sewage treatment facilities that large quantities of inadequately treated sewage are released into any available stream. It is a rare municipality indeed that does not have a serious water pollution problem (Fig. 8-6).

From the standpoint of balance in the stream, an overload of decomposable organic matter means an increase in the number of heterotrophic microorganisms, because these decomposers build up their populations from the organic materials. At first glance, this factor would seem to be a self-regulating one that would work to the stream's advantage: the more organic matter to be decomposed, the more heterotrophic organisms to accomplish the task. Indeed, within limits, this situation does develop. But there is another side to the picture, namely, the increase in oxygen consumption and carbon dioxide production by these decomposers. With a sizable increase in the metabolic activity of heterotrophic microorganisms, the consumers are deprived of oxygen. Furthermore, the inorganic substances made available through decomposition encourage the growth of algae, which also consume large quantities of oxygen.* In addition, the excessive amounts of carbon dioxide produced in the metabolism of all organisms involved create profound chemical changes in the aqueous environment. The net result is a sharp drop in consumer productivity at all levels. If the situation persists (as it usually does), the river eventually becomes a vast and sterile wasteland.

Needless to say, rivers are only one of the many types of habitat that may become seriously "unbalanced" in an ecological sense. At the present time in the United States, some alarming changes are occurring in all three major types of habitat: aquatic, terrestrial, and aerial. We shall consider a few specific examples in a later section of this chapter.

---

* This situation might seem paradoxical, inasmuch as algae are autotrophic and therefore produce oxygen in photosynthesis. However, the oxygen that they produce during daylight hours is largely lost to the atmosphere; and, at night, they constitute a pure drain upon the oxygen dissolved in the water as they carry on respiration. The result is a considerable net deficit in oxygen due to the algae alone, to say nothing of that required by heterotrophs in the water. Quite frequently, and especially with chemical and thermal changes in the water, large masses of algae thus produced die from oxygen deprivation and pollute the water even further through their decay.

(a)

(b)

Figure 8.6. (a) A sewerage pipe opening into the Arkansas River from a city located on that river. The scum, obvious at the left-hand side of the photograph, is a mixture of oily waste and sludge. Such a scene is common along virtually all major streams in the United States. (Courtesy Arkansas Department of Pollution Control and Ecology.) (b) View of Cadron Creek, one of the many free-flowing streams in Arkansas. Such pollution-free recreational areas are rapidly disappearing from the American scene. (Photograph by Robert T. Kirkwood.)

269

8.1D Ecological Metabolism

As we have noted, elemental substances tend to undergo cyclic changes in nature that frequently attain a high degree of complexity. These changes occur especially whenever a given atom becomes involved in the synthesis of an organic molecule containing perhaps hundreds or even thousands of individual atoms—for example, when a carbon atom is incorporated into a molecule of chlorophyll, of hemoglobin, or of DNA.

Fortunately, and of necessity, such "natural" molecules do not, as a rule, imprison their constituent atoms forever, or indeed for very long. Over the millions of years that living forms have evolved the capacity to synthesize complex molecules, other organisms (especially decomposers) have evolved enzyme systems that degrade such molecules step by step until all of the atoms reappear in the form of inorganic compounds that are usable by producers. A simplified illustration of such a process is shown in Fig. 8-7. Thus, as long as a given atom is kept in ecological circulation, it is subject to change, *no matter how complex the molecule of which it may be a part.* In other words, synthesis and decomposition are a part of nature's self-regulating or "balancing" system, and it is a system that works with ε

Figure 8.7. The synthesis-decomposition cycle of nature, greatly simplified. In the case of most complex organic molecules, a large number of individual steps must be performed in the degradative process. Compare with Fig. 4.16.

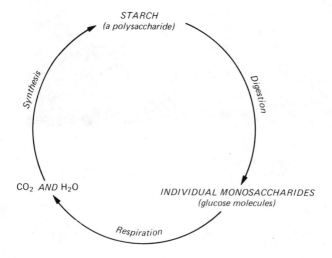

high degree of efficiency. At least, it did so until the mid-19th century, when chemists learned how to synthesize organic compounds.

Like virtually all technological advances made by man, the triumphs of organic chemistry have paid rich and immediate dividends to human welfare. Once having mastered the basic techniques of altering natural compounds in certain specific ways, or of building completely new molecules, chemists have been able to construct thousands of new substances. Most of these substances were merely curiosities, but some have become highly useful as drugs, dyes, insecticides, or industrial reactants. Still others have been developed into highly beneficial tools to further chemical theory and practice. To say the least, the field of organic synthesis has been one of the most active and beneficial areas of scientific endeavor to be exploited by man during the past century.

Nevertheless, the sudden appearance of new organic substances in nature has created ecological problems. Evolution is painfully slow; organisms (whose genetic systems must be altered by chance mutations) simply do not "learn" to cope with new molecules overnight. As a result, most synthetic molecules that find their way into the cellular makeup of an organism are passed over by the metabolic machinery, surrounded by fat molecules and stored, or transferred from cell to cell in a series of metabolic operations. If the organism is fortunate, it may eventually manage to eliminate such molecules into its environment, where they are subject to ingestion by still other organisms.

Because living systems are marvelously adaptable, they usually seem to cope with foreign molecules remarkably well. Furthermore, most synthetic molecules are produced by man in such small quantities that their ultimate disposal is no great problem. At the very least, such deleterious effects as these molecules might produce are hardly noticeable in the world of life taken as a whole. But the known exceptions to this general rule are becoming more numerous. Since man himself ingests quite a number of synthetic molecules (chiefly in the form of medicines and various drugs that he unwittingly takes in with his foodstuffs), he runs an increasing risk of self-contamination.

Let us consider a concrete example, that of the synthetic insecticide DDT (dichloro-diphenyl-trichloro-ethane). The long technical name of this compound gives some indication of its chemical complexity. It was first synthesized in 1874, but its usefulness as an insecticide was not realized until 1939. Because few really effective insecticides had been developed to that point, DDT was employed very widely, and with dramatic results, against almost every form of undesirable insect life.

During the several decades that have passed since its introduction, thousands upon thousands of tons of DDT have been released into man's environment. Its indiscriminate use, especially at first, caused a number of human casualties; and the shotgun approach so frequently employed, again mostly at first, tended to destroy beneficial organisms along with those at which it was primarily aimed. Consequently, ecological chaos was produced in many ecosystems, with the final result often being worse than the first one after the passage of only a brief period of time. Perhaps an actual case history will serve to emphasize this point.

During the 1960's, a concentrated effort was made in East Borneo to wipe out malaria, whose causative agent is carried by mosquitoes. Quantities of DDT were sprayed, with the desired result that mosquito populations dropped to practically zero. However, cockroaches that inhabited houses also picked up a certain amount of the insecticide. Unlike mosquitoes, which are highly susceptible to DDT, the cockroaches were generally able to withstand the dosages to which they were exposed. They were not killed but were merely slowed down. This development enabled the geckos (lizards) that normally inhabit the houses of that region to catch and eat large quantities of cockroaches. As a result, the geckos became the recipients of the DDT, which, in turn, slowed *them* down, enabling the domestic house cats to catch and eat them readily. It so happens that cats are very susceptible to DDT. Before long, hardly a cat existed in the entire region. Consequently, of course, there was a sharp increase in the mouse and rat populations, with the result that bubonic plague, carried by fleas that infest rats, reached epidemic proportions. Nor was this all. At about the same time, the thatched roofs of the houses began to leak because certain insect larvae were consuming the straw. An enterprising ecologist called in by the government discovered that these larvae are normally kept in check by the geckos, which by now had been eaten by the cats, . . . and so went the complicated story.[2]

Unfortunately, such examples are legion, and many convey far more serious consequences than the mere loss of domesticated cats and thatched roofs, or even temporary epidemics of bubonic plague. For one thing, the effects of DDT go on and on, through organism after organism, because— and this point should be kept in mind clearly—*most of the DDT ever synthesized is still present on earth.* It is a nonbiodegradable substance; that is, organisms do not possess enzyme systems capable of decomposing it to its constituent atoms.

When one considers the quadrillions of DDT molecules that are in the earth's atmosphere, the soil, the water, and within the bodies of organisms, the total ecological implications are truly staggering. Let us suppose, for example, that a cereal crop is dusted with DDT in order to protect it from insect predators. The grain is later utilized in the preparation of poultry feed, and a certain amount of DDT becomes incorporated into the eggs thus produced. By this means, man ingests the chemical and becomes subjected to its potentially harmful effects. In the same manner, almost any of man's common foodstuffs—milk, meat, even vegetable substances—are potential and, almost universally, actual carriers of DDT or other synthetic molecules of whose specific biological action within living systems we know but little.

What does DDT do within the human body? We simply do not know. Some of it is excreted, perhaps to begin its cycle through nature once more; and still more is buried in the fat stores of the body. But in its rounds, it comes into contact with body tissues, such as liver, kidney, and brain. Evidence is mounting that the cells of these organs pay a heavy price for having to deal with DDT. It seems a fairly safe guess that medical research will uncover quite a number of specific, deleterious effects of the insecticide in human tissues within the next few years, especially as the average residual load per human increases. It also seems a reasonable conjecture that the most dramatic effects will be seen in embryonic growth, since the finely balanced biochemical reactions that accompany early development are quite vulnerable to metabolic interference. Already, much available evidence shows a direct relationship between DDT accumulation in the eggs of certain birds and the failure of these eggs to hatch. DDT apparently prevents the formation of hard shells. It is virtually certain, therefore, that some species of birds will become extinct within only a few short years because of this single factor.

We have chosen to use DDT as an example because its effects have been studied more widely than those of other complex insecticides. But there are other synthetic substances—dieldrin, chlordane, aldrin, endrin, malathion, to name a few—that are similar to DDT. And these chemicals are only one class of compound. When one considers the number of widely employed medicinal substances (for example, common aspirin) against which pharmacological evidence is mounting rapidly, there is ample cause to wonder whether the field of organic synthesis may not prove to be more of a curse than a blessing in the long run.

8.2 SOME ECOLOGICAL IMPLICATIONS

In the foregoing discussion of ecological principles, we have necessarily touched on some of the environmental problems presently faced by man. However, much more needs to be said, because the "fallout" in this case is so important to human affairs. In fact, it is becoming increasingly apparent that an alteration in the present trends that are developing between man and his environment may well be critical to his survival as a species.

Most professional biologists of the present day find it difficult to avoid attitudes of defeatism and outright panic, because the picture is an alarming one. Fortunately, there are some encouraging signs. At this writing, communication between scientists and industrialists (who are often directly involved with sources of pollution) is increasing and with beneficial results. However, any real hope for improvement in present ecological trends lies in education of the lay public; and hopefully, responsible action will eventually result. Toward this end, let us consider at least briefly the problems that presently appear to be major ones.

8.2A Pollution

In a highly technological society, it is inevitable that quantities of industrial wastes will be discharged into the atmosphere, the water, and the soil. Some of these are alterable, at least in time; others are not. The seriousness of the problem is directly proportional to the size of the population within a given area, to name one factor. It is also related to the nature of a population's industries, the number of automobiles driven, the topography of the community, and so on.

AIR POLLUTION

Thus far, such highly industrialized and mechanized societies as the United States and Great Britain have fared reasonably well, because they have been able to use the world's atmosphere and oceans as waste depositories. However, if all countries possessed the level of technology that has been developed by these two nations, it is doubtful that human beings could live in most of the earth's atmosphere. The present trend is toward more industrialization among the so-called underdeveloped nations, and so the problem of air pollution will probably get much worse before it can be expected to improve.

Just what is air pollution? One of the major substances involved is carbon dioxide from organismic respiration and from the combustion of fuels. We tend to think that there is a "balance" between oxygen and carbon dioxide, but it has been estimated reliably that the carbon dioxide content of the atmosphere has been raised by about 11 per cent within the past century, mostly from the increased combustion of petroleum, natural gas, coal, and wood. This change might appear to be insignificant, but it represents an alarming trend toward a condition in which the rate of carbon dioxide production exceeds the rate of photosynthesis. If this condition ever occurs, with a resulting drop in oxygen content of the atmosphere, it will impose serious limitations upon all life, including man. Furthermore, carbon dioxide in the atmosphere acts as a shield for the earth: It allows *radiant* energy to pass inward but prevents *thermal* energy from passing outward into space. Therefore, an increase in atmospheric carbon dioxide means an inevitable increase in the earth's temperature. The rise in temperature, in turn, has quite a number of serious implications, but consider just one. The President's Science Advisory Committee estimated in 1965 that present trends in increased carbon dioxide production may possibly raise the earth's temperature high enough to melt the polar ice cap, a phenomenon that would raise the sea level by 400 feet. Of course, this change would occur over a period of time, but (the report states) even if 1,000 years were required to melt the cap, the sea level would rise some 4 feet every 10 years. Calculate, if you will, how soon complete inundation would occur in Atlantic City, New Jersey; Galveston, Texas; Norfolk, Virginia; and Seattle, Washington, all of which presently stand at about 10 feet above sea level, on the average.[3]

Of more immediate concern in air pollution are the many poisonous substances that are increasing daily. A few of these are certain noxious substances associated with the combustion of automobile and airplane fuels, as well as those resulting from the use of rubber tires. Analysis of air over all large American cities reveals the presence of tremendous quantities of acids, organic materials, oxides of sulfur, phosphorous and nitrogen, ammonium compounds, aldehydes, and a variety of even more poisonous substances. When such a mixture is exposed to sunlight, the poisonous ingredients of smog are formed. Given certain atmospheric conditions, the results are deadly to human beings, especially those with severe respiratory diseases. There is little doubt that a large number of clinical and subclinical health symptoms can be traced to air pollution. Virtually any physician in any large city will testify to this fact.

WATER POLLUTION

It is also inevitable, in a technological society, that bodies of water eventually suffer the effects of pollution. To illustrate the present deterioration of aquatic areas in the United States, let us consider some concrete examples. The Hudson River in the northeastern United States, once a model of beauty and cleanliness, has deteriorated to the status of a gigantic sewerage line. Some aquatic life remains, but it is inadvisable to eat fish caught from this stream except in a few areas where towns and cities along the banks are some miles apart. In the same general region, Lake Erie has been polluted to such a point that one public official has termed it "the world's largest cesspool." Even the Mississippi River, largest in the United States, has undergone a marked change in biotic characteristics. For example, during the mid-1960's, chemical pesticides that were leached into the river from cotton fields in its valley all but wiped out the catfish populations in the river (catfish are particularly sensitive to such chemicals). Furthermore, the production of shrimp in coastal areas where streams carry pesticides into the ocean waters has been greatly curtailed within recent years, and doubts have been raised about the advisability of allowing the consumption of those shrimp that are harvested in such areas. Unfortunately, such examples as these could be multiplied almost endlessly.

It might seem that the disruption of such an ecosystem as a river, a lake, or a harbor is a small price to pay for the benefits that accrue to a city through its growth. However, there are some extremely serious ramifications that extend far beyond the mere disappearance of wildlife, serious as that may be. For one thing, the accumulation of human wastes increases the opportunity for pathogenic (disease-causing) microorganisms to multiply and endanger the health of a community. There is no doubt that many American cities run a constant risk of serious epidemics. To cite an example, health authorities in Southern Mississippi found the Pascagoula River so badly polluted in the early 1960's that they forbade oyster fishing in the sound into which this river flows. Not long after their order was given, several cities throughout the Southern United States experienced serious outbreaks of infectious hepatitis, a viral disease. It was traced eventually to oysters that were taken from the sound and sold in violation of the health order. These oysters, subject as they were to a constant bath of human wastes, had picked up the hepatitis virus and were harboring it in their tissues.

SOIL POLLUTION

Soil pollution is probably a less serious problem at the present time than air and water pollution, mostly because our dependence upon soil is more indirect. Nevertheless, some alarming trends are becoming evident. As soils become loaded with pesticides, accompanied by a reduced population of consumers and decomposers necessary to the recycling of elements that are essential to adequate soil fertility, they become less productive. In areas where irrigation practices are necessary and where the arid climate results in a rapid evaporation of moisture into the atmosphere, there is a tendency for salts to accumulate. In the southwestern United States, many thousands of acres of land brought to fertility by irrigation within the present century have already been abandoned because the salt concentration precludes successful agricultural operations. Thus, the optimism created by the promise of blooming deserts, widely heralded only a short time ago as the ultimate answer to the problem of feeding an expanding population, was hardly justified.

In addition to such pollutants of air, water, and soil as we have mentioned, there is an additional, and relatively new, factor that requires special consideration. This factor is the radioactive material now present in substantial amounts within every human environment. It constitutes a special case because of its unique biological effects. Since these effects are not widely understood or appreciated, let us digress momentarily and consider them.

The atoms comprising most elements are remarkably stable, and their subatomic particles (protons, neutrons, and electrons) remain in constant proportion. For example, an ordinary atom of carbon ($_6C^{12}$) contains six protons and six neutrons packed into the atomic nucleus, and six electrons located in "shells" (Fig. 4-4). However, a small but constant proportion of carbon atoms are $_6C^{14}$; that is, the nucleus contains six protons and *eight* neutrons. Atoms of $_6C^{14}$ originate at a constant rate in the earth's atmosphere due to the creation of neutrons resulting from cosmic-ray bombardment. Thus, $_6C^{14}$ (carbon-14) is an isotope of $_6C^{12}$; and it is a *radioisotope* at that, because it tends to be unstable. The half-life of carbon-14 is 5,760 years; that is, one-half of the atoms making up a given quantity of carbon-14 revert back to nitrogen-14 in this length of time. The imbalance between protons and neutrons in an atomic nucleus tends to cause that nucleus to be unstable, with the result that high-energy particles are emitted from the nucleus. Certain of these particles are highly penetrating; they travel at very high rates of speed and frequently interact with other atomic nuclei, causing *them* to become unbalanced. It is this emission of high-energy, high-velocity particles that we term radioactivity.

Actually, carbon-14 itself is of relatively little importance in the total radioactivity of nature; we have merely used it as an example. Let us consider a far more important source of high-energy particles, uranium-235 ($_{92}U^{235}$). Whenever this element is subjected to bombardment by neutrons, as happens when a thermonuclear device is set off, the nucleus of each atom is split into two parts. Not only does this event cause the release of tremendous amounts of energy, but it also initiates a chain reaction wherein various types of high-energy particles bombard other atomic nuclei with the production of a large variety of isotopes. One such series is shown in Fig. 8-8.

Members of the series shown in Fig. 8-8 (krypton-90, rubidium-90, barium-144), as well as many of the subsequent products indicated by the dotted arrows but not listed, are very short-lived. In other words, they are so unstable that they disintegrate rapidly, thus changing into other elements and emitting high-energy particles in the process. But strontium-90 is an

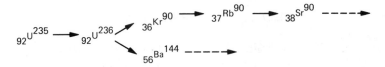

Figure 8.8. The normal decay sequence of uranium-235, greatly simplified. It first changes to uranium-236, which subsequently decays to krypton-90 and barium-144. Barium then decays according to a sequence.

exception. It possesses a half-life of approximately 28 years; that is, one-half of a given amount of this element will have disintegrated in that length of time.

In the fallout of radioactive materials from a thermonuclear device, strontium-90 is apparently of little direct importance. Unfortunately, however, it behaves in living systems very much like its chemical relative, calcium ($_{20}Ca^{40}$), with the result that it is assimilated by producer organisms. Eventually, through a variety of possible food chains, man ingests a certain quantity of strontium-90. For example, one of the most important pathways is grass → cow → milk → man. Like calcium, strontium-90 becomes concentrated in the bones, where its slow disintegration ensures a long exposure of the tissues of the body to the high-energy particles (in this case, fast electrons) resulting from the distintegration of strontium-90 nuclei.

In general, high-energy particles resulting from radioactivity are detrimental to living systems. The extent of any damage is related to the nature of the particles, the nature of the tissue, and the total quantity of irradiation, among other factors. Cells that are active in division are the most susceptible, as a rule, and are more easily killed than are cells in an interphase condition. For this reason, certain cancer cells, which tend to remain in a state of constant division, are particularly susceptible to irradiation.

But there is one especially important aspect of this phenomenon: Radiations are mutagenic. If a mutation occurs within a somatic (non-germinal) cell of a human being, it may only result in the death of that cell. However, if the cell is changed through this mutation in such a way that its normal synthetic controls are thrown into chaos, the cell and its progeny may divide wildly. The resulting growth is a cancer, to use a very general term, and many types of cancer (including the dreaded blood disease, leukemia) are inducible by irradiation. If a mutation occurs in a somatic cell of an embryonic human being, that cell's progeny (destined to become, say, a limb) may form a highly abnormal organ. Furthermore, if a mutation occurs in a sperm or an egg that becomes involved in fertilization, it will be carried into *all* cells of the resulting individual and will almost certainly constitute a "bad" gene.*

All human beings are exposed to a certain amount of radioactivity through cosmic rays that reach the earth from outer space and through extremely small amounts of radioactive elements that are widely distributed throughout the earth's crust. The widespread use of X rays in diagnostic and therapeutic procedures adds still more to the radioactive exposure of the average person. Finally, radioactive wastes from thermonuclear explosions and from industry (where disposal is becoming a tremendous problem) further increase this danger—hence they must be regarded as a form of pollution. The unique effects upon biological systems, chiefly through mutagenesis, is the reason we consider radiation a special case.

Actually, the radioactive fallout resulting from bomb tests and nuclear reactor wastes constitutes only a small percentage of the radiation to which humans are exposed. One can say with assurance, however, that this fallout is one case of pollution in which, from the biological standpoint, any pollution at all is too much. The data collected over the past few decades indicate quite clearly that there is no amount of radiation so small that it does not do somatic and genetic damage to human beings. One expert in this field has estimated (conservatively, by his standards) that radioactive fallout within a 25-year period has produced 12,000 genetically defective babies and 100,000 cases of leukemia and bone tumors.[4] Other estimates are far less conservative, and it must be remembered that these figures do not take into account "hidden" recessives or other radiation-induced abnormalities.

Our responsibility with regard to this form of pollution is clear, at at least in principle: **Any type of radiation is an extremely dangerous form of pollution and is to be avoided whenever possible.** Of course, the use of X rays in medical practice is often essential; but, even here, the physician should be extremely discriminating. It is encouraging that the medical profession has taken a great deal of responsibility in this regard, insisting upon more effective shielding in the manufacture of X-ray machines and has frequently substituted less hazardous diagnostic procedures than those involving radiation. For example, skin tests for the detection of tuberculosis have been widely substituted for the annual chest X rays that were once considered routine for the general population. It is also commendable that nuclear physicists have, as a group, shown a high degree of responsibility

---

* Of course, in a diploid system, this gene would probably not exert its undesirable effects immediately. Most mutant genes are recessives. (Can you postulate a reason as to *why* they are recessives?) Therefore, the effects of most germinal mutations are delayed.

and professionalism with regard to potential and actual hazards of radiation.[5]

The testing of thermonuclear devices, with its attending radioactive fallout, carries grave political implications. Whether it is better to subject the world's population to more radioactivity in order to gain military advantage through the testing of weapons or to risk falling behind militarily in order to avoid increased radioactivity is a difficult decision that must sometimes be made by a nation's leaders. In the United States, since the 1940's, a degree of tension over this issue has existed between military personnel and scientists. Without attempting to set forth the arguments on both sides, we can only say that it behooves every citizen to become informed about the biological effects of radiation as well as the military urgency of any particular moment.

We can only view with total dismay the possibility that mankind should ever indulge in a nuclear war. The military aspects alone of such an eventuality are alarming, since even a limited conflict involving nuclear weapons would probably be devastating in its direct effects. At Hiroshima, 70,000 persons were killed outright, and a large area of the city was actually vaporized; yet, the bomb employed was a "primitive," low-level type that was only a fraction as powerful as those stockpiled today. But dreadful as the destruction would be, it is entirely possible that the genetic effects would do more damage to the human species in the long run than merely killing a few thousand or million people. For generations following such a holocaust, the induced mutations in germinal tissues (mostly recessive, mostly harmful) would keep cropping out.

Actually, we have no way of knowing with any reasonable degree of accuracy the extent of damage, either direct or indirect, that a nuclear war might inflict upon mankind. But from what we know about the effects of radiation upon living systems, including man, such an eventuality must be avoided at all costs. Surely no political crisis is so insurmountable that it cannot be resolved in some other way.

8.2B Overpopulation

"The explosive growth of the human population is the most significant terrestrial event of the past million millennia," ecologists Paul and Anne Ehrlich wrote in 1970. "Three and one-half billion people now inhabit the Earth, and every year this number increases by 70 million" [*Population, Resources, Environment* by Paul R. Ehrlich and Anne H. Ehrlich. (San Francisco, Calif.: W. H. Freeman and Co., Publishers, 1970)].

Mankind is presently in the throes of what biologists call a *logarithmic growth phase*. This phenomenon is a common pattern in natural populations of plants, animals, or bacteria whenever the reproduction-death ratio becomes sufficiently great that the rate of increase is exponential rather than arithmetic.

By estimate, the world population of *Homo sapiens* was some 5 million in 8000 B.C., at about which time it is supposed that man's agricultural activities began. It has been further estimated that perhaps 200 million people existed at the time of Christ; this increase is attributed to the rise of agriculture and its stabilizing influence upon the species. By 1650 A.D., this figure had slightly more than doubled to 500 million. Let us note that over a period of some 10,000 years, it required about 1500 years, on the average, for the human population to double. Had this trend continued, the year 3000 would have come and gone before the world's population reached 1 billion.

However, for reasons that are not altogether clear (although certain factors such as industrial and agricultural revolutions undoubtedly played a part), the total population doubled in a mere 200 years; the 1 billion mark was reached by 1850. The next doubling (to 2 billion) was reached in 1930, only 80 years later; and the *next* will evidently occur around 1975. If the trend continues, the year 2000 will be ushered in by some 8 billion souls (Fig. 8-9), most of whom will be too hungry and too preoccupied with problems of overcrowding to participate very joyously in the celebration.

SOME FACTORS RELATED TO OVERPOPULATION

It is significant that, in nature, no plant, animal, or bacterial population ever maintains a logarithmic phase of growth indefinitely. Some factor or combination of factors—food shortage, disease encouraged by overcrowding, accumulation of poisonous waste materials, or decimation of the ranks by an enemy—inevitably and invariably bring about a leveling process. Most students of population biology predict that such a process will occur in the human situation long before the year 2000—perhaps sooner than 1980. In any event, there seems to be no question as to *whether* it will occur, but *when* and *how*.

At the present time, the world faces an acute food shortage. This shortage seldom occurs to the majority of people in a generally affluent society where bounty is such a way of life that the government often feels obliged to pay farmers *not* to raise food (although acute hunger and even starvation are not uncommon in the United States). But it is a stark reality that more than one-half of the present 3.5 billion people on earth do not get enough to eat and that upwards of 20 million human beings starve to death each year (Fig. 8-10). True, we are learning how to produce more food by a variety of means; but the overall picture is hardly an encouraging

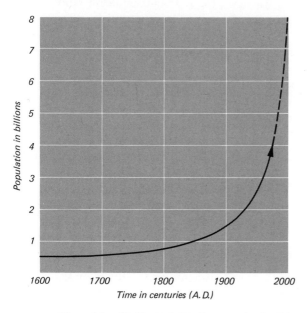

Figure 8.9. World population figures and rate of increase since the year 1600. The dotted line represents a projection of human population increase based on past and present trends.

one, since each year we are currently producing 70 million more people (births over deaths). Furthermore, there are many factors that tend to cancel out our technological advances in food production.

People require living space, and living space subtracts from productive land area. The world presently gains about 135 people every minute, some 200,000 per day, close to 6 million per month. *This means that a new Chicago is added to the world each month, and a new Brazil* (about 70 million people) *each year.* Unfortunately, we are talking about *people,* not land area. How much space is required for each new person on earth? No reliable figure can be given, but ecologist LaMont Cole estimates that approximately 1 million acres of land are removed annually from the cycle of photosynthetic production, largely through paving. (For example, a mile of four-lane highway requires some 50 acres, and this land is usually the most level and productive available.) In truth, the greatest improvement in the technology of food production that we can presently envision will not begin to counterbalance the factors of population increase and land removal. It is true that water areas of the world can be made more productive, as can certain land areas, but many experts believe that

Figure 8.10. The two-year-old boy in this picture, victim of a famine due to drought that occurred in India in 1956, is dying from starvation. According to present indications, scenes like this will become more common during the coming decades. (Photo courtesy Food and Agriculture Organization of the United Nations.)

we are nearing the practical limits of productivity in both types of environment. At any rate, increasing amounts of pollutants added to the earth's waters may constitute a factor that will result in *less* aquatic productivity, not more.*

It is becoming increasingly apparent that man is caught in a vicious, and self-limiting, ecological cycle. The more people we have on earth, the more food is required and the more serious becomes the pollution problem. When more food is raised, more pesticides are applied, which only adds to the total pollution. The more people, the less land there is in production; the more pollution, the less productivity there is in both land and

---

* Quite recently, it has been found that DDT and other compounds of its general class interfere seriously with the photosynthesis of the most important marine algae. Since at least 70 per cent of all photosynthesis on earth is carried on by marine algae, this interference has serious implications for the continued production of oxygen, to say nothing of the complex food web of the oceans.

water. Thus, it is probably only a matter of time until the usual factors that interfere with logarithmic growth set in: food shortage, accumulation of toxic materials, widespread disease, and (quite conceivably) wars brought on at least in part by crowding. Any one of these factors would probably be sufficient to change the trend of population growth. All four are not only possible, but likely, within the present century.

IMPLICATIONS FOR THE FUTURE

There may be some cause for optimism over the long run, disregarding for the moment the possibility of irreparable genetic deterioration of the human species and nutritional damage.* Hopefully, the species would recover following what now appears to be almost certain calamity before the year 2000 and will find a way to stabilize the world's population at some optimal figure. In the meantime, however, it appears that we are on a collision course with at least two unavoidable consequences of overpopulation and that these catastrophes will occur well before the year 2000. The first consequence is a high degree of social chaos and human suffering; the second is a severe deterioration in the quality of human life. We say "unavoidable"; there is one slender chance, and only one. This chance would come from a sharp, and immediate, curtailment in the production of more human beings.

It is one thing to prescribe a remedy, and quite another to enact it. How shall we go about limiting human reproduction? Of course, if some overall board of authority were to assume immediate control and dictate the terms, prescribing widespread sterilization together with enforced contraception and abortion, the problem might be solved (assuming an army of physicians were recruited to carry out these tasks). But it is highly unlikely that many human beings can be expected to look with favor upon such a solution, even assuming it to be a desirable one, since it involves a serious curtailment of human freedom. Another possibility is the voluntary abstention from reproduction; but the vast majority of mankind does not possess the knowledge, the motivation, or the means for participation in such a program. As biologist David Prescott has pointed out,

> In the achievement of population growth control, the least infringement on individual freedom would result from some voluntary regulation such as advocated in family planning programs, although it is

---

* It is now well established that malnutrition causes permanent damage to human tissues. The most dramatic example of this phenomenon is seen whenever an undernourished woman bears a child or when a child itself suffers from malnutrition. Children who are the victims of these conditions suffer a marked loss of nerve cells in the brain, sometimes as many as 50 per cent of the total number originally formed during embryonic development.

unlikely for a number of social and cultural reasons that voluntary programs will ever produce any significant results among any except the more highly educated people of this world. To depend, moreover, on the individual voluntary restraint on reproduction would be unjust in the face of *ad libitum* reproduction by the ignorant or uncooperative. Voluntary restriction of reproduction for other than reasons of individual self-interest is not likely to be much more successful than voluntary payment of income taxes.[6]

Mankind as a whole simply is not conditioned to thinking in such self-limiting terms. In many parts of the world, the procreation of numerous children is the only dependable form of social security for old age, and no amount of education or temporary reward is going to change the attitudes of those concerned. Moreover, in many parts of the world, religious beliefs are involved; these beliefs usually center around the conviction (formally imposed by the religious institution itself, in many cases) that chemical or mechanical means for preventing the union of gametes is unnatural and sinful. Still another factor, widely overlooked, is the psychological factor of the male ego; perhaps the majority of men feel a deeply ingrained need to justify their manhood through the production of children.

One possibility for controlling the population is through abortion, as has been demonstrated by Japan, which made this procedure legal, inexpensive, and readily available in 1948. Since that time, their rate of population increase has been curtailed sharply. However, there are difficulties in this proposed solution. The religious heritage of Japan is far different from that of much of the world, where strong resistance to any suggestion of abortion may be expected. Furthermore, as psychologist James Archer has pointed out, Japan is a highly civilized country with an inhabitant-physician ratio of 900:1. In contrast, Ethiopia, as just one example, has a ratio of 96,000:1.[7] Where the number of physicians in a society is this small, they cannot even satisfy the need for contraceptive information and prescription; they cannot provide for the insertion of intrauterine devices, much less perform abortions. By the time such societies increase the inhabitant-physician ratio, the major population crisis of the world will probably have occurred.

All things considered, it now appears that there simply is not time to avoid a great deal of human suffering as mankind shifts from a logarithmic growth phase to one of populational stability. In the meantime, and certainly eventually, individual men and women, religious institutions, societies, and governments will be obliged to make some hard decisions. To quote once more from Prescott,

The institution of population control will probably evolve through economic pressures such as the abolishment of the income tax dependency allowance for children, followed by the introduction of other financial penalties. It seems inevitable that sterilization must be imposed on some equitable basis for reproduction control to be completely effective. The relinquishment of the right to reproduce at will represents the loss of a major individual freedom, but this is still small in comparison to the losses of individual freedom that will be forced on our descendants in a nation and world in which the population has been allowed to expand to a limit imposed only by material resources.[8]

8.2C Conservation Ecology

In 1962, the late Rachel Carson published a highly controversial book entitled *Silent Spring*. Miss Carson pointed out the dangerous extent to which man persists in changing the face of the earth, especially through the careless destruction of natural resources and the indiscriminate use of pesticides. As might have been expected, she was hailed as a prophet by a relatively small segment of the population, mostly conservationists; and she was roundly damned by perhaps a still larger group, a remarkably high percentage of whom maintained vested interests in land development or the manufacture of pesticides. Miss Carson did indeed paint a grim picture, and even some of her supporters felt that she might have overstated her case.

In retrospect, it appears that her views were amply justified. True, we have not suffered for our misdeeds according to her predictions partly because of reforms and restraints that would never have been initiated had it not been for her warnings and those of other concerned individuals. Nevertheless, her direct prophecies may yet be fulfilled. Ecologists sometimes speak of a "pollution lag," which is an ecological version of the biblical statement that "whatsoever a man soweth, that shall he also reap." In another metaphorical context, we have treated nature abusively; one day, she will have her vengeance, and in spades.

THE HISTORY OF CONSERVATION IN AMERICA

Man tends to be extremely careless when dealing with the earth's resources. This carelessness is partly through sheer greed and lack of concern, partly through ignorance and shortsightedness. The ignorance, at least in the United States, can be attributed in large part to a lack of understanding of basic ecological principles, coupled with a feeling that man is really not a part of nature and can therefore ignore everything except his own interests. This last factor is, quite curiously, an expression of religious piety, and deserves a closer analysis than it has usually received.

America came to her greatest strength at a particularly strategic moment: She discovered her great natural resources almost precisely at the same time that technology advanced the means for their rapid exploitation. Also at this time (the mid-19th through early 20th centuries), the prevailing economic and social philosophy was built around the doctrine of *laissez-faire,* the inherent goodness of man, the equation of progress with good, and (during a fair portion of this time and in certain influential circles) the pseudo-Darwinian concept that might makes right. Regardless of whether man was considered a product of evolution or of special creation, it was generally agreed that he stood so far above anything in nature that he was no longer a part of it. Because America was a land of seemingly endless bounty, such a philosophy was tolerable for at least the time being.

This is not to say that America lacked conservation programs. Selective cutting and reseeding of forests, contour plowing on hillsides, filling in pits that had been formed by mining operations—these and other measures represented a developing American conscience toward the conservation of natural resources. Thus, well before the year 1900, a reasonably successful conservation movement had begun. Generally, the aims of this movement were to use natural resources wisely and for the benefit of the most people. This viewpoint and the measures it promoted have been called *traditional conservation;* as an ideal, it cannot be challenged seriously. In fact, the traditional conservation movement has been successful to a large degree in preventing the waste and plunder of natural resources that would undoubtedly have occurred without its influence.

In the meanwhile, the nations of Western Europe, which had been obliged to guard their more limited resources with great care from the beginning of the technological revolution, were driven to seek even more effective avenues of conservation. It was during the latter part of the 19th century that European biologists developed the basic theoretical concepts that crystallized ultimately into the science of ecology. Since that time these theoretical concepts have found wide practical application in the area of conservation. The result is a workable synthesis called *conservation ecology.*

THE NEW CONSERVATION

How, one might ask, does the "new" conservation differ from the traditional approach? In the first place, it should be understood quite clearly that ecologists have no quarrel with the *aims* of traditional conservation—only with the methods. They contend that it is not enough merely to employ wisdom in the development and use of our natural resources (mineral reserves, water, land, forests, animal and plant life as a whole), however good and essential this might be. On the whole, with an expanding population, the methods of traditional conservation can only postpone the evil day of resource depletion. Instead, ecologists have argued, the only permanent solution is to effect something of a harmonious balance in any given natural situation. Of course, this approach is somewhat irrelevant to the problem of mineral depletion, but it becomes highly meaningful in all other areas of conservation.

In the area of wildlife management, it has become apparent in the United States that traditional methods of control are inadequate to maintain balanced populations of animals. However, conservation ecologists have achieved notable success through the application of basic ecological principles to the problems encountered in this very difficult area of endeavor. By studying predator-prey relationships, population density allowances, the influence of environmental factors, natural food chains, natural succession in habitats and niches, and the several complex interrelationships that exist between wild animals and their natural environments, ecologists are now able to make recommendations that would have astounded conservationists of two generations ago. As a result of these recommendations, and proportional with the degree to which they have been put into practice, such animal populations as deer, pheasant, and several species of prized freshwater fish are now under effective control in most areas of the United States (Fig. 8-11).

With regard to the conservation of forest reserves, the ecological viewpoint has also paid great dividends. Even if trees are cut selectively and measures are taken to ensure their replacement, this method is often inadequate for good management over a long range of time. Ecologists insist upon a consideration of erosion effects, the upsetting of balance among plant species, the eradication or dislocation of animal species normally associated with a forest, the effects of moisture and temperature changes on the ecosystem, and the several other ecological factors involved in a massive logging operation or an extensive burn (Fig. 8-12).

Unfortunately, conservation ecology is often difficult and expensive to implement, and it can seldom promise short-term results. Furthermore, it often runs counter to the "common sense" intuitions of those who are unschooled in theoretical ecology. As a result, it is frequently difficult to sell this general philosophy of control to governmental and private organizations. Many of the laws governing the use of natural resources were enacted before the insights of conservation ecology were available (and some of these laws are even inconsistent with the fundamental principles of traditional conservation). As a consequence, some of them are in need of revision.

Figure 8.11. Group of elk on a refuge at Jackson, Wyoming. By the application of wise conservation principles, such animal species can be controlled for the greatest public good. (Photo by E. P. Haddon, courtesy U.S. Department of the Interior, Bureau of Sport Fisheries and Wildlife.)

IMPLICATIONS FOR THE FUTURE

In view of the urgency attending the need for the wise use of our natural resources, it behooves every citizen to take an active part in guarding the little that remains to us. So often, commercial interests or even presumably well-intentioned governmental agencies work against the long-range public interest without protest on the part of the public. In a complex society where elected officials are obliged to listen to the voices of their constituents, it is only natural that vested interests often speak louder than the general citizenry. In view of the increasing problems of overpopulation and pollution, it will be difficult indeed to maintain any semblance of conservation within the coming decades, even with the employment of more effective measures. One can only hope that it is not too late already.

It is often claimed that, in a highly industrialized society such as ours, to strive toward the goals of conservation ecology is merely visionary and impractical. Technology has created our problems—so runs the argument—let us look to technology for their solution.

289

(a)

(b)

Figure 8.12. (a) This mature forest in Idaho was logged in the early 1930's. It was replanted in 1939 by the Civil Conservation Corps. (b) Same view, photograph taken in 1949. (c) Same view, photograph taken in 1969. (d) Forest Service crew planting Ponderosa pine after a burn in an Arizona forest. (All photos courtesy U.S. Forest Service.)

(c)

(d)

Figure 8.12. (cont.)

Unfortunately, technology cannot reverse most of the environmental changes that it has caused, even if it wished to do so. No amount of inventiveness will restore the bald eagle or peregrine falcon to life, once these species are rendered extinct through the destruction of their nesting sites and through their ingestion of DDT (Fig. 8-13). There is no presently conceivable way that Lake Erie can be restored to a balanced, productive condition, short of a thousand years of natural events that man cannot hasten. The DDT now residing in the fat stores of virtually every animal on earth will hardly be removed by technology. The forest put to the bulldozer for the construction of yet another housing development is gone forever; even if the houses were torn down and the concrete removed, generations would be required before restoration of the area would even begin to approach its original condition.

To many people, such considerations as these are hopelessly romantic and unrealistic, betraying a nostalgia for the past, a longing to stop the wheels of progress. Who cares—they say—that there are fewer than 100 whooping cranes in all the world, that the last blue whale will have died before the close of this century, that the American alligator may well suffer the same fate?

Although excellent arguments can be advanced from an aesthetic viewpoint for the preservation of endangered species and forest areas, more is involved here than mere nostalgia. Disappearance of wildlife and the natural areas that support it are symptomatic of man's present ecological illness. Regardless of how convinced he may have been in the past that he was not a part of nature, man had very well better face up to the truth of the matter: **He is a part of nature. As he destroys the crane, the whale, and the alligator, so he destroys himself.** True, he is not critically dependent upon the very environments to which these animals are restricted, but he cannot survive the destruction of them all. More important, the attitudes of carelessness and wanton destruction that lead to animal and plant extinction will inevitably bring man to his own ecological destruction.

In a more immediate and practical sense, however, what can be done in a complex society to maintain a growing population at a reasonably high standard of living and yet avoid the dangers against which Rachel Carson warned? Clearly, a farmer whose subsistence depends upon periodic and liberal applications of powerful insecticides cannot eliminate his spraying program merely because he reads dire warnings against DDT; nor can city planners very well outlaw the use of bulldozers and land-fill machinery.

In agriculture, much can be done that is not being done. Many farmers are guilty of indiscriminate spraying; if they would limit the application of their insecticide or herbicide to a short, critical period of vulnerability on the part of the organism involved, they might spare the countryside a great deal of pollution, as well as save themselves time and money. Quite

(a)

(b)

Figure 8.13. (a) Bald eagle. (b) Peregrine falcon. These are two of the many birds threatened with extinction due to DDT ingestion. (Photos by Luther C. Goldman, courtesy U.S. Department of the Interior, Bureau of Sport Fisheries and Wildlife.)

often, agricultural experts are capable of furnishing the necessary information if the farmer will trouble himself to get it. In many other cases, more research (which farmers and farm organizations should support actively) is needed in order to find ways of limiting spray operations. Moreover, with very little research, a biodegradable pesticide might often be substituted for one that is sure to create problems, such as DDT. For example, the natural substance pyrethrin (obtainable from a plant, *Pyrethrum,* and certain related genera) is quite effective against a great many insects, and its effectiveness might be increased with very little more research. Undoubtedly, other "natural" pesticides could be developed so as to render completely unnecessary the use of DDT-type pesticides.

It is not always necessary to use chemicals in combatting insect pests. A classic example of effective control is the eradication of the screw-worm fly, which infests cattle, from the southeastern United States. Because it is very difficult to combat this insect with sprays, agricultural entomologists began in the early 1950's to seek other means for dealing with it. In studying this parasite, they discovered that female screw-worm flies normally mate only once during a lifetime. It had occurred to one of the entomologists some years earlier that irradiation is an effective means for sterilizing animals; why not rear thousands of male screw-worm flies, sterilize them with radiation, release them from airplanes over infested areas, and hope that they would mate with female flies? If successful, this procedure would prevent females from producing any offspring at all. A pilot program was undertaken, with very promising results. Once the techniques were mastered, it became possible to completely eradicate the parasite from the region under consideration.

Of course, not all entomological problems can be solved this neatly. But many could be, if enough effort were expended, with the ideal goal being to eliminate all use of pesticides. In comparison with the vast amount of research that has gone into the development of spray chemicals, almost nothing has been spent in developing "biological" pesticides: viruses, insect predators,* such natural substances as pyrethrin, or hitherto unsuspected plant and animal enemies of undesirable species. A close study of the life cycle of a given undesirable organism (as in the case of the screwworm fly) might reveal a critical stage of vulnerability to radiation, light of a certain intensity, temperature shock, or some other nonchemical lethal agent. We do not suggest that agricultural engineers have not been responsive to suggestions by ecologists. Many of them are, themselves, well-versed in ecology. The major problem is chiefly one of attracting funds for research from both public and private agencies and recruiting sufficient talent to carry out worthwhile research programs.

In the utilization of land for construction purposes, city planners and engineers might show a considerably higher degree of responsibility than has often been the case. It is much easier to level all vegetation than to leave trees and shrubs, but a prior construction plan that places houses and streets among existing vegetation is usually feasible. To their credit, many planners of housing, business, and highway construction have acted responsibly toward that portion of the environment with which they deal. Hopefully, increasing concern will be shown for preserving and growing vegetation wherever it is possible to do so.

Unfortunately, most Americans still tend to think and act toward environmental problems in 19th-century terms. In a democratic society, therefore, agencies and institutions generally reflect these same attitudes. Consequently, the public must be educated to think in 20th-century ecological terms. However, education is a slow process at best; even a Rachel

---

* To a limited extent, such insects as the praying mantis (Fig. 8-14a), parasitic wasps (Fig. 8-14b), and the lady-bird beetle, all of which prey voraciously upon a large variety of insect pests, have been reared in quantity and released within local situations. Basic research on this type of control, however, has been poorly supported, and it deserves more attention than it has received.

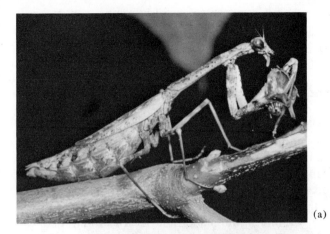
(a)

(b)

Figure 8.14. (a) Praying mantis feeding on an insect pest. (Courtesy Carolina Biological Supply Company.) (b) A parasitic wasp depositing its eggs in an alfalfa weevil larva. Eggs hatch into larvae within the body of the host, and then kill it. (Courtesy U.S. Department of Agriculture.)

Carson, employing the shock treatment of a *Silent Spring,* cannot reach more than a relative handful of people. Perhaps at this late stage, we can only hope that a part of our ecosystem, at least, may be kept from destruction.

Nevertheless, it is the strength of a democracy that individual voices are sometimes heeded. Quite frequently, public officials would be happy to oppose special interest groups bent on further abuse of natural resources if they felt that they had any support at all. Even a single voice raised in protest will sometimes be sufficient to stop a move that is not in the public interest. However, since there is strength in numbers, and because several minds are better than one at clarifying the basic issues involved, the concerned individual does well to identify himself with some club or society that is dedicated to the promotion of conservation methods.* If conservation is left entirely to government, no matter how ideal its form, there can be no great hope for really effective curbs on pollution or the further preservation of wilderness areas.

On the other hand, individuals and organizations should be extremely careful to ensure that protests are based upon sound ecological theory. Not infrequently, well-intentioned objections to agricultural programs are completely unrealistic and only interfere with any progress that might be made. Tension and distrust is created between conservation societies and governmental agencies; as a result, there is frequently confusion. We emphasize, therefore, the need for an understanding of ecological principles among the lay public. Furthermore, an individual or an organization should be very careful to study any given problem thoroughly before lodging a protest. Otherwise, discussions become more emotional than reasoned, and meaningful achievement becomes difficult.

8.3 SOME GENETIC AND EVOLUTIONARY IMPLICATIONS

Is man a part of nature? In attempting to resolve this question, we have answered it affirmatively as we traced the development of ecological thought. It seems fair to say that *only* when man thinks of himself as one organism among many, and as a species of animal occupying the world ecosystem, is he in a favorable position to ensure his continued existence on earth.

---

* Some of the national organizations that are active in the cause of conservation are the National Audubon Society, the National Parks and Conservation Association, the National Wildlife Federation, the Sierra Club, and the Wilderness Society.

From an entirely different (although not unrelated) viewpoint, that of human genetics and evolution, man is *not* a part of nature. This seeming reversal of our earlier position contains a great many reservations. Biologically, man *is* an organism; his genes mutate; the various genetic types appearing throughout his species are subjected to selective pressures; he obviously occupies his place among other organisms as a result of evolution. And yet, there is a very important sense in which man is *not* a part of nature. Let us explore this paradox.

8.3 A The Rise of Eugenics

In 1865, the same year that Mendel reported his genetic research to the Natural History Society of Brünn, an Englishman named Francis Galton (1822–1911) published a lengthy discussion of human genetics in a popular British magazine. Galton, who was a cousin of Charles Darwin, started with the assumption that general vigor, native intelligence, musical ability, mathematical genius, and similar human qualities are under the control of heredity, although he was as ignorant of genetic mechanisms as was the rest of his generation. Nevertheless, Galton proceeded to seek ways of improving the human gene pool; in 1883, he coined a new term to describe this area of activity: *eugenics.*

Despite his limitations in genetic theory, Galton made quite a number of observations that are worth considering. Remember, he was operating in a climate of biological thought that was completely dominated by the idea of natural selection. In pondering the implications of Darwinian natural selection for man, Galton discovered that medical practice works counter to natural selection: In wild animal species, the weak and sickly die; but, thanks to the healing arts, many inferior human beings live to procreate. If this practice continues, Galton wondered, will it not eventually weaken the species? Since the answer seemed obvious, and since it was unthinkable that man should abandon medical practice, Galton advocated a double prescription: encouragement of those with superior genetic endowments to have more children and encouragement of those with inferior genetic endowments to have fewer. Since his time, the former course of action has been termed *positive eugenics;* the latter, *negative eugenics.*

We need not tarry over the several complex recommendations Galton made over the years for implementing eugenics programs. Suffice it to say that the eugenic ideal became widely accepted, especially among those persons in European and American society who took for granted that it was easy to identify superior genetic stock: was it not those men who had succeeded in their society, the captains of industry, the financial magnates, the successful politicians, the intellectual giants of university faculties?

Given Darwinian natural selection, superiority would rise to the top like cream.

8.3B The Problem of Biological Fitness

In the meantime, genetics began a development of its own after 1900, the year Mendel's paper was discovered anew. For many years, the principal work in genetics was done with the easiest organisms—fruit flies, maize, an occasional small mammal—and the more complicated area of human genetics was widely avoided. The secrets of basic genetics were wrested from organisms more favorable for experimental work than man; had the small group of qualified geneticists diffused their labors over the complexities of human genetics, it is doubtful that much would have been accomplished. As a result of this general avoidance of human genetics, the eugenics movement proceeded somewhat independently, and somewhat ignorantly, on its way. Operating mostly on assumption, American eugenicists urged legislation for sterilization of the "unfit" and for the prevention of marriage between certain types of individuals. Several states enacted such legislation, but many of these laws were based upon genetic myths, and almost all of them were doomed to failure from the start. In a free society, how does one manage to encourage reproduction among the fit or discourage it among the unfit?

By the 1930's, it had become increasingly apparent to most students of evolution that Darwin's expression "survival of the fittest" was an unfortunate term (Darwin himself had lived to regret its use). It was very misleading even when dealing with species of organisms existing under natural conditions. When the expression was applied to *human* evolution, genetics, or social affairs, it was nothing short of disastrous in its connotations. The distinction between "fit" and "superior," on the one hand, and "unfit" and "inferior," on the other, may have seemed perfectly clear to 19th-century Englishmen and Americans; by the 1930's, however, evolutionists and geneticists of both countries had uncovered the basic flaw of reasoning: *What is meant by superior? Superior in what way?* After all, the fittest in nature are those genetic types (organisms, races, subspecies, species) that reproduce more successfully than their competitors. Are we ready to accept the humiliating standard that reproduction defines superiority among human beings? This attitude would have struck Francis Galton, who was a genius by any reasonable standard, as a supreme bit of irony—he died childless.

The problem of defining superiority remains the basic difficulty for those who would improve the human species genetically. Even if one assumes that human reproduction can be weighted in a certain direction—no small achievement in itself since any really effective program would almost certainly violate the accepted ethical standards of practically all human societies—where does one begin? What criteria should be used? Despite the major advances in human genetics during the past few decades, present-day scientists are really in no better position to answer this question, and they are considerably less confident than the Galtonians that any meaningful answer can be provided.

Consider, however, Galton's assumption that medical practice works counter to the principle of natural selection, that man runs the risk of preserving weakness to beget weakness. Is there anything to this belief? The answer is undoubtedly affirmative. It is in this sense that man is not a part of nature. Galton observed quite correctly that medicine prevents the "natural" elimination of physically defective individuals. This observation is far more true now than it was a hundred years ago. Does this compel man to choose between what geneticist Theodosius Dobzhansky terms a genetic twilight and a moral twilight; that is, should we refuse treatment to genetic weaklings and thus become murderers, or should we run the risk of weakening the species to the point of extinction? [9]

In point of fact, this dilemma is more imagined than real. In the first place, medicine probably saves as many "good" genes as "bad" ones, perhaps more. In the second place, for man to become extinct in a true evolutionary sense, he would have to fall victim to one or more competitive species; at the present time, no animal species appears to be a serious competitor to man's superiority. In fact, the human species ceased to have real competitors in nature quite some time ago; and so, if man becomes extinct, this event is not likely to come about through natural selection. One thing seems fairly certain: Man is not likely to forsake his moral and ethical values and his medical technology for a return to pre-human conditions. For better or worse, he is moral and technological man. If he is to be saved from extinction, it must be through a greater degree of morality and technology, strange partners though these may seem to be.

To a very great extent, although not entirely, man has removed himself from the evolutionary forces of nature. He began long ago to forsake nature for culture, of which medicine and morality are both a part. This is not to say that man is not evolving; he is. But it must be remembered that he reached his present biological status at least 100,000 years ago, if one may trust the calculations of physical anthropologists. In contrast, man's cultural evolution did not begin in earnest until some 10,000 years ago. If rapidity of change is any criterion, cultural evolution has been the more important factor for quite some time now.

However, eugenic attempts are neither unnecessary nor unwise. Eugenics did receive a bad name earlier in this century when both geneticists and social scientists realized the extent to which eugenic thinking was based on a fallacy. As a result, most geneticists turned away from human genetics as a whole. Now this trend is being reversed, and there is a tendency in genetics to review the human scene in the light of newer knowledge.

8.3C Genetic Counseling

At the present time, the most fruitful approach to eugenics is through genetic counseling. For example, suppose a couple has a child who is afflicted with the genetic-metabolic disease phenylketonuria, which is characterized by the inability to metabolize properly the amino acid phenylalanine. This condition leads to serious mental retardation unless the child is placed on a very rigorous, near-phenylalanine-free diet. It results from the presence in the child of a recessive gene in the homozygous condition. If both parents are assumed to be normal with regard to phenylalanine metabolism, each parent is obviously heterozygous for this gene. If they contemplate having more children, the genetic counselor can inform them that the probability of their having another child afflicted with the disease is one in four, and that the probability of their having another child who carries *one* of these recessive genes is two in four. Although the counselor must ultimately leave it to their judgment as to whether having more children is worth the risk of passing this gene onward, he may suggest very strongly in this case, at least, that the risks are very great in terms of potential human misery.

How effective can we expect genetic counseling to be in improving the species generally? Unfortunately, the outlook is not an optimistic one. For example, it is estimated that in the United States, there is one phenylketonuric in 10,000 to 20,000 of the general population. Let us take the lower figure for illustrative purposes; the frequency of phenylketonurics may thus be expressed as 1 per 10,000. Suppose all phenylketonurics are eliminated from the breeding population by sterilization. Through a complex process of mathematical calculation, it can be shown that this procedure would reduce the frequency of phenylketonurics from 1 per 10,000 to 1 per 10,001 in a single generation. Calculate, if you will, the length of time required to reduce the incidence of the disease by one-half (1 per 20,000), assuming a generation time of 25 years! Such calculations do not even take into account the fact that the mutation rate from "normal" to "phenylketonuric" would almost certainly keep pace with the elimination of this gene from the population. Of course, it is of some help that heterozygous carriers may be identified and discouraged from further reproduction, but it does not presently appear that the most rigorous selection against deleterious recessive genes can reduce their frequency significantly. Negative eugenics, therefore, is not the answer to genetic improvement of the human species.

We are not claiming, of course, that genetic counseling itself is futile. If a counselor can prevent further misery to a single family, he more than justifies his professional existence in society. In addition, he is frequently able to alleviate unfounded apprehensions or dispense meaningful knowledge to those who might be helped by such assistance. In terms of human need, the present tragedy is that qualified genetic counselors and counseling centers are a scarce commodity; and even where they are available, people (including, unfortunately, medical practitioners) are often ignorant of their potential for human service.

After having reviewed the evidence indicating that elimination of undesirable genetic traits from a population has a minimal effect upon improvement of the species as a whole, human geneticist Curt Stern comments as follows:

> If the hopes and fears of the eugenics movement seem greatly exaggerated in the light of a numerical treatment of the problems, it should not be forgotten that the idealism which concerns itself with the genetic fate of future generations has a sound core. To say that the loss of supposedly desirable genotypes in one or even many generations of differential reproduction is small does not mitigate the fact that it is a loss which may be regrettable and, possibly, even have serious consequences. To state that reproductive selection against severe physical and mental abnormalities will reduce the number of the affected from one generation to the next by only a small percentage does not alter the fact that the small percentage may represent tens of thousands of individuals. Conversely, even a slight increase of desirable genotypes, through progressive eugenic measures, would be a social gain. [From *Principles of Human Genetics* (2nd ed.), by Curt Stern. (San Francisco, Calif.: W. H. Freeman and Co., Publishers, 1960).]

Thus, Stern extends a cautious hope that positive eugenics (he prefers the term "progressive eugenics") may hold some promise for improvement of the species. However, he is not very explicit in his recommendations for an effective program—and for good reason. Although great strides have been made in human genetics, scientists are still unable to identify superior genotypes with any degree of success. Even if there is agreement on a definition for "superior," it would be difficult to implement a meaningful program in our present society. Hopefully, more knowledge will be at our disposal within a few years. Perhaps then it will become feasible to take at least some steps toward positive eugenics. In the meantime, about all science can do is to educate more people to an awareness of the problem, encourage more research in human genetics, and alleviate or prevent need-less human suffering wherever it is possible to do so.

8.3D Nature Versus Nurture: The Heredity-Environment Controversy

One other basic premise of Galtonian eugenics deserves some com-ment: namely, the assumption that "superior" human qualities (intelli-gence, musical ability, and so on) are genetically determined. To what extent is this assumption borne out or refuted by modern genetical re-search?

Let us remember that Galton himself held no clear-cut notion as to *how* such traits might be inherited. When he began thinking about the problem, he felt justified in assuming that they were. After all, society had before it any number of examples: the long line of musical Bachs, the Bernoulli family that produced a number of brilliant mathematicians, the Galton-Darwin family itself with several noteworthy members. On the negative side, studies were made (in 1875) of the feeblemindedness in families labeled the Jukes and Kallikaks. It seemed obvious that genius as well as dullness is inherited. After Mendelian genetics became known, it was even claimed that single-gene inheritance was the basis for such traits, and attempts were made through analysis of family pedigrees to establish 3:1 ratios.

This simplistic interpretation of human heredity ran into difficulties well before the 1930's. Genetic research itself failed to make a clear-cut case for the inheritance of such traits as the eugenicists had in mind. Fur-thermore, the rise of behavioristic psychology emphasized the role of environment in the development of such traits. The eugenics movement was lagging for a variety of reasons, and behaviorism was gaining strength for a different variety of reasons. The net result was a decided swing to environmentalism among the intellectuals of Europe and America. Begin-ning in the 1930's or thereabouts, the role of heredity in human behavior was discounted heavily; the role of environment was emphasized to the exclusion of all other considerations. After all, one could explain both the Bachs and the Bernoullis, and the Jukes and the Kallikaks, quite readily—it was all a matter of environment.

It now appears that the environmentalists of this period were over-confident. More recent studies (especially those involving identical twins) by psychologists *and* geneticists indicate beyond reasonable doubt that many behavioral traits of man, including various types of intelligence, *are* genet-ically determined. True, there are difficulties; for example, how can one define intelligence? How does one devise a test that rules out cultural and general environmental influences? However, despite these difficulties, it seems clear that certain aptitudes are gene-related; apparently, in almost all cases, large numbers of genes are involved for any given trait, which makes analysis difficult.

The heredity-versus-environment, nature-or-nurture controversy that raged earlier in this century was typical of the way intellectual clashes evolve. First, there is a militant "either-or" attitude. Secondly, a period of disillusionment and confusion follows as more data are forthcoming than can be fitted into place immediately. Then finally, there is a reconciliation of issues, a realization that it is not "either-or," but "both-and." The history of ideas is replete with examples of this kind; the heredity-environment controversy merely adds to the list.

Although there are still psychologists who insist that mental qualities and behavioral traits of human beings are determined *entirely* by environment and there are biologists who seem to feel that genetics is all-important, there has been wide reconciliation on this point. Geneticist Charlotte Auerbach summarizes this synthesis of thinking as follows:

> To the geneticist, questions like "Is criminality inherited? Is cancer a hereditary disease? Is intelligence the result of education?" make no sense. They presuppose an antithesis which he knows to be wrong, the antithesis between heredity and environment, between "nature and nurture." ... Every trait, normal or abnormal, is the result of developmental processes, and these are controlled by genes as well as by environment. It is true that the relative contributions of heredity and environment to any particular trait differ widely, but few traits are determined entirely by heredity, even fewer by environment. A bullet wound is caused by an outside agency, but the wounded person may have been involved in a brawl through his aggressive disposition, which at least in part may be inherited. Moreover, the effects of the wound on his general health and spirit and the speed of recuperation depend on his constitution, and this is partly hereditary. At the other end of the nature-nurture scale we have a number of traits that, at least under present conditions, are wholly gene-determined, such as blood groups, eye color, and diseases like Huntington's chorea. For some of these, environmental remedies may be found in the future; for others, this may not be possible because the connection between the gene and its observed effect is too direct for human interference. Between these extremes lies the vast majority of characters that are due to an interplay between genes and environment.

And then, employing a striking analogy, Dr. Auerbach continues:

> We should look upon our genes as the cardplayer looks upon the cards that have been dealt out to him and with which he will have to do the best he can.... We start life with a hand of genes as the

cardplayer starts a game with a hand of cards. Occasionally, the hand may be so bad that even moderate success is out of reach. Even more rarely, it is so excellent that little or no exertion is required for success. Mostly, success depends on the skill and experience of the player. True enough, the limits of his achievement are set by the hand he holds and by the hands of the other players; but how near he comes to reaching these limits depends on his skill, and a good player may achieve a better score with poor cards than a poor player with good ones. In the game of life, the "playing" of the genes is only in part done by human efforts; the rest has to be left to circumstances which we cannot, as yet, control. Progress in this direction is, however, rapid. Smooth hair can be "permanently" curled, dark hair can be bleached. More important: speech defects caused by hereditary harelip can be prevented by operation, and the gene that causes susceptibility to infantile paralysis can be made harmless by polio vaccination. The more we find out about the way genes act and the manner in which they respond to environmental conditions the more we shall learn to bring out the effects of the good genes and mitigate those of the bad ones.[10]

Great strides have been taken in genetics since Dr. Auerbach wrote these lines. It is now possible to identify and treat many of the defects of which she speaks. While the goal of genetic engineering—that is, the successful alteration of undesirable genotypes—has not yet been achieved for man and the more complex animals, it no longer seems as remote a possibility as it did a few years ago. Genetic counseling is being widely accepted, and it is broadening its base of knowledge continuously. While the principles that she emphasizes are valid and even prophetic, we are now in a much better position to deal with the problems she identifies.

8.3E Implications for the Future

We have mentioned the hope that man may one day be able to undertake a kind of genetic engineering. Whereas he can now alter the defects caused by undesirable genes, he will then be able to alter the genes themselves within gametes or organisms. There are still other possibilities: for example, identification of "carriers," or heterozygous individuals, for potentially harmful genes. Through genetic counseling, such individuals might be advised not to have children, or at least, not by another individual with the same heterozygous condition. Some of these developments are not attainable within the foreseeable future, but eventually, they may go a long way toward saving man from any worsening of his present genetic condition. And perhaps none too soon. Even if medical technology does not weaken the species, increasing amounts of radiation may well do so.

However, it would appear that man's greatest present biological danger is not genetic but environmental. We have noted the problems related to the factors of overpopulation and pollution. Perhaps the need is not so much to worry that the species will become weak genetically but to realize that there may be no species of man to worry about at all.

What chance is there that man will evolve into a higher form or, put another way, that he will progress rather than regress? One of the popular themes of science fiction is the appearance of human beings perhaps 10,000 years from now who possess huge brains and small bodies—veritable human computers, as it were. Is this change a likelihood?

If by evolution we mean *organic* evolution, such a development seems unlikely. In the first place, the average capacity of the human cranium has not changed discernibly in 100,000 years; and yet, for most of that time, man has been under the major influence of natural, not cultural, selection. In the second place, the idea is purely Lamarckian. It implies than man has a built-in tendency toward progression, that greater use promotes a continued increase in size. Let us remember the definition of natural selection: **It is essentially the differential reproduction of genetic types.** In order to show that the species as a whole can experience an increase in the size of the brain, one would have to assume a correlation between intelligence and brain size. It would then have to be shown that *the more intelligent people consistently have more children than those with less intelligence.* He who expects brain size and/or intelligence to increase in modern man on this same basis puts forth a dubious hypothesis indeed.

Of course, we have no way of knowing what man may look like 100,000 years from now, assuming that he is still around. Unless, however, his cultural evolution has unforeseeable effects upon his organic evolution (for example, it is conceivable that artificial selection for intelligence might be undertaken), it appears safe to predict that few physical changes will be evident.

QUESTIONS FOR REVIEW AND DISCUSSION

1. What are the four components of a pond ecosystem? What type of nutrition characterizes each of the three types of biotic components?

2. The ecologist M. Kleiber has estimated that if a man lived on chicken eggs alone for a year, about 7 acres of land would be required to feed him. In contrast, enough grain could be raised on 0.3 acre to feed a man for a year, and only 0.002 acre would be required if he subsisted only on algae. Explain these figures in terms of the food chain-pyramid of numbers concept. Can you suggest an explanation

for the considerable difference in the areas required for raising grain and algae?

3. Why is it more realistic to speak of *food webs* rather than *food chains* in describing an ecosystem?

4. Why are synthetic compounds, such as DDT, more likely to constitute an ecological hazard than natural compounds, such as pyrethrin?

5. Eradication of the screw-worm fly from the Southeastern United States was a great technological achievement that was dependent on "pure" scientific knowledge. What was this knowledge? What does this imply for the relationship between science and technology?

6. Why is strontium-90 of particular significance to man? How does this radioisotope originate in man's environment?

7. At the present rate of increase in the human population, it has been estimated that there will be one human being per square yard of Earth's land surface by the year 2500. Obviously, something will be done to alter the rate of increase before such a population is reached. What do you think this "something" will be?

8. What four factors may be involved in the "leveling off" of a population growth curve? Which of these factors do you feel is most likely to become effective in curbing the present rate of human population growth before the year 2000?

9. How does conservation ecology differ in outlook from "traditional" conservationism?

10. Is man a part of nature? How do the authors justify their answer to this question as both "yes" and "no"?

11. Suppose a government decided to allow only selected women to bear children, with selected males serving as sperm donors. Without considering the ethical problems, state the biological difficulties that might be inherent in such a eugenic program. Would the phenomenon of recombination have a bearing on the success of such a program?

12. Early in this century, a certain individual heard a lecture on genetics, and exclaimed, "Why, genetics is simply a kind of scientific Calvinism!" What do you suppose he meant? In consideration of Charlotte Auerbach's analogy of a hand of cards, do you agree with the individual's statement? To what extent do you feel that it is an oversimplification?

REFERENCES

Carson, R. *Silent Spring*. Boston: Houghton Mifflin Co., 1962. A classic protest against environmental abuse.

Detwyler, T. R. *Man's Impact On Environment.* New York: McGraw-Hill Book Company, 1971. A thorough consideration of human ecology.

Ehrenfeld, D. W. *Biological Conservation.* New York: Holt, Rinehart and Winston, Inc., 1970. This book sets forth the principles of the "new conservation" discussed in this chapter, and contrasts it with traditional conservation.

Ehrlich, P. R. and A. H. Ehrlich. *Population, Resources, Environment.* San Francisco: W. H. Freeman and Company, 1970. An authoritative work by two renowned experts in human ecology.

Hardin, G. *Nature and Man's Fate.* New York: Rinehart and Company, Inc., 1959. A challenging book that relates biology and evolution to the social and political problems faced by man in the 20th century.

Odum, E. P. *Ecology.* New York: Holt, Rinehart and Winston. 1963. An excellent little volume by an outstanding ecologist.

Weisz, P. B. (ed.). *The Contemporary Scene.* New York: McGraw-Hill Book Company, 1970. A book of readings on human nature, race, behavior, society, and environment. Several of these readings are cited independently in this chapter (see appendix).

NINE

The Social Scene

The fallout of practical applications from the great conceptual schemes of biology has been impressive indeed. We have made no attempt to review these applications, partly because some of them are so well known. It is common knowledge, for instance, that modern techniques for the study and treatment of cancer are traceable to the so-called cell theory and that hybrid corn became possible through an application of Mendelian genetics.

It is less widely known that biological thought has exerted a profound effect upon social trends and social philosophies. These effects have been especially noticeable within the past century. Perhaps more important, it now appears quite likely that biology will influence man's thinking to an even greater extent in the near future. Many problems in philosophy, theology, psychology, sociology, and political science are fundamentally biological ones; failure on the part of some people to recognize this fact in the past has often resulted in confusion, at best, and, at the worst, in pure nonsense.

Perhaps the root of the problem has been, and continues to be, the understandable tendency to remove man from nature. Somehow one forgets that philosophers, theologians, and psychologists are first of all human beings, that human beings are animals, and that animals are a part of the biological world. Put another way, man is an organism in a world of organisms. If he can be said to transcend his biological nature in any meaningful sense, at least it should be remembered that he cannot escape it completely (notice, we say *completely*). If man is only a little lower than angels, he is also only a little higher than apes.

Nevertheless, man is not what paleontologist G. G. Simpson calls a "nothing but" animal; that is, those who say that "man is nothing but an animal" are surely wrong.[1] That he *is* an animal cannot be denied; but he is an *ethical, social* animal who is apparently unique among his fellow organisms in being able to think upon his origin, his destiny, his moral responsibilities, and his place in nature. Man's attempts to formulate meaningful questions and answers about such matters constitute what we call the "social scene." Let us endeavor to relate biological science to this general area of human interest.

9.1 PHILOSOPHY, RELIGION, AND BIOLOGY

9.1A Biology and Philosophy: A Problem of Communication

We have pointed out that science and philosophy exerted a strong reciprocal influence during the late Renaissance when modern scientific tradition was just beginning to emerge. At that time, philosophy was probably more helpful to science than science was to philosophy. In one sense, such philosophers as Bacon, Descartes, and Kant *were* the authors of modern science. Nevertheless, the work of Galileo was profoundly stimulating to the philosophers of the 17th century. Later on in the same century, the physics propounded by Isaac Newton was important to the philosophy of that time because it reinforced the mechanistic view of the world within which most philosophers operated.

Biology did not mature as a science until later, although 17th-century philosophers had some early influence. Descartes, for example, drew much of his initial inspiration from William Harvey, whose elucidation of blood circulation in the human body (published in 1628) was the first great achievement of experimental biology. Perhaps it is fair to say, however, that biology was overshadowed by physical science throughout most of the 17th, 18th, and 19th centuries as a source of inspiration for philosophy. Unfortunately, as a result, some philosophers developed thought-systems that might never have gained prominence if more biological insight had been available. For example, John Locke (1632–1704), who has had great influence upon modern Western thought, based his philosophy on the premise that the human mind is completely blank at birth. Perhaps it is blank in the sense that Locke meant it; but it is extremely doubtful, in the light of even an elementary knowledge of the human nervous system, that his general premise was justifiable in a biological sense. To cite another example, Cartesian dualism (everything is either mind or matter), although subject to numerous criticisms on other grounds, is not a meaningful distinction in the light of modern biology.

The first really great impact that biology made upon philosophy was through Darwinian evolution. Although his influence has waned considerably since the 19th century, Herbert Spencer (1820–1903), a contemporary of Darwin, was for a time extremely influential as an evolutionary philosopher. However, evolutionary thought permeated the whole of philosophy and generated problems that led to the formulation of thought-systems that have been more enduring than those of Spencer. Foremost among the philosophers for whom the concept of organic evolution was a major stimulus are Henri Bergson (1859–1941), John Dewey (1859–1952), and Alfred North Whitehead (1861–1947). To explore their respective ideas would divert us from our theme, but it is enough to say that their total influence upon philosophy has been profound.[2]

Perhaps biology has not yet matured sufficiently in a philosophical sense to exert a very powerful influence upon philosophy as a whole. It may well be that Whitehead was justified in stating in 1925 that "the science of living organisms is only now coming to a growth adequate to impress its conceptions upon philosophy." [3] However, this picture is almost certain to change as biology makes a greater impact upon the world of ideas as a whole. Even now, it seems reasonable to say that many philosophical problems (for example, the free will-determinism controversy, the mechanism-vitalism dichotomy, the nature of the mind) would not seem nearly so great to philosophers if they were well-versed in modern biology. We do not claim, of course, that biology has solved these problems—far from it. But the philosopher who examines them without the insights of modern biology fails to make the most of his opportunity.

Perhaps the problem of interaction can better be stated in terms of philosophy and science as a whole. For example, one of the enduring problems in philosophy is whether or not human thoughts and actions are *determined* or *free* (the free will-determinism controversy). Proponents of determinism point to the many biological mechanisms that are known to control human behavior. Their argument is, essentially, that if all the mechanisms were known, there would be no grounds for maintaining that free will exists. In other words, the human mind is purely a mechanism. Those who insist that free will is a reality usually base their arguments on common-sense observations. They maintain that the human mind is more than a mere sum of its parts. In other words, "mind" is an emergent property.

The problem may be resolved quite satisfactorily, operationally, in the same manner that scientists resolve their most difficult problems. Under some circumstances, it is more fruitful to act as if human thought and behavior are determined; under other circumstances, it is more profitable to act as if a given individual is free to choose his course of action. This is not to say that such an approach "really" solves the problem, but to recognize that, in our present state of knowledge, it is not possible to determine which of these alternatives—determinism or free will—is "true." In fact, this may never be possible. Scientists generally learned long ago to avoid "either-or" alternatives and to settle for operational and provisional conceptual schemes. Philosophers might profit from this example.[4]

However, it must be stated in all fairness that the problem of interaction between biology and philosophy is to a great extent one of communication, and much of the blame must be placed upon biologists rather than philosophers. Perhaps the real blame should be placed on society's encouragement of an educational system that in effect fosters anti-intellectualism through the deliberate compartmentalization of knowledge. In many universities, a given discipline (such as biology, or even one of its subfields) is so isolated that it ignores all knowledge except its own. Fortunately, many universities have now seen the dangers of extreme compartmentalization and are making serious attempts to return to the ideal of a liberal education. If this trend gains momentum, the reciprocal influence of biology and philosophy will undoubtedly increase.

9.1B Biology and Religion: A Problem of Dogmatism

In view of the fact that a majority of the present population of the United States profess a connection with some organized religious body (and well over 90 per cent profess a belief in God), the subject of religion within any context would seem to be a relevant one.[5] Traditionally, science has remained indifferent to the entire subject of religion—and for good reason, since the basic assumptions of each area are not useful to the other and, indeed, have often seemed contradictory. Nevertheless, unless a person professes to accept only science or only religion (which is rare either way), he will see that problems in both areas are overlapping.

In 1896, following more than three decades of controversy that centered around the implications of organic evolution, an American historian, Andrew D. White, wrote a lengthy and perceptive work entitled *A History of the Warfare of Science With Theology in Christendom*. White surveyed the history of ecclesiastical opposition to scientific ideas: the Copernican revolution, the shape of the earth, the naturalistic approach of medicine to human diseases, the application of historical and scientific methods to the study of the Bible, and organic evolution with its evidences and implications. He came to the general conclusion that the historic conflict did not really involve religion at all, but rather, *dogmatic theology*. Religion itself, White argued, cannot quarrel with science; theology, however, is another matter altogether. Any system of thought that *rules out empirical evidence in advance* (you will recall our previous definition of dogmatism in Chapter 1) is by its very nature in conflict with the spirit of scientific inquiry. White's distinction is surely a valid one. What has often been termed the conflict of science and religion is largely, if not entirely, misnamed. The conflict is between science and dogmatic theology.

Since a survey of the historic conflict between science and dogmatic theology lies beyond the scope of this book, let us concentrate on a single vital point: namely, the controversy in Christendom that continues to the present time over the concept of organic evolution.

THE HISTORY OF BIBLICAL INTERPRETATION

In Chapter 7, we made the statement that the concept of organic evolution is probably accepted by only a minority of people in the Western world. In contrast, "everyone" accepts the other conceptual schemes we have introduced: biogenesis, the cell concept, and Mendelian genetics. At least, there is no widespread prejudice against these broad hypotheses. Why the difference?

Western civilization as we know it developed around the Christian religion, and a very important part of that religion is the Bible. The Old Testament, which was held in great reverence by the Jews, was carried over into the Christian Church as a body of sacred literature. By the fourth century A.D., the books presently included in the New Testament had been agreed upon by authoritative Church councils, and were added to those of the Old Testament. Well before the later Middle Ages, the Church had proclaimed the entire body of the Bible to be the authoritative Word of

God and had solved the problems of interpretation by the dogmatic methods so characteristic of the medieval Church. However, this dogmatism did not take the form of a slavish literalism. Thomas Aquinas himself, who did more to shape the theology of the Roman Catholic Church than anyone else, held that the Scriptures might have meanings other than literal ones. The point is that the Church proclaimed itself to be the sole reliable interpreter of the Bible. Thus, in Roman Catholic theology, the authority of the Scriptures has traditionally been subordinate to the authority of the Church.

It was against this concept of authority that Martin Luther revolted in the early 16th century, and his revolt led to the Protestant Reformation. From the very first, the Protestant churches emphasized the authority of the Scriptures over the authority of a church hierarchy; and, as a result of this emphasis, the Protestant Reformation became characterized by a fervent Biblicism that contrasted rather sharply with Roman Catholicism. Although there is no reason to believe that Roman Catholics of the Renaissance period took a less literal view of the creation account in Genesis, Protestants became committed to such a view as a part of their very reason for existence as a separate religious movement. Thus, it is within the Protestant framework that the loudest and most vehement objections have originated.

While science was full of ferment during the 17th and 18th centuries, theology was relatively quiescent. Both Roman Catholicism and Protestantism remained authoritarian. Within the ranks of the latter, differences over interpretation of various biblical passages led to the rise of different Protestant denominations. There was little disagreement, however, over the basic posture: the Bible is the revealed Word of God and is inspired in all its parts. Coupled with this attitude was an inconsistent literalism. Protestants may have differed among themselves on the content and significance of The Song of Solomon and Revelation, but they were almost unanimous in their literal view of the Genesis account of creation.

In the meantime, and beginning especially in the early 19th century, a "new" Christian theology arose, namely, the field of biblical criticism. Scholars began to study the ancient documents objectively in order to establish dates, authorships, and origins of the biblical writings. As a result of this impartial approach to biblical studies, which used the tools of historical and scientific research, a wave of liberal religious thought began to sweep through Protestant Europe. However, it was confined in large part to the world of scholarship. By the time the *Origin of Species* appeared, the new theology still had made little impact on the average parish parson. This fact accounts for the genuine shock that greeted Darwinian evolution in ecclesiastical circles.

The specific point of conflict centered around the account of the creation in the book of Genesis. According to the traditional and literal interpretation of this account, God first created the inanimate earth and then proceeded around 4000 B.C. to create living forms successively; preparation of the earth for these forms and their creation occupied a period of six days. Also traditional with this viewpoint, although really only implied rather vaguely in the actual account, was the interpretation that living forms are immutable. Obviously, the traditional interpretation of the Genesis account was directly challenged by Darwinian evolution.

The greatest opposition to the concept of organic evolution came from the Protestant churches; Roman Catholicism remained generally aloof from the whole controversy. In 1909, the problem was settled for the Roman Church when a special Biblical Commission, which had been appointed by Pope Leo XIII, issued a statement that in effect gave Catholics freedom to accept or reject the evolutionary concept as it applied to the organic world and to the human body as long as the creative power of God was acknowledged. As for the Protestant churches, most of them eventually rationalized the concept in one way or another, and by the end of the 19th century, the uproar had gradually subsided.[6]

THE FUNDAMENTALIST MOVEMENT

In Protestantism, dogmatic theology has largely taken the form of *fundamentalism*. Although fundamentalists have never been in complete theological agreement among themselves, the following points are generally accepted: The Bible is the divinely inspired and dictated Word of God; the bible is historically and scientifically inerrant; any scientific, historical, or critical evidence that is not in strict agreement with the literal teaching of the Bible is to be rejected summarily. To anyone who is acquainted with the Bible and with modern science (to say nothing of the fields of historical and biblical criticism), it should be obvious that fundamentalists are committed to living with some grave difficulties.

Throughout the latter part of the 19th century, within a variety of denominations, there existed a hard core of fundamentalists who resisted both the new theology and the new biology *in toto*. By the turn of the century, their position had become untenable because of the mounting evidence against the validity of biblical literalism. In America, to a greater degree than in Europe, fundamentalism, therefore, became strongly militant shortly after the turn of the century. In the meantime, liberal theology began to decline in scholarly popularity. Having viewed the extremes of liberalism and fundamentalism, most theologians settled down to some sort of middle course. Since liberalism had never been strongly militant anyway, the fundamentalists, at least in the United States, had the field of popular religion almost to themselves by the mid-1920's. Almost every Protestant denomination either was influenced by fundamentalism or aligned itself with the movement. Although the movement was strongest in the United States, it had a powerful influence in Europe as well.

The fundamentalist movement has lost much of its former strength and militance, but its basic premises are still relevant for many people. To them, in fact, fundamentalism *is* the Christian religion. Thus, the science-versus-religion conflict is still very real.[7]

The foregoing discussion is not meant to suggest that only ignorant and prejudiced people are fundamentalists. As a matter of fact, their ranks include many highly competent scientists and theologians who have made positive contributions to their respective fields. The intent of fundamentalism is a laudable one: to preserve the integrity of a great body of literature that represents, to them, the only certainty in a world characterized by shifting values and arbitrary ethical standards. Unfortunately, however, fundamentalists ignore or explain away the viewpoints of such individuals as the biologist who says that the human species is older than some 6,000 years and that the human body bears the scars of long years of organic evolution, the Hebrew scholar who points to the strong evidence for a different cultural origin for Genesis 1 and Genesis 2, and a careful student of the New Testament who discovers certain discrepancies in narrative among the four Gospels. By commitment, the fundamentalist can allow no amount of empirical evidence to impinge upon his basic dogmatic assumptions.

There is a tendency among professional biologists to assume that fundamentalism is a dead issue, but it is not. For example, as recently as 1969, the California State Board of Education, apparently under pressure from fundamentalists, voted unanimously to require biology teachers in the public schools to devote as much time to the concept of special creation as to evolution. Millions of people in the United States and Europe remain allied with fundamentalist assumptions; and, for better or worse, both science and theology must take this fact into account. As far as the fundamentalist himself is concerned, he is, of course, free to believe whatever he will. But he should be aware that his loyalty to the basic tenets of fundamentalism commits him to a dogmatism that cannot be reconciled with the spirit of impartial inquiry that is essential to the scientific process.

On the other hand, dogmatism is not limited to theology. As we shall see presently, it is to be found in political systems, and—paradoxical as it may sound—even in science. Many biologists, for example, meet theological dogmatism with empirical dogmatism, asserting with authoritarian conviction that organic evolution (or biogenesis or the latest concept of the atom) has been "proved." Perhaps every area of human endeavor has its share of those whom Eric Hoffer has called the True Believers—individuals who are so emotionally constituted that they feel obliged to embrace one set of dogmatic assertions or another.[8] We leave it to the psychologists to explain this foible of human behavior. To say the very least, it is inconsistent with the spirit of scientific endeavor.

Organic evolution continues to be opposed in the Western world, therefore, almost solely by Christian fundamentalists, both Catholic and Protestant.* Less dogmatic religious people have taken the view that the Bible loses nothing of its integrity through a nonliteral interpretation of those passages that conflict with modern science, and that the Christian religion as a whole does not suffer by considering the Bible in the light of modern scholarship. This view is expressed by theologian Daniel Stevick:

> These words [the Bible] have their authority and significance as witness. As historical reporting, they may be inaccurate. As science, they may be dated and naïve. But, as witness to the redeeming activity of God, they are final, self-authenticating, and carry the authority of the God whose Word they are.[9]

Perhaps an even more basic conflict arises between advocates of science and religion whenever there is failure to recognize that each of these two subjects must be approached according to a different temperament. We shall have more to say in the next chapter about the tendency of scientists to regard their truth as the only truth, but it is appropriate to recognize the principle at this point. Theologian Reinhold Niebuhr states it as follows:

> ... the religious symbols of ultimate meaning are poetic rather than exact and scientific, and the fearfully pious are always tempted to buttress their validity by a frantic adhesion to some outmoded science, against the challenge of a marching science, which always has immediate truth on its side but which always threatens to construct a scientific world picture in which no meaning can be found for man in his grandeur and his misery.[10]

9.2 BIOLOGY AND THE SOCIAL SCIENCES

One has only to contemplate mankind's present tendency toward overpopulation to realize that social problems are fundamentally biological

---

* Although Roman Catholics are under no obligation to accept the Genesis account of creation literally, many of them oppose the concept of organic evolution. It must be remembered that the Roman Church includes a number of fundamentalists, with attitudes toward problems of biblical interpretation that are not greatly different from those of their Protestant counterparts. The major difference is theological: The arch-conservative Catholic is essentially a *Church* fundamentalist, and the arch-conservative Protestant is essentially a *Bible* fundamentalist.

ones. As a special example, note the cases where rioting begins in an overcrowded city slum, quite frequently touched off by some minor incident. Evidence is mounting, much of it from animal studies, that overcrowding has an adverse biological effect upon the complex mammal. The net result is an abnormal stress upon the nervous system that may intensify aggression patterns or other syndromes, thus leading to antisocial behavior. It is difficult to investigate this area, because there are many uncontrollable variables and a multiplicity of possible causal factors.

We do not intend merely to point out the importance of biology to social science, although we feel justified in saying that sociologists, political scientists, and psychologists who fail to take the biological basis of human behavior into account may be wasting their time. Rather than enter into an analysis of these complex fields, let us dwell on some revealing case histories of biological and social interaction.

9.2A An Intellectual Disaster: Social Darwinism

It seems apparent that one reason Charles Darwin procrastinated about setting forth his views on evolution was his apprehension that they would be distorted and misapplied. His fears were amply justified. In the decades immediately following publication of the *Origin of Species,* there was complete turmoil in the intellectual world over the idea of evolution. Indeed, it was a rare field of endeavor that escaped its influence completely. Every aspect of human culture was cast in developmental terms: language, religion, ethical systems, political systems, the whole spectrum. In fact, evolution became something of an intellectual fad during the latter part of the 19th century. The major part of the trend, called *social Darwinism,* was based on the premise that the principles of organic evolution are operative among human societies in precisely the same manner as they are operative in the world of animal life.

A number of reasons might be advanced for the advent and sweeping success of social Darwinism. For one thing, the concept of organic evolution *was* a tremendous idea that had numerous implications for the human species. Furthermore, it involved both science and history; this involvement is a rare thing in science. All of the social sciences—sociology, political science, psychology, history in its dynamic sense—were in a very early stage of development during the latter half of the 19th century, and each was struggling to become more scientific. Hence, a conceptual scheme and a method were lifted directly from biology, the natural science with which the social sciences are most closely identified.

The greatest immediate stimulus to social Darwinism came from Herbert Spencer, an English philosopher who had been thinking about evolution long before 1859, although mostly in Lamarckian terms. It was he who coined the term "survival of the fittest" that Darwin borrowed. He became intrigued with proposing a general law of evolution that would be applicable to the whole of society. In his *Social Statics,* published in 1850, he attempted to justify *laissez faire* economics from biological principles. In 1862, the first of several volumes composing his *Synthetic Philosophy* appeared. *The Principles of Sociology* was published in three volumes between 1876 and 1896; *The Principles of Ethics* appeared in two volumes between 1892 and 1893. Spencer was a prodigious writer; in addition to these highly influential works, he wrote numerous other books and articles. His social views can be summarized rather concisely without doing them great injustice: He believed that natural selection and the whole of evolutionary theory are directly applicable to the human species in all of its interactions.

In general, Spencer's social theories were consistent with his basic premise. He believed very strongly in a *laissez faire* economy with free and open competition in the labor market, and he was vigorously opposed to governmental controls on society because these are "unnatural." Therefore, he opposed state-supported education, postal systems, tariffs, and welfare aid. On this last point, it was his contention that the poor are nature's unfit (why else had they not become rich?), and government only violates the laws of nature to maintain them even at the subsistence level.

Although social Darwinism became fairly popular in Europe, it was received with especially strong enthusiasm in the United States. The temper of the times was particularly favorable to the reception of Spencer's views. The post-Civil War era saw great fortunes made by men who had worked long and hard. There was enough opportunity in the land, and sufficient freedom, that the difference between success and failure was in fact frequently a matter of industry and resourcefulness on the part of an individual. Thus, throughout the business, industrial, and intellectual communities, there was widespread sentiment that nature rewards individuals in direct proportion to their own efforts. It is small wonder that such expressions as "struggle for existence" and "survival of the fittest" took on special meaning in America.

However, America's intellectual community as well as much of American society as a whole became disenchanted with social Darwinism well before the end of the 19th century. A succession of economic panics, labor riots, and other social disorders forced thoughtful leaders to take a new and strong look at the *laissez faire* doctrine. It became obvious that unbridled competition in social affairs could (and often did) lead to results that were nothing short of monstrous in terms of individual human welfare. The religious community, which was developing more social concern, began to realize how much human suffering was caused by free competition. The fundamentalist element, of course, had never accepted this basic Darwinian premise anyway. Initially, Spencer and social Darwinism had won over the American public by a type of default. The 1860's and 1870's were a time of great stress for American society, and social Darwinism was proposed as a possible solution to social problems. By 1890, however, the whole Spencerian scheme had lost much of its popular appeal; interest in social Darwinism declined, with one important exception: The eugenics movement, which was not Spencerian in origin but which must be classified as one aspect of social Darwinism, retained its strength for some decades past the turn of the century.

In Europe, where the social scene was different, social Darwinism never reached the degree of popularity that it did in the United States. However, it was embraced enthusiastically by a number of people, and such popularity as it enjoyed roughly paralleled that in America.

Although social Darwinism itself was a temporary fallout effect of Darwinian evolution,* it had a fallout all its own whose effects extend even to the present day. It should be readily apparent that an extension of social Darwinism to international affairs would justify military imperialism. Although Spencer himself (who was a pacifist) explained away this implication by saying that human society had already passed through its militaristic stage of evolution, other writers were not so squeamish. Another logical extension of social Darwinism was the concept of the superior race. This combination of militarism and racism reached a high point of popularity in the United States during the latter part of the 19th century. It was a strange mixture of super-patriotism, racism, Spencerian evolution, and Manifest Destiny (the doctrine that God had chosen the American people, a superior breed, to bring enlightenment to the heathen by annexing their lands). Nor was this feeling limited to the United States. Both sides in the Franco-Prussian War (1870–1871) justified their actions by appealing to Darwinian evolution. As is well known, a considerable amount of militarism based on the concept of racial superiority was preached in Germany before both World War I and World War II, although historians continue to debate the extent to which the German militarism of the present century has sprung directly from these ideas. Social Darwinism, nevertheless, undoubtedly has exerted a certain degree of influence in all civilized countries within the past hundred years.

Pure racial bigotry, which continues to be such a disturbing factor especially in the United States and South Africa, is undoubtedly motivated

---

* Somewhat ironically, Spencer never embraced the total Darwinian conceptual scheme. Apparently in defense of certain theories of learning and his belief that acquired intelligence is inherited, he remained a Lamarckian all his life. His social theories, therefore, were not truly Darwinian at their base.

in part by a kind of lingering social Darwinism. The feeling runs something like this: Whites must be superior to blacks—since the former have the upper hand, this fact must prove their superiority. Thus, with a simplistic rationale that defies both history and evolutionary theory—to say nothing of genetics—the champions of this doctrine make a leap of faith from social dominance to biological superiority.

There is no doubt that millions of people today long for a Spencerian world, whether their basic motivation is racial, military, social, or economic. Part of this longing, at least, undoubtedly can be traced to the days when Herbert Spencer was enjoying his greatest popularity. Social Darwinism was dead in intellectual circles before 1900, but its ghost lives on in the minds of those whose psychic hungers are fed by the emotional security that derives from a superiority complex.

How much of the blame for social Darwinism can be laid at the feet of Darwin himself? It seems fair to say that none of it can be, if indeed "blame" must be imputed. Darwin did not claim to be a philosopher or social scientist, and he carefully avoided any extension of his theory into these areas. In addition, his retiring manner prevented him from making a vigorous protest at the abuses of his theory, although it is well established that Darwin was totally unsympathetic toward the transplantation of his theory from the purely biological realm to the social arena. On one occasion, shortly after publication of the *Origin of Species,* Darwin wrote his friend Charles Lyell, the geologist, as follows:

> I have received in a Manchester newspaper rather a good squib, showing that I have proved "might is right," and therefore that Napoleon is right, and every cheating tradesman is also right.

It would appear that Darwin was no more sympathetic to the social applications of his theory than were some of the men who, decades later, would curse his memory. He insisted, whenever he had an opportunity, that he had used in completely metaphorical sense the expressions "struggle for existence" and "survival of the fittest" (neither of which was original with him). In fact, he said so in the later editions of the *Origin of Species.* Darwin was himself the kindliest of men; and, if we may be allowed to speculate, we would hazard the guess that his very temperament prevented him from endorsing the major tenets of Spencer's use of his theory.

In summary, the social Darwinians made at least two grave blunders. First of all, they equated "fittest" with "strongest" or "most brutal," whereas Darwin merely used the term to describe those that are best adapted to a given environment. Today, of course, we draw an even finer line: The "fittest," biologically, are those who compete best reproductively. The second blunder of social Darwinians was assuming that men somehow achieve social progress by competing with each other. They failed completely to take into account the struggle of man with his environment. Of course, there were other blunders as well. Historian Richard Hofstadter, whose book *Social Darwinism in American Thought* is a definitive one, concludes with this summary and warning:

> Whatever the course of social philosophy in the future . . . , a few conclusions are now accepted by most humanists: that such biological ideas as "survival of the fittest," whatever their doubtful value in natural science, are utterly useless in attempting to understand society; that the life of man in society, while it is incidentally a biological fact, has characteristics that are not reducible to biology and must be explained in the distinctive terms of a cultural analysis; that the physical well-being of men is a result of their social organization and not vice-versa; that social improvement is a product of advances in technology and social organization, not of breeding or selective elimination; that judgments as to the value of competition between men or enterprises or nations must be based upon social and not allegedly biological consequences; and, finally, that there is nothing in nature or a naturalistic philosophy of life to make impossible the acceptance of moral sanctions that can be employed for the common good.[11]

The historical lesson of society's experiences with social Darwinism should not be lost on modern man. It is dangerous to draw analogies too freely between the natural sciences, where causal factors are difficult enough to ascertain, and the social sciences, where they become so complex that they are almost impossible to analyze. Analogies are particularly hazardous when the basic premise is only an approximation, a first statement, in the scientific area from which it is taken. Darwin's theory of evolution lacked completeness even for biology; how much more inappropriate it proved to be as a social theory is surely one of history's clearest lessons.

9.2B An Ideological Disaster: Death of a Science in Russia

In a previous discussion concerning radiation effects (see Section 8.2A), we pointed out that biological problems often have a direct bearing upon political science. Let us now consider how political science may affect biology. A number of case histories might be cited in order to demonstrate the interaction of biology and politics, but the most interesting one transpired within the present century and assumes a special significance. This case is the clash that has occurred between genetics and communist ideology in the Soviet Union.

Perhaps a little background in the history of Russian politics will be helpful. For centuries, Russia was ruled by a succession of czars, but this system of government was overthrown by revolutionaries in 1917 following a disastrous military experience that was a part of World War I. After a few years of political confusion, Russia became dominated by the Communist party, which imposed a strict socialism upon the country. There was to be no private ownership of land, and society would be a classless one. The most influential figure in this movement was Nikolai Lenin, who drew heavily upon the economic and political theories of the 19th-century German socialists Karl Marx and Friedrich Engels. Essentially, Marx and Engels had reacted to capitalism; they claimed that, in a competitive society, wealth tended to concentrate more and more in the hands of a few, at the expense of the masses. Thus, the Communist party espoused a doctrine of total equality, at least in principle.

As a social ideal, the goal of human equality is a laudable one. Surely this ideal is what the framers of the American Declaration of Independence had in mind: equality in opportunity and equality before the law. But it is very easy to distort this lofty ideal. Many persons, both American and Russian, have extended the concept of equality into the biological realm where it would mean that all men begin life as equals in genetic potentiality. Within the framework of communist doctrine, this leap from the social to the biological realm became an ideological necessity; in theory, a classless society must be composed of equal individuals. For all practical purposes, the Communist party leaders of the 1920's and 1930's proclaimed that all men *are* biological equals; their party line actually started from this basic premise.

In the meantime, rapid progress was being made in genetics. The grand synthesis of fundamental genetic theories came during the early 1930's, and some of the finest geneticists of that period were Russians. By that time, it was widely realized that the Darwin-Mendel conceptual schemes were based on the premise that individuals within a population or within a species differ (remember Darwin's emphasis on variation) and that differences often have a genetic base (which Darwin assumed and Mendel confirmed). This synthesis of genetics and evolution placed the Russian geneticists in a delicate position. Fortunately for them, however, there were few, if any, Communist party leaders who recognized the basic conflict. For the most part, the geneticists worked with fruit flies, cereal grains, and cabbages, and their work seemed harmless enough. But just when they were getting along rather well, they made a fatal mistake: They ventured into the field of human genetics.

As is well known among geneticists and psychologists, the best way to study the relative effects of heredity and environment in human beings is to compare identical twins, preferably those that have been reared apart from infancy. Such a study was badly needed in the 1920's, if for no other reason than to help settle the eugenics question. Russia was a particularly favorable locale for such a study, because the social turmoil following the revolution of 1917 had separated many families. Consequently, a large-scale investigation was launched by Russian geneticists in the early 1930's; by 1934, about 1,000 pairs of identical twins had been studied. The results of this study showed very clearly, among other things, that genetic differences *do* exist among human beings.

Dwellers in a free world would automatically suppose, perhaps, that such massive evidence against the notion of biological equality would have a profound effect upon political ideology, but such was not the case. *Biology did not change the party line; the party line changed biology.* All work in human genetics was suspended in Russia at the end of 1936; the Moscow institute that had sponsored the massive twin studies was disbanded shortly thereafter. In 1937, its director was committed to prison, where he died.

Long before these events transpired, a Russian agronomist named Trofim Lysenko had begun maneuvering his way to the top of Russian science. Lysenko espoused a strange mixture of Lamarckianism, mysticism, anthropomorphism, and romantic nonsense. For example, he maintained that plants are educable, that they choose their sexual partners, and that they "will" the genetic nature of their progeny.

Yet, it was Lysenko who engineered the downfall of the leading Russian geneticists in 1936. Afterwards, he moved to the top position in agricultural affairs and shortly after this triumph became a member of the Supreme Soviet. For the better part of three decades thereafter he was the darling of Soviet science, and was retained in a position of authority by both Josef Stalin and Nikita Khrushchev. It was not until February, 1965, four months after Khrushchev was deposed, that Lysenko was dismissed from his position as director of the Institute of Genetics of the U.S.S.R. Academy of Sciences. By that time, the condition of Russian agriculture was an international scandal, chiefly because of Lysenko's consistent refusal to countenance the application to agriculture of genetic principles that had led to the development of hybrid corn and superior animal breeds in the Western world. There is reason to believe that Lysenkoism played a considerable role in Khrushchev's downfall.[12]

In the meantime, the science of genetics had died a slow and painful death in Russia between 1936 and the early 1960's. Stalin instituted a general political purge in 1938 that removed many of the most courageous geneticists; others simply disappeared during the war years of the 1940's.

In 1948, Lysenko reiterated and strengthened his position that biology and genetics must yield to the Communist party line, and the few remaining adherents to the accepted genetics of the Western world either managed to keep their thoughts under cover, recanted, or were liquidated.

What is the picture in Russia today? It is not an easy one to ascertain, but there is reason to believe that genetics is making a comeback. For one thing, the regime that took over from Khrushchev permitted a thorough revision of biology textbooks used in high schools, and these books affirm the Mendelian genetics that Lysenko denied. Furthermore, genetic research is now being reported from Russia that would not have been tolerated between 1936 and the early 1960's. Thus, even with the handicap of three lost decades in genetics, Russian biology is making its adjustment to reality. As for Russian society itself, there are distinct signs that it is moving away from the rigid party line of pure communism. It seems doubtful that the doctrines of Lenin and his forebears are convincing to the present generation in Russia. In many ways, this move away from pure communism as an ideal parallels the American move of the past half-century away from pure capitalism as an ideal. Many political scientists predict that both Russia and America will some day live under a system of government that represents a compromise between their respective former positions.

To the biologist, the account of genetics in Russia, Lysenkoism, and communist ideology is a part of the history of conflict between science and dogmatism. It is reminiscent of the attitudes that were expressed against Copernicus and Darwin by the dogmatic theology of their respective times. *Our thought-system demands an earth-centered universe, an instantaneous creation, the equality of human minds,* says the dogmatist, *and wishing will make it so.* Then, when empirical evidence becomes so overwhelming that even the dogmatist can no longer resist it, he seeks to preserve the integrity of his thought-system through subtle modification or through a denial that he ever really opposed the conceptual scheme that has been vindicated. Such is human nature.

The very doctrinal basis of pure communism is an ideological disaster, because it is a basic denial of human freedom. We do not say that Marx and Engels were wrong in their evaluation of certain evils of capitalism or in their quest for greater equality of opportunity and material blessing among the earth's downtrodden masses. But the communist dream turned out to be a nightmare for the Russian people as a whole. Much of this unfortunate situation can be laid to the fact that communist ideology is based upon a concept of human nature to which modern genetics bears no witness. The biological basis of human freedom is human individuality, and no people will ever be free unless they recognize the right of each individual to be different. Biologist Garrett Hardin has expressed the matter with fitting eloquence:

> We must, in a deep sense, accept our humanity, our *variable* humanity. In the past we have not been notably successful in this, and the least successful have been the theologians, the moralists and the political scientists, who have, with rare and uninfluential exceptions, built their systems to fit only some fictitious "normal" Man, and then wondered why *men* did not behave like *Man*. We will never solve the moral problems of men until we accept, in our bones, the insights of the biologist and the geneticist.[13]

Perhaps men will not do so even then, but Hardin's main point is surely correct. To be truly moral, a man must be free, and to be truly free is to be recognized as an individual whose uniqueness and dignity are inviolate.

9.2C A Moral Problem: Genetic Variability

As biological science accumulates impressive evidence that human behavior stems in part from genetic influences, the implications for all of the social sciences become serious indeed. Let us consider one problem area, namely, antisocial or criminal behavior.

It has been known for years that criminality is gene-related. In the 1930's, a massive twin study was carried out in the United States and Europe that confirms this relationship beyond reasonable doubt. The method was as follows: An investigator would examine prison records in search of individuals who had a twin, either fraternal or identical, then he would search out the twin and find out if he or she had been convicted of a crime. In such studies, twins who "match" (that is, both have criminal records in this case) are said to be *concordant,* those who do not are said to be *discordant.*

Of course, merely to find a high incidence of concordance among twins would tell us very little. We would expect to find a higher degree of concordance than among any two groups chosen at random in society, or even among brothers and sisters, because members of a twin pair are usually subject to very similar environmental influences. But we can turn this very fact to advantage. The influence of the environment on *identical* twins would be approximately the same as the influence of the environment on *fraternal* twins. If, therefore, we regard the identical twins as our experimental group, fraternal twins constitute the closest approximation to a control group that we could hope for.

The results of these twin studies are revealing, if not astonishing. With regard to a criminal record, *fraternal twins were 34 per cent concordant and 66 per cent discordant; identical twins were 72 per cent concordant and 28 per cent discordant.* Furthermore, in a number of cases, concordant identical twins had often been convicted of the *same type of crime,* even though (in many instances) both individuals had turned to crime long after they had gone their separate ways.[14]

There has also been a relatively new development in genetics. During the early 1960's, it was learned that two relatively rare types of chromosomal combination, the XYY and XXYY syndromes, are frequently accompanied by a high degree of aggressiveness on the part of the individual who possesses either syndrome.* This aggressiveness often takes the form of antisocial behavior or criminality of one sort or another. For example, a group of geneticists found in 1966 that 21 out of 942 men in two British institutions for dangerous, violent, or criminal patients possessed two Y chromosomes. Since the combined incidence of the XYY and XXYY syndromes in society as a whole is about 5 in every 10,000 males, this means that the incidence of such individuals in these two institutions showed about a 40-fold increase (about 2 per cent as compared with about 0.05 per cent). These data, among others, indicate very strongly that the possession of two Y chromosomes by a man is correlated with criminality.[15]

If one accepts a genetic basis for human behavior, and the conclusion seems inescapable, some of our most cherished traditions thus are challenged. In past ages, men thought their destinies to be controlled by the stars or by the gods. Civilized people shook off these superstitions long ago and built their social institutions on the assumption that a man's destiny is his own. Should one admit that scientists and philosophers have been wrong, that a man's genes and chromosomes constitute a kind of determinism? Is an XYY individual predestined to a life of antisocial behavior? Or if a man's identical twin commits murder, is it inevitable that he, too, will commit a murder some day? Is the human will really not free? If a person who possesses an XYY syndrome robs a bank, can he plead with the judge that it is not he who is guilty, but his chromosomes? How fair is a legal system that *assumes* the equality of both genes and environment for all human beings?

These are complicated questions. Some of them cannot be answered in terms of present knowledge, and still others probably can never be answered in simple terms, if at all. Our point is this: Genetic factors in human behavior are quite real, and they must be considered. Perhaps it is more relevant to ask questions such as these: How shall I, as a parent, a

---

* Apparently, the XYY combination arises whenever a sperm carrying two Y chromosomes fertilizes an egg. The Y chromosomes failed to separate during the second meiotic division, and both were carried into the same sperm. The XYY individual would be a male, of course, with a total of 47 chromosomes in each of his body cells. The XXYY combination ($2n = 48$) arises by a similar, but cytologically different, process. There is independent evidence that the Y chromosome carries genes that contribute to male aggressiveness; thus, it would appear that the XYY or XXYY male gets a double dose of these genes.

social worker, a minister, a juror, or a judge respond to a problem of demonstrated genetic difference? How much of the other person's behavior am I willing to assume *may be* genetic in the absence of clear evidence to the contrary? Of course, it would be unrealistic to ascribe *all* human behavior to genes and chromosomes; some of the eugenicists foundered on this assumption. But it is just as unrealistic to ignore genetic factors.

Some recent events may be significant in their import. During 1969, a Frenchman possessing the XYY syndrome was convicted of murder. The jury recommended a reduced sentence of seven years' imprisonment based on the reasoning that "a man thus unbalanced from birth should not be severely punished for his transgressions." During the same year, an Australian was acquitted of a murder charge on the same grounds. Although these judgments raise a number of grave problems (for example, how to protect society from such individuals without abusing the individuals' rights), it is encouraging that society is showing signs of accepting the phenomenon of human inequality.

The implications of these problems, if not their answers, should be clear. Biology *is* a social issue. Society must seek ways to recognize and accept human inequalities at the same time that it seeks to promote equality of justice and opportunity. The biological factors are now so obvious that they can be ignored no longer.

9.2D Psychology: A Special Case of Biology

In historical retrospect, it is clear that every social science that presently makes a claim to legitimacy has struggled through a considerable amount of confusion in establishing its sphere of operations and its methods. Certainly, this development has been true of psychology, which (as it is usually pursued) is the science of the human mind and behavior. Let us examine at least a few of the biological implications for this field.

Psychology has no definite birth date. Its roots go back to Aristotle and continue through Descartes, Locke, and a host of other philosophers. Certainly, Descartes has played an important role in psychological thought, inasmuch as the mind-body relationship has been one of the most difficult problems. In fact, one of the "fathers" of modern psychology, G. T. Fechner (1801–1887), conducted laboratory investigations in what we would now call experimental psychology because he wished to find out whether the "mind" could be approached through scientific methodology. It is significant that great strides were made during the 19th century in animal physiology. Fechner and his immediate successors, therefore, relied very heavily on this field in their attempts to enunciate rational explanations for human behavior.

It is beyond the scope and aim of our present consideration to attempt a survey of the history of psychology. There were many influences during the course of the 19th century, and psychology entered the 20th century as a respectable academic discipline that had attracted a number of distinguished scholars to its ranks. From that time to the present, its development has been marked by numerous schools of thought. Structuralism, functionalism, Freudianism, behaviorism, Gestalt psychology—these and several other labels denote some important emphasis or other by certain groups of psychologists. As a rule, each school of thought has had its origin as a protest against a presumed excess on the part of another school of thought; not infrequently, each school has acted as if its particular truth was the only truth about human behavior. This attitude is not unusual, of course. It is a necessary accompaniment of growth, and biology as a whole has undergone much the same experience. For example, between 1900 and 1920, at least a dozen schools of thought existed in biology over the issue of organic evolution alone. It is from the conflict of different ideas and viewpoints that any science derives its richest blessings.* Certainly, psychology has provided men with some of their greatest insights.

Regardless of the various emphases, schools, and viewpoints of psychology, it appears in historical retrospect that psychologists have tended to align themselves with one or the other of two approaches. There is no convenient label that can be applied to these approaches, especially since the best labels almost always oversimplify, and the difference in viewpoint here is definitely not simple. However, perhaps they can be summarized briefly without doing either of them a grave injustice.

One of these two underlying modes in psychological thought rests upon the assumption that human behavior can best be explained through an elucidation of the fundamental mechanisms of the thought processes. Philosophically, this approach denies that mind and body are two different entities. Operationally, it affirms that behavior must ultimately be studied and explained as an extension of physiology. Thus, psychologists following this rationale have tended to rely heavily upon experimental studies conducted at the level of nerve synapses, reflex arcs, hormones, and so on. At least one modern psychologist, H. J. Eysenck, simply terms the proponents of this viewpoint *experimental psychologists,* although this label may be unfair to proponents of the other viewpoint, since it would imply that they do not pursue experiments.

The other division of psychological thought has laid great stress on considering behavior as a whole. In general, its followers have recognized the validity of experimental investigations in attempting to get at the

---

* Alfred North Whitehead, in discussing the so-called conflict between science and religion, counseled tolerance: "A clash of doctrines is not a disaster—it is an opportunity." [16]

fundamental mechanisms of behavior, but they have insisted that those investigations largely miss the point of psychology. As a result, they have tended to orient their activities around measurements of similarities and differences that involve the overall behavior of individuals and groups of individuals. Eysenck has termed these psychologists *personality theorists.*

To an objective biologist, who has the advantage of viewing these two approaches to psychology from the outside, it would appear that both are necessary. Each approach to the understanding of behavior has its own particular value, and neither viewpoint gains stature by denying the legitimacy of the other. Yet, a certain degree of tension persists. Eysenck, writing in 1967, comments as follows:

> It may seem obvious and indeed inevitable that psychology is equally concerned with both these approaches, but this view does not seem to be at all widely held. Experimental psychologists often seem quite unaware of the problems created by individual differences; personality theorists seem equally unconcerned with the lack of relationship between their concepts and those of the experimentalists.[17]

Undoubtedly, these apparently contrasting schools of thought will eventually effect a synthesis, as is characteristic of scientific developments whenever each of two conflicting viewpoints is a fruitful conceptual scheme in its own right. Actually, the tension in psychology merely reflects the tension in biology as a whole. However, as would be expected, the main stream of biology words the issues differently, because its major concern is not with the nature of behavior but with the nature of life.

Even though there has been close affinity between biology and psychology with regard to physiology and certain other biological subfields, psychologists have generally tended to ignore one crucial area, namely, genetics. Genetics was almost totally undeveloped before 1900, and several decades of intensive work were required before it was able to take its rightful place in biological thought. In the meantime, psychology was developing its own schools of thought *without* genetic insights, save those of eugenics (which mainly served only to disillusion those who attempted to incorporate it into their thought-systems). Since that time, of course, it has been amply demonstrated that heredity plays a very important role in human behavior. Yet few psychologists have been willing to give the factor more than grudging admittance. Having built their concepts upon an underlying philosophy of environmentalism, they have been reluctant, on the whole, to alter these concepts to accommodate genetic insights. Although both schools of psychology have been slow to accept genetics, this attitude seems particularly true of the experimentalists. Psychologist Jerry Hirsch attributes their bias mainly to the behaviorists (who have been, for some decades, the leading experimental group):

The "opinion leaders" of two generations literally excommunicated heredity from the behavioral sciences. Understandably, they objected to amateurish labeling of behaviors as instincts without proper experimental analyses. Also, they were repelled by the pseudo-genetics of Hitler and other purveyors of race prejudice . . . . behaviorism still makes the gratuitous uniformity assumption that all genetic combinations are equally plastic and respond in like fashion to environmental influences.[18]

It would appear that Hirsch and others of a relatively new school of thought called *behavior genetics* are effectively counteracting the strong environmental bias that has characterized traditional psychology for so many decades. It seems possible that they may be able to bring about a synthesis between the experimentalists and the personality theorists. Another potentially strong current in psychology is *ethology,* which is the study of animal behavior from the standpoint of social interaction. The ethologist has certain advantages; he can manipulate animal associations to suit the conditions of his experiment and then make objective observations. To the extent that animal studies are relevant to the problems of human behavior, this approach can be exceedingly fruitful.

In summary, we have attempted to show some of the interactions of biological science with those areas of interest that are often called the social sciences. It is not our intent to be critical of these fields, but all of the social sciences, as well as philosophy and theology, have ties with biology that have often been ignored. Hopefully, we have revealed the significance of at least some of these ties.

QUESTIONS FOR REVIEW AND DISCUSSION

1. We have emphasized repeatedly in this book that intellectual clashes involving "either-or" alternatives usually end in a "both-and" compromise. Evaluate the free will-determinism controversy in this light.

2. What is fundamentalism? How does the fundamentalist outlook impinge on biological science?

3. Why was social Darwinism received so enthusiastically in the United States shortly after the Civil War?

4. If natural selection is operative in nature, why are social scientists not justified in assuming and even encouraging its operation in human societies?

5. The American Declaration of Independence states these words: "We hold these truths to be self evident, that all men are created equal. . . ." In what sense is this a valid and praiseworthy statement? In what sense is it subject to criticism?

6. Why was the science of genetics suppressed in Russia for the better part of three decades?

7. Evaluate this statement by Garrett Hardin: "We will never solve the moral problems of men until we accept, in our bones, the insights of the biologist and the geneticist." Does this imply that science may legitimately deal with ethical and moral questions?

8. Is criminality inherited? Explain.

9. What is an XYY syndrome? Let us suppose that it were possible to identify all XYY individuals during childhood. What do you think should be done with (or for) them?

10. What is "environmentalism"? What criticisms do the authors level at the field of psychology as a whole, based on its traditional environmentalistic outlook?

REFERENCES

Hardin, G. *Nature and Man's Fate.* See reference at end of Chapter 8.

Hofstadter, R. *Social Darwinism in American Thought* (rev. ed.). Boston: The Beacon Press, 1955. A classic study in American social thought as it has been influenced by evolutionary concepts.

Medvedev, Z. A. *The Rise and Fall of T. D. Lysenko.* New York: Columbia University Press, 1969. The story of Soviet genetics in the period 1929–1966, written by a Russian scientist and translated into English by an American geneticist, I. M. Lerner.

Stern, C. *Principles of Human Genetics* (2nd ed.). San Francisco: W. H. Freeman and Company, 1960. Although now several years old, this book continues to serve as one of the major reference sources in human genetics.

Stevick, D. *Beyond Fundamentalism.* Richmond, Va.: John Knox Press, 1964. A theological treatment of fundamentalism from a historical viewpoint.

Williams, R. J. *You Are Extraordinary.* New York: Random House, 1967. A distinguished biochemist discusses inborn traits that are responsible for human individuality.

Zirkle, C. *Death of a Science in Russia.* Philadelphia: University of Pennsylvania Press, 1949. Although this book was written well before the downfall of T. D. Lysenko, it is an authentic account of the rise of Lysenkoism in Russian science.

TEN

The Scientific Scene

In employing the analogy of a radioactive fallout to illustrate the effects of biological concepts upon various areas of human endeavor, we need to make yet another point: The radioactive products of a thermonuclear explosion often react with each other. It seems appropriate to examine the scientific scene itself within this framework of thought and to extend our discussion of science, and especially biology, to include certain implications for the present and for the future.

As you will recall, we have constantly emphasized the dependence of science upon certain basic assumptions, two of which we introduced in Chapter 1 as the first and second principles of science. Let us first try to provide a philosophy for science; then we shall continue with a critique of science in the modern world.

10.1 PHILOSOPHICAL PROBLEMS OF SCIENCE

There is a common notion that science is its own justification, that its basic assumptions need no defense or clarification, since science is so spectacularly successful. This attitude is an outgrowth of the definition of science as being merely organized knowledge of the material universe. But, as we have tried to show in this book, science is much more than organized knowledge. Furthermore, it should be abundantly clear by this time that science does have serious implications for other areas of human endeavor, and that it is obliged to examine its basic assumptions in the light of these implications. The history of science has shown rather clearly that whenever science has ignored or neglected its own philosophy, it tends to become dogmatic. And, perhaps needless to say, dogmatism is an attitude that science cannot afford.

Since it is beyond the scope of this book to deal with the philosophy of science as a whole, we shall merely present a few sample problems with an emphasis upon those that are of concern to biological science.

10.1A Issues in Biology

MECHANISM VERSUS VITALISM

Ever since the time of Aristotle, and no doubt before then, men have argued over the question: Is the life phenomenon explicable in terms of physics and chemistry, or is it necessary to invoke a supernatural agent for its explanation? This question has not always meant the same thing from one period of history to another. It has depended upon the state of knowledge in physics, chemistry, *and* biology. For example, Descartes was a thoroughgoing mechanist in his interpretation of the material universe, but what could mechanism possibly mean in Cartesian terms? The physical science of his day, and for some time following, was formulated in very simple concepts: The universe is a machine, and so are organisms. This framework was reinforced later in the 17th century by Newtonian physics, whose machine-like constructs were taken for granted in science until the 20th century.

That Cartesian mechanism was an oversimplification became apparent to many biologists long before physical science was obliged to alter its own views drastically. As a consequence, vitalism was often embraced out of default; it seemed more reasonable than the simple machine analogy. Furthermore, it fitted in nicely with the view that ultimate reality is not of a physical nature, a concept that was a logical accompaniment of a theistic outlook in religion.

Nevertheless, as biology continued to develop, it became increasingly apparent that vitalism would not do as a working frame of reference, because it is totally sterile in producing testable theories; that is, it is scientifically fruitless. For example, consider the area of cell biology, which we discussed in Chapter 5. Suppose one examines numerous living cells, notes their marvelous adaptability to changing environmental conditions, their ability to divide, and so on. It would be quite tempting to formulate a hypothesis that goes something like this: "There must be *something* about cells that is not amenable to rational explanation, a causal quality that will forever defy analysis in chemical or physical terms. I shall call it a *nurisma*." One could then speak learnedly to his colleagues of cellular *nurismae,* but the concept would never be of the least value in explaining the cell in physicochemical terms.

Consequently, in our own consideration of the cell, we formulated the conceptual scheme of a clock and admitted from the start that the concept was thoroughly mechanistic. Philosophically, it is possible to debate the vitalism-mechanism issue from either side. Good arguments (at least, negative ones against the opposing viewpoint) can be offered either way. But scientifically, it is no contest. The scientist is obliged to *act as if* living systems are mechanisms—not *machines,* perhaps, but mechanisms nevertheless.

However, one encounters levels of organization in biology where neither mechanism nor vitalism is satisfactory—for example, at the level of cellular interaction. Perhaps an illustration will serve to clarify this point. One can macerate a young living sponge in a bowl of sea water and thus separate the several cells from each other. Then, in order to ensure that the cells are *really* separated, the mass of material can be strained through a cloth whose pores are just large enough that a single sponge cell can squeeze through each pore. The several hundred cells are filtered through the cloth into a dish of sea water; *then, as if by order, they begin to orient themselves into a certain organized pattern.* Within a short time, the cell mass has become a sponge once again.

Quite clearly, this phenomenon raises some questions. To postulate a *nurisma* or even a *super*-nurisma will obviously serve no useful purpose. Yet, these cells are certainly not acting like the wheels and gears of a machine—what machine ever assembled itself after having been thoroughly wrecked?

The difficulty is overcome in an operational sense if one realizes that vitalism and mechanism may not be the only alternatives in the search for a conceptual base in biology. You will recall that we spoke of *emergent properties* of living systems in Chapter 5 when we discussed levels of organization that come about with complexes of cells. An emergent property is one that appears in a living system as a result of cellular, tissue-level, or organ-level interaction. Operationally, it is a means, and a very fruitful one, of conceptualizing phenomena that arise at successively more complex levels in living systems.

Some convinced mechanists will object that the compromise of emergence is simply vitalism in a different dress; and conversely, some vitalists see it as merely a different level of mechanism.* However, most of these objections seem to come from persons who are committed to finding the *real* basis of life, from persons who are so constituted that they are not satisfied with mere operational definitions. Unfortunately, however, at least for those who think in "either-or" terms, there is no way to determine whether vitalism or mechanism is the "real" explanation for life. The recognition of emergent properties of living systems is simply a convenient and fruitful way of organizing one's experience and working through to tangible results. Whether emergent properties are "real" is quite beside the point.[1]

TELEOLOGY: THE BIOLOGY OF PURPOSE

It is tempting to ascribe purposefulness to every level of protoplasmic organization. For example, if one probes an amoeba with a microneedle, it withdraws from the point of stimulus. One's first impulse is to say that it *tries* to get away from the irritating stimulus. Teachers of biology often fall into the habit of using teleological language rather loosely. For example, it is sometimes said that the leaves of a plant exist "for the purpose" of carrying on photosynthesis. Of course, if pressed, the laboratory investigator or the teacher will admit to loose phraseology. Nowadays, no one really ascribes purpose to an amoeba or to a plant, because to do so implies consciousness, and we are not willing to grant this property to these organisms.

To a great extent, the problem is a semantic one. Human language developed as a means for communicating on the level of *human* problems; it is poorly adapted to describing the life phenomenon at its several levels. As a result, biologists have felt obliged to coin many new terms. However, the problem goes deeper than mere semantics, as we shall see.

Teleological explanations in biology go back a long way in history.

---

* The emergent viewpoint is often called *organicism* or *holism*. Almost any introductory textbook of philosophy includes a discussion of mechanism, vitalism, and organicism, and you may wish to pursue the matter further through such reading.

Aristotle's thought-system demanded teleology; and, as we observed in Chapter 1, the Romans Pliny and Galen were very fond of dealing in teleological explanations. In the Middle Ages, almost all references to nature as a whole were cast in a teleological framework, and this characteristic has carried over into our own time.

A reaction to teleological thinking set in with the advent of mechanism. Organisms are machines, so it was said, and machines are not purposive. Even at the present time, teleological expressions are largely omitted from the biological vocabulary, although few biologists think in the same mechanistic terms as did the generation that rejected all teleological explanations. Teleology, in fact, is widely equated with vitalism and is found guilty by association.

It now appears that biologists may have overreacted in rejecting teleology *in toto*. Clearly, there are certain phenomena that seem to require an explanation that involves purposiveness at *some* level of definition; for example, the sponge cells that reassemble themselves into a whole sponge certainly *act* as if they are goal-directed. At the level of the higher animal body, any structure that fits into an overall pattern of function is purposive to the larger system and must be so explained.

Most of the confusion can be eliminated by recognizing that some forms of teleology are useful to biology, and some are not. If, by teleology, one means externally imposed goals and purposes on the part of a higher intelligence, this definition is not useful because it is a supernatural concept. It may be the true order of things in nature, but science can neither demonstrate the validity of this viewpoint nor use it as a profitable conceptual scheme. If one means by teleology that a given organism possesses a man-like consciousness, this definition is clearly naïve and degenerates into a sterile anthropomorphism. But if, by teleology, one means that the function of a cell, a tissue, an organ, or even an organism is best explained by showing how it fits in with the other members of its system, this definition seems valid.

The entire subject of teleology in biology really needs to be reconsidered. It received a bad name during a time when it represented, for the most part, an attempt to explain nature in vitalistic terms. When it became obvious that teleology clearly would not do for inanimate objects, it was soon eliminated from consideration for the world of life as well. But teleology is a valid and even necessary conceptual framework at certain levels of biological organization, and hopefully, the concept will be developed and used more fully within the next few years.

Many biologists consider the subjects of mechanism, vitalism, and teleology to be passé and quite fruitless within the framework of modern biological thought. Unfortunately, there is a tendency to regard these philosophical problems as "solved." The solution usually says that mechanism is the true state of affairs in living systems and that there is nothing to teleology. This viewpoint thus degenerates all too readily into a dogmatism that refuses to take new developments into account. As we have intimated, the question of teleology is badly in need of review; it may well be that certain aspects of vitalistic thought will also be productive in biology. It is worth noting that these philosophies seem to die, then come back to life periodically. To dismiss them as totally fruitless is to court dogmatism.[2]

10.1B The Limitations of Science

Science is the study of natural phenomena and aims to discover among those phenomena interconnected relationships that are useful both in explanation and in predictability. By implication, this definition of science (or, for that matter, *any* comprehensive definition of science) limits its operational sphere to things that have a material or energetic existence. For example, science has no way of approaching the following questions: Is there a God? Does the universe exist for a purpose? Are there absolute and "given" moral values for man? Although these questions are meaningful, they lie outside the realm of science. The scientist, *as a scientist,* must *act as if* they have no meaning for him. Confusion in understanding science sometimes results because people (including some scientists) take this operational, "act as if," attitude quite literally. Actually, there are many legitimate areas of human thought where science is powerless, and it is best that we identify these limitations.

To a great extent, the problem of recognizing the limitations of science revolves around a deeper philosophical problem: the nature of reality. As we saw in Chapter 3, Immanuel Kant challenged both science and philosophy on this issue in the latter part of the 18th century. We can never get at ultimate reality, the "thing-in-itself," Kant said, because even empirical knowledge is conditioned by reason. Kant went on to criticize those who would limit knowledge to the world of material realities.

Although most working scientists have ignored philosophers, there is an extremely important principle here. Because scientists are obliged to *act as if* their physical objects (or forms of energy, or whatever they may be working with) are "real," and because this type of reality is the only one with which science is equipped to deal, it is easy to assume that no other reality exists. Or scientists often assume that because scientific methodology has been so markedly successful in dealing with the material universe, it can be applied to *all* areas of human endeavor.

MATERIALISM

Materialism is the view that the only reality that exists is matter and that every phenomenon of human experience is to be explained as "matter in motion." This view goes at least as far back in the history of thought as Democritus, who proposed that everything consists of indivisible particles ("atoms") dispersed in space. Materialism has had numerous proponents since the time of Democritus, although his primitive views of matter have given way to more modern concepts. Nevertheless, the basic posture of materialism remains essentially the same: Every phenomenon in the universe is to be explained by the laws of physics. On the negative side, the materialist categorically denies the legitimacy of such concepts as purpose and design in the universe. Whatever happens (including what goes on in human minds) does so because of preceding physical causes. The philosophy of materialism is, at best, an attempt to be consistent. At worst, it is arrogant, because it assumes that there is only one kind of thing in existence and only one set of methods for approaching reality.

Sir Arthur Eddington, a British physicist, challenged the consistency of this viewpoint with an analogy:

> Let us suppose that an ichthyologist is exploring the life of the ocean. He casts a net into the water and brings up a fishy assortment. Surveying his catch, he proceeds in the usual manner of a scientist to systematize what it reveals. He arrives at two generalizations: (i) No sea creature is less than two inches long. (ii) All sea creatures have gills . . . . An onlooker may object that the first generalization is wrong. "There are plenty of sea creatures under two inches long, only your net is not adapted to catch them." The ichthyologist dismisses this objection contemptuously. "Anything uncatchable by my net is *ipso facto* outside the scope of ichthyological knowledge, and is not part of the kingdom of fishes which has been defined as the theme of ichthyological knowledge. In short, what my net can't catch isn't fish." [3]

Again, consider this analogy by theologian Robert Wicks, who maintains that it is a fallacy of thinking to conclude from the workings of a material universe that no other reality (such as a higher intelligence) exists:

> Suppose a man endeavored to understand a machine like a newspaper press. From what his senses could tell him he would learn that every wheel and gadget set other wheels and gadgets moving, so that every part was determined by some other part; and the whole was driven by some natural, impersonal force like steam which had no moral purpose whatsoever. All this information could be gathered without knowing the purpose in the minds of the editorial staff. No study of the machinery by itself could reveal such a purpose, and a man might assume it did not exist. However, if from some other source he became acquainted with the editor's intentions, he could see how an impersonal machine might have a hidden purpose work-

is philosophically naïve. It rests upon the presupposition that material reality is ultimate reality and that "things-in-themselves" are actually knowable. This viewpoint is possibly true, and Kant may have been entirely wrong; there is no way to "prove" the issue one way or the other. But almost all proponents of materialism ignore the Kantian arguments, as well as the considerations of other philosophers, and, in effect, hold that their position is a self-evident one. Hence, materialism becomes a form of dogmatism and thus eliminates itself from qualification as a scientific viewpoint. This attitude is nothing less than ironic. Those who seek to be rigidly "scientific" through the viewpoint of materialism fall easily into the trap of dogmatism, which is anathema to the fundamental attitudes of science.

Science is essentially a method, a way of dealing with the discernible phenomena of a material universe. As such, it is eminently successful within its own domain. But to claim that it deals with ultimate reality (as the materialist does) or that all human problems can be approached scientifically (as the proponent of scientism does) is to rely upon a dubious philosophical base indeed. In either case, the viewpoint constitutes an intrusion into the realm of speculative metaphysics, the very thing that the materialist would seek to avoid.

10.2 SCIENCE IN HUMAN AFFAIRS

We have attempted in this book to show something of the tremendous development that the scientific outlook, especially in the biological sciences, has undergone since the days of the ancient Greeks. As a result of this development, we presently live in what has been aptly termed the Age of Science; as a consequence, we are the beneficiaries of numerous material blessings. The past century alone has seen the virtual conquest of most infectious diseases, the widespread use of electricity, a major revolution in agricultural methods, and the conquest of outer space—to mention only a few of the benefits from science. If these and other direct benefits to mankind's standard of living are deemed technological rather than scientific, it is no matter. Technology is the application of scientific concepts to practical problems; and, without the development of new concepts, there could be little advance in technology.

Because science is, by its very nature, an ongoing activity, perhaps it is relatively easy for a scientist to be optimistic about the future. Certainly, there is good reason for optimism in a society that rewards science and technology as handsomely as ours has done in the past. If recent decades are any indication, science will continue to increase its penetration into the voids of empirical ignorance by geometric rates of progression.

Of course, this picture is not entirely reassuring at the time of this writing. Involvement with war and the dangers of an inflationary economy hang like a shadow over most of the research programs in the United States. The great activities of the early 1960's have not been carried into the decade of the 1970's. If the general moratorium on basic research in the sciences continues, the whole enterprise may be in trouble. However, perhaps we dare hope that this obstacle to progress will be lifted in due time.

W. D. McElroy, writing in 1971 from his vantage point as Director of the National Science Foundation, develops a perspective that he shares with his fellow scientists:

> We are in a decade of transition and what will finally evolve is as hard for me to perceive as it is for you. I do know that the rate of change—and its potential for good and ill—is accelerating at a rapid pace. We can only dimly perceive the kind of society we will have a decade or so hence. But we can see the directions of change. The issues moving to the fore in our time have in common a concern with the quality of life, and I believe we are moving into an era in which the quality of life for every citizen will move far ahead of the gross national product as the measure of our well-being. Increasingly, some of the classical views of property may be modified, giving way to the view that resources are not free for the taking but belong fundamentally to all the people. Increasingly, this will mean that technological innovations are not automatically considered improvements, nor will the marketplace be a sufficient test of their value. We will demand that technological innovations—both in use and in the process by which they are created—enhance the public good. Or, to put it more accurately, we will demand that they function with the least possible hazard to ourselves and the environment. . . .
>
> First and foremost—and despite the seduction of popular appeal—the scientist must hold fast to those simple truths of scientific methodology, disciplined training, and critical review. If we compromise with these first principles, all is lost. . . .
>
> As a citizen of our college or university we can strengthen not weaken those ties which make for a community of scholars. Scientists, more than any other academic group, have been accused of giving their highest allegiance to their discipline. . . .
>
> As a research scientist, the future role of the biologist should emphasize an increasing sensitivity to society's problems. While acknowledging the central need for fundamental disciplinary work, I believe interdisciplinary research offers unusual opportunities to grapple with the complexity of, for example, environmental problems. There are a number of reasons why scientists are likely to welcome involvement in interdisciplinary research on socially relevant problems. Pollution, health care, population growth, urban development

are matters that concern us as citizens, and when opportunities open for connecting one's research interest with a social problem, an important satisfaction can be added to that of discovery for its own sake. Interdisciplinary involvement, it has perhaps been said too often, also affords exposure to different viewpoints and approaches, and hence to fresh perspectives toward one's own field.[6]

Thus, among other things, McElroy identifies an urgent need for present-day science: fuller involvement with social problems. There is good reason to believe that the great majority of scientists are completely sympathetic with this recommendation, but society as a whole is evidently not as fully aware of the urgency of the problem. As citizens, we support some enterprises that promise immediate practical benefits for a segment of mankind, but we prefer not to think about problems of poverty, injustice, and the deterioration of values in a large segment of our society. Perhaps the main difficulty is that while "everyone" grants the urgency of these problems, and there is even some grudging support for their study, few are willing to endorse spending the vast amounts of money required to devise and implement such programs as are needed. To make matters even more difficult, value judgments are often involved. How, for example, does the government or even some private foundation tell society that it "ought" to adopt this or that set of moral or ethical values? To fight pollution of the water, soil, and atmosphere are difficult enough. How does a society go about fighting pollution of the spirit?

Perhaps science and scientists should not concern themselves with these areas, but a number of thoughtful people (both scientists and non-scientists) disagree. Science *as science* cannot help society decide a question of values, but scientists as human beings can. Unless the academic community is willing to take a large share of responsibility for the development of standards and norms around which any enduring society must be structured, there may soon be no stable society in which to do scientific work or anything else.

A great deal of this problem is related to our tendency toward compartmentalization in education, of which we spoke earlier. It may be necessary in the organization of an educational system that different areas of learning be kept administratively segregated from each other, but this separation often translates itself to students and professors alike as a license for unconcern about any knowledge outside their field of choice.[7]

We must remember that science and technology, despite their tremendous contributions to the quality of modern life, cannot solve all of mankind's problems. It is urgent that the natural sciences cooperate not only with the social sciences but with the humanities as well. All of these areas should have much to say to each other, and the establishment of clearer lines of communication among natural scientists, social scientists, and humanists may well be critical to mankind's survival as a species, or at least, as the *human* species whose future cultural evolution is well-nigh limitless in potential. The anthropologist Loren Eiseley, who is well qualified to speak as a scientist-humanist, warns against the sentiment that man is capable of finding his salvation in material progress alone:

> In the West of our day only one anachronistic force threatens man with the ruin of [his] hope. It is his confusion of the word "progress" with the mechanical extensions which represent his triumph over the primeval wilderness of biological selection. This confusion represents, in a way, a reversion. It is a failure to see that the triumph of the machine without an accompanying inner triumph represents an atavistic return to the competition and extermination represented in the old biological evolution of parts. . . . [This attitude] persists in the notion that something called gracious living is solely associated with high-powered automobiles and the social amenities available in the very best clubs. . . .
>
> Transcendence of self is not to be sought in the outer world or in mechanical extensions. These are merely another version of specialized evolution. They can be used for human benefit if one recognizes them for what they are, but they must never be confused with that other interior kingdom in which man is forever free to be better than what he knows himself to be. It is there that the progress of which he dreams is at last to be found. It is the thing that his great moral teachers have been telling him since man was man. This is his true world; the other, the mechanical world which tickles his fancy, may be useful to good men but it is not in itself good. It takes its color from the minds behind it and this man has not learned.[8]

For Eiseley, at least, scientism holds no answer for the deepest of human problems. He attempts to formulate what might well be called the fourth principle of science: namely, that **science derives its true meaning and value from the totality of human experience, not from its own special viewpoint alone.**

QUESTIONS FOR REVIEW AND DISCUSSION

1. Why do many biologists regard both vitalism and mechanism to be unsatisfactory philosophies? Does the viewpoint of emergence really solve the problem?

2. In what sense is teleology a naïve interpretation of nature? In what sense is it a useful viewpoint?

3. What was Eddington attempting to illustrate with his analogy of a fish net?

4. Why do the authors maintain that materialism and scientism are inconsistent with the spirit of science?

5. W. D. McElroy lists a number of social problems for which he feels that science should seek a fuller involvement. Can you identify other social problems to which biologists, particularly, might address themselves profitably?

6. Summarize and evaluate Loren Eiseley's statement. Do you feel that it is legitimate for a scientist to speak with as great a degree of conviction about values as Eiseley does?

REFERENCES

Bronowski, J. *Science and Human Values* (rev. ed.). New York: Harper and Row, 1965. A classic essay by a distinguished scientist and humanist.

Potter, V. R. *Bioethics: Bridge To The Future.* Englewood Cliffs, N.J.: Prentice-Hall, Inc., 1971. An innovative exploration of ideas, in which the author attempts to bridge the gap between biological science and ethics.

Simpson, G. G. *This View of Life.* New York: Harcourt, Brace and World, 1963. An outstanding evolutionist and paleontologist discusses biology within a philosophical framework.

Snow, C. P. *The Two Cultures and A Second Look.* New York: Cambridge University Press, 1964. The author's thought-provoking and controversial Rede Lecture of 1959 together with his later reflections.

APPENDIX

Footnote References in Text

Chapter-end references in this text are limited to a relatively small number of works that have been specially selected because of their immediate relevance. Whenever a given work is referred to by superscript number, that work will be listed at the end of the chapter under consideration. In other cases, superscript numbers refer to anecdotal material, or to references listed under chapter headings other than the one immediately involved. In these cases, the references are either cited directly or they are identified according to appropriate chapter.

1 THE ANCIENT WORLD

1. See Jones for a thorough discussion of the pre-Socratic Greek natural-philosophers.

2. Most historians of biology, including Nordenskiold, seem unduly critical of Aristotle. The advantages of hindsight often carry with them a certain degree of intellectual arrogance.

3. See Singer, p. 64 ff., for a brief but illuminating discussion of the relationship between early Christianity and ancient science.

4. Our main reason for including this account of the Judeo–Christian heritage is to prepare the reader for the events that transpired in the Middle Ages and the Renaissance. Since the dogmatism that marked those periods stemmed largely from the Church, it is easy to make Christianity the villain of the drama. However, there is another side to the story. Whitehead and others have pointed out that modern science began with an act of faith: that the universe possessed order and could be interpreted by rational minds. This act of faith was borrowed directly from Christianity, and it is significant that the major architects of modern science (for example, Copernicus, Galileo, and Newton) were devout men of Christian faith. For a fuller exposition of this idea, see Whitehead, pp. 4–15 (Mentor Edition), and Eiseley (see reference at end of Chapter 7), p. 62.

2 THE LONG SLEEP

1. See Jones, Introduction to Vol. 2, for a fuller exposition of this idea.

2. For an extended discussion of Thomas Aquinas, see Jones, Vol. 2, p. 208 ff.

3. C. E. K. Mees (*Electrical Engineering, 53* [1934], 383) attributes this story to Francis Bacon. Another version of the story says that the monks consulted only Aristotle. If this is so, it was unfortunate (for their purposes) that they did not consult Pliny, who *does* discuss horses' teeth. The irony is, of course (if we may indulge in the construction of imaginary history), that both Aristotle and Pliny would probably have advised them to follow the suggestion of the young friar!

4. For example, early in the 17th century, Galileo (see Chapter 3) wrote to his fellow-astronomer Johannes Kepler from the University of Padua, which at that time remained a stronghold of Scholasticism: "Oh, my dear Kepler, how I wish that we could have one hearty

laugh together! Here at Padua is the principal professor of philosophy, whom I have repeatedly and urgently requested to look at the moon and planets through my glass, which he pertinaciously refuses to do . . . What a glorious folly! And to hear the professor of philosophy at Pisa labouring before the Grand Duke with logical arguments, as if with magical incantations to charm the new planets out of the sky."

5.   For an account of William of Ockham, see Jones, Vol. 2, p. 316 ff.

3   THE GREAT AWAKENING

1.   See Conant, pp. 10–13.
2.   *Ibid.,* pp. 45–47.
3.   See Butterfield, p. 31 ff.
4.   See Conant, p. 234 ff., for a fuller exposition of the controlled experiment in biology.
5.   *The Critique of Pure Reason,* Part II, Chapter III.
6.   See Durant, p. 96 ff.; Jones, Vol. 3, p. 73 ff.
7.   See Jones, Vol. 3, p. 154 ff.
8.   See Jones, Introduction to Vol. 4 and Chapter 1, "The Age of Reason," for a fuller exposition.
9.   See Durant, p. 253 ff.; Jones, Vol. 4, p. 14 ff.
10. Whitehead (see reference at end of Chapter 1) levels a devastating criticism at science on this score: "Science repudiates philosophy. In other words, it has never cared to justify its faith or to explain its meanings; and has remained blandly indifferent to its refutation by Hume. . . . If science is not to degenerate into a medley of *ad hoc* hypotheses, it must become philosophical and must enter upon a thorough criticism of its own foundations" (pp. 17, 18, Mentor Edition).
11. For a lucid exposition of this idea, see Eiseley (reference at end of Chapter 7), p. 13 ff. Also, for a brief account of Linnaeus, see Eiseley, pp. 16–26.

4   LIFE

1.   See Beck, Chapter 8, for a concise and understandable discussion of the nature of life.
2.   See Waddington, Chapter 1, for a brief but lucid treatment of philosophical aspects of the life phenomenon.
3.   See Beck, Chapter 10, for a lucid treatment of explanation in science.

4. See "Spontaneous Generation" in Knobloch for a brief history of the controversy.

5. Baker and Allen present a clear, concise discussion of organization extending from energy and atoms through enzymes and nucleic acids. This brief book presents the chemical models that a beginning student of biology needs for an understanding of properties that emerge at higher levels of organization.

6. See Giese, Chapter 4, for a more detailed treatment of the colloidal properties of a living system.

7. See "The Origin of Life" in Haynes and Hanawalt, also Section IX in Knobloch. The latter reference consists of five papers by different authors on the origin of life.

5 LIFE AND CELL

1. See Part I in Gabriel and Fogel for a chronology of the development of the cell theory and papers by a number of the men who contributed to its final formulation. See also Chapter 1 in Brown and Bertke for a brief historical sketch of the development of the cell theory.

2. See Hooke's paper in Gabriel and Fogel.

3. See paper by Dutrochet in Gabriel and Fogel.

4. See paper by Schwann in Gabriel and Fogel.

5. "On the Nature of Disease," *Texas Reports on Biology and Medicine, 12* (1954).

6. See Wilson and Morrison for a clear, concise description of general cell morphology and of the structure and function of cell organelles. See also Jean Brachet's paper, "The Living Cell," in Kennedy.

7. See the paper by Morowitz and Tourtellotte, "The Smallest Living Cells," in Kennedy.

8. See Robertson's paper, "The Membrane of the Living Cell," in Kennedy.

9. See Green's paper, "The Mitochondrion," in Kennedy.

10. See Wilson, p. 40, for a discussion of plastids.

11. *Ibid.*, p. 58, for a discussion of the endoplasmic reticulum.

12. *Ibid.*, p. 71, for a discussion of the Golgi complex.

13. See DeDuve's article, "The Lysosome," in Kennedy.

14. See Brown, p. 394, for a discussion of centrioles.

15. See Giese for a more detailed and sophisticated treatment of cellular metabolism.

16. See Lehninger's paper, "How Cells Transform Energy," in Kennedy.

17. See Section IV in Kennedy for several articles by different authors dealing with protein synthesis.

18. See Arnon and Bassham's paper, "Photosynthesis," in Kennedy.
19. See Mazia's paper, "How Cells Divide," in Kennedy.
20. See Swanson *et al.* for a more detailed analysis of cell reproduction and its significance. The sections dealing with mitosis and meiosis are quite lucid.
21. See Grobstein for a clear and well-illustrated treatment of the concept of levels of organization and emergent properties.

6   LIFE, CELL, AND HEREDITY

1. See Carlson for a rather complete history of the gene concept.
2. Mendel's paper is included in the collection of Peters.
3. See Chapter 1 in Carlson.
4. *Ibid.,* Chapter 3.
5. See Sutton's paper in Peters.
6. See Carlson, Chapter 7; see also the paper by Sturtevant in Peters.
7. See Bridges' paper in Peters.
8. See Carlson, Chapter 19.
9. See Beadle's paper in Haynes and Hanawalt.
10. See the paper by Beadle and Tatum in Peters.
11. See Bonner, Chapter 2.
12. See the paper by Avery *et al.* in Peters.
13. See articles on the nucleic acids by Crick and other authors in Haynes and Hanawalt.
14. See Swanson *et al.* for a lucid presentation of the cell as a genetic unit.
15. See Part III, "Gene Action in Protein Synthesis," in Haynes and Hanawalt.
16. See the paper by Changeux, "The Control of Biochemical Reactions" in Haynes and Hanawalt; see also Chapter 2, "The Operon," in Carlson.

7   LIFE, CELL, HEREDITY, AND EVOLUTION

1. Garrett Hardin (see reference at end of Chapter 8) states in his prologue, "Even today, a century after its birth, the great majority of mankind either has not heard of the theory [of evolution] or thinks it false." Hardin wrote these words in 1959; there is no compelling reason to believe that the situation has changed significantly since that time.

2. For a fuller exposition of the ideas of Buffon, Erasmus Darwin, and Lamarck, see appropriate passages in Eiseley.

3. See appropriate passages in Eiseley and Hardin (reference at end of Chapter 8) for details of Darwin's personal life, and of the events surrounding the publication of the *Origin of Species.*

4. "Great revolutions in science are scarcely ever effected but after their authors have ceased to breathe" (William Swainson, 1834).

5. For a fuller exposition of the synthetic theory of evolution, see the books by Huxley, Ross, Simpson, and Stebbins.

6. *Origin of Species* (Mentor Edition), pp. 69–70.

7. *Ibid.,* p. 134.

8. See T. Dobzhansky. *Genetics and the Origin of Species* (2nd ed.). New York: Columbia University Press, 1941, p. 189 and bibliography for references to this work.

8   THE HUMAN SCENE

1. Odum, H. T. "Trophic Structure and Productivity of Silver Springs, Florida," *Ecological Monographs, 27* (1957), 55–112.

2. See Weisz, p. 281.

3. Detwyler, p. 168 ff., points out that the carbon dioxide "greenhouse effect" is a very complex consideration, the possible implications of which may well have been overemphasized. However, our point is essentially the same as Detwyler's: that man's impact upon his environment is increasingly great, with unforeseeable results.

4. Cited in Ehrlich and Ehrlich, p. 137. See also Walter R. Guild, "Biological Effects of Radiation" in Fowler, J. M. (ed.). *Fallout.* New York: Basic Books, Inc. 1960.

5. See Fowler, cited above, for numerous expressions of concern by physical scientists. Also, as a further indication, *The Bulletin of the Atomic Scientists,* a journal which was begun in 1945, has expressed continued editorial concern for radiation hazards to man.

6. Prescott, D. M. "Control of Human Population Growth," *Bioscience, 19* (March, 1969), 205. Also included in Weisz, p. 319.

7. Archer, J. E. "Can We Prepare For Famine?" *Bioscience, 18* (July, 1968), 685–690. Also included in Weisz, p. 316.

8. Prescott, *op. cit.;* in Weisz, p. 320.

9. See "Man and Natural Selection," *American Scientist, 49* (1961), 285–299. Dobzhansky does not, himself, subscribe to the reality of this dilemma. He merely poses it, and then goes on to note that the terms of the dilemma constitute an oversimplification.

10. Auerbach, C. *The Science of Genetics.* New York: Harper and Row, Publishers, 1961. Excerpts from pp. 121–130.

9 THE SOCIAL SCENE

1. *The Meaning of Evolution* (see reference at end of Chapter 7), p. 284. Also discussed by Simpson in *This View of Life* (see reference at end of Chapter 10), p. 24. It should be emphasized that Simpson does *not* subscribe to the "nothing but" interpretation of man's biological nature. He uses the expression to launch a discussion on man's uniqueness.

2. See Jones, Vol. 4 (reference at end of Chapter 3), or other histories of philosophy, for the thought-systems of Bergson, Dewey, and Whitehead, as well as for the influence of evolutionary thought on philosophy.

3. *Science in the Modern World,* Mentor Edition, p. 41.

4. For a thoughtful analysis of this problem, see "The Freedom of the Will" in Feigl, H. and W. Sellars (eds.). *Readings in Philosophical Analysis.* New York: Appleton-Century-Crofts, 1949.

5. According to *Statistical Abstract of the United States,* 63 per cent of the population claimed church membership in 1968.

6. For a fuller account written for the lay reader, see the articles by R. M. Grant, J. T. McNeill, and S. Terrien in the introductory section of *The Interpreter's Bible* (Vol. 1). New York: Abingdon Press, 1952.

7. See Stevick for a theologian's viewpoint of this conflict, and for the history of fundamentalism.

8. Hoffer, E. *The True Believer.* New York: Harper and Row, Publishers, 1951.

9. *Beyond Fundamentalism,* p. 106.

10. Niebuhr, R. "Christianity and Darwin's Revolution" in *A Book That Shook the World.* Pittsburgh: University of Pittsburgh Press, 1958, p. 33.

11. *Social Darwinism in American Thought,* p. 204. Reprinted by permission of the Beacon Press, copyright © 1944, 1955 by the American Historical Association.

12. See Lerner, I. M. *Heredity, Evolution, and Society.* San Francisco: W. H. Freeman and Company, 1968, p. 282. See also Medvedev, p. 223 and other sections.

13. *Nature and Man's Fate,* p. 188.

14. See Stern, pp. 603–605, for a summarization of twin-studies data on criminality.

15. Casey, M. D., L. J. Segall, D. R. K. Street, and C. E. Blank. "Sex Chromosome Abnormalities in Two State Hospitals for Patients Requiring Special Security," *Nature, 209* (1966), 641.

16. *Science in the Modern World,* Mentor Edition, p. 185.

17. From Eysenck, H. J. *The Biological Basis of Personality.* Springfield, Ill.: Charles C Thomas, Publisher, 1967. Courtesy of Charles C Thomas, Publisher.

18. "Behavior Genetics and Individuality Understood," *Science, 142* (1963), 1436. Copyright 1963 by the American Association for the Advancement of Science.

10 THE SCIENTIFIC SCENE

1. See Waddington (reference at end of Chapter 4), p. 17 ff. for a thoughtful discussion of mechanism, vitalism, and emergentism.

2. See Simpson on the subjects of vitalism, mechanism, and teleology.

3. Eddington, A. S. *The Philosophy of Physical Science.* New York: Cambridge University Press, 1939, p. 16.

4. *The Interpreter's Bible,* Vol. 11, p. 97. New York: The Abingdon Press, 1953.

5. From *Religion and Science,* p. 175, by Bertrand Russell, published by Oxford University Press, 1935.

6. "Science, the Public, and the New Realities," *Bioscience, 21(2)* (January 15, 1971), 59–61. Reprinted with permission of author and publisher.

7. For a powerful treatment of compartmentalization in American and British higher education, see Snow. The entire book is a protest against educational fragmentation, but see especially p. 10 ff.

8. *Darwin's Century* (see reference at end of Chapter 7). © by Loren Eiseley. Excerpts from pp. 350–351.

Glossary

The terms included in this glossary are those that are used frequently in the text, or those that require a concise, operational definition. For terms that are not included, the student should consult the index and/or an unabridged dictionary.

abiogenesis: The concept that life may originate spontaneously, within a very short space of time (hours or days), from nonliving antecedents. Historically, proponents of this concept have been opposed by those holding to the concept of *biogenesis.*

algae: A group of photosynthetic organisms, largely aquatic, most of which are relatively simple in structure. Classically, they have been considered the simplest of the photosynthetic plants. However, within recent years, many biologists have come to regard them as members of the kingdom Protista, which includes those organisms that do not fit readily into the animal or plant kingdoms. Most protistans (hence, most algae) are microorganisms.

allele: One member of a contrasting pair of genes. For example, of the gene pair *Aa,* either gene can be called an allele to the other.

anatomy: The field of biology that is concerned with the structural parts of an organism or group of organisms.

anthropomorphism: A philosophy or means of interpretation according to which the actions of an organism or the conditions of existence of an object are presumed to arise from an intelligence similar to that of man.

Aristotelianism: A static, as opposed to a dynamic, view of nature that assumed that empirical knowledge is finite, that nature can profitably be studied according to dogmatic methods, and that function in the world of life can be explained teleologically. It should be noted that this viewpoint is more readily identifiable with medieval Scholasticism than with Aristotle himself.

arthropods: Members of the phylum Arthropoda, which includes more species than all other animal phyla combined. Arthropods are characterized by paired, jointed appendages, and by a firm exoskeleton composed of a substance called *chitin.* Representative arthropods are insects, spiders, and crustaceans (for example, lobsters and crayfish). Many of the arthropods are microscopic in size.

autotrophic nutrition: A mode of nutrition wherein organic compounds are synthesized from inorganic materials, with carbon dioxide serving as the sole source of carbon. Most autotrophic cells or organisms utilize radiant energy in their synthesis, in which case the process of "capturing" this energy and converting it to chemical energy is called *photosynthesis.*

behaviorism: Historically, a position within psychology that has relied on objective experimental methodology and has emphasized the study of overt behavior as distinguished from mentalistic and subjective phenomena. In contemporary psychology, behaviorism has become more deeply involved with experimentation involving the biochemical and cytological mechanisms of human and higher animal responsiveness.

biogenesis: The concept that life comes only from life under conditions that prevail presently on earth. Historically, proponents of this concept have been opposed by those holding to the concept of *abio-genesis.*

biopoiesis: The process by means of which life is held to have arisen through naturalistic means under the conditions that prevailed on earth 3 to 5 billion years ago.

Cartesianism: The rationalistic philosophy of René Descartes. See also *rationalism.*

compound: A combination of two or more different kinds of atoms or ions in a definite ratio, bonded together chemically.

conceptual scheme: A broad hypothesis with far-reaching implications. Organic evolution in biology and relativity in physics are examples of scientific conceptual schemes.

cytology: The field of biology that is concerned with the study of cells.

Darwinism: The theory of evolution, propounded by Charles Darwin, that holds that the major feature of evolution as a process is natural selection. See also *natural selection.*

deduction: A process of drawing a conclusion from a set of premises; in science, a process of reasoning that begins with a generalization (theory or law) and predicts a future event as a logical extension of that generalization.

diploidy: The condition of a cell or organism whose chromosomes exist in pairs; that is, there are two "sets," or genomes, of chromosomes.

dogmatism: A framework of thought that rules out in advance the possibility of discovering or accepting empirical evidence that might weigh against the belief in question.

dualism: A viewpoint that holds that there are two distinct kinds of reality, as in the thought-system of Descartes. These two kinds of reality are usually expressed as "mind" and "matter."

ecology: The field of biology that is concerned with organisms and their relationships to their environments.

ecosystem: A segment of nature—for example, a pond, a stream, or a desert—that is prescribed and delimited for ecological study.

emergence: The viewpoint or philosophy that recognizes the existence of qualities that belong to a whole entity—(for example, an organism)—that could not have been predicted from a knowledge of the separate parts of that entity. Stated simply, it is the view that a whole may be more than a mere sum of its parts, and as a biological philosophy, it holds that biology rests on principles that cannot be reduced to more basic principles of chemistry and physics. Historically, the emergent viewpoint arose as a reaction to *reductionism.*

empiricism: The viewpoint that holds sense perception to be the most important source of human knowledge. In its most extreme form, it holds sense perception to be the *only* source of human knowledge. Historically, empiricism arose as a reaction to *rationalism.*

endergonic reaction: Any chemical reaction in which energy is required from a source external to the reactants. Whole series of reactions may be classified as endergonic if the net result is that energy must be put into the system. For example, protein synthesis within the cell is energy-requiring; therefore, the entire process may be referred to as an endergonic reaction.

enthalpy: The total energy content of a physicochemical system.

entropy: Disorganization or randomness. For example, the second law of thermodynamics holds that closed energy systems (those in which energy is prevented from coming into the system) tend to proceed from low to high entropy, that is, the energy of the system goes from more energetically organized to less energetically organized states.

enzyme: An organic catalyst, that is, an organic molecule or compound (specifically, a protein in living systems) that alters the rate of some chemical reaction without undergoing chemical alteration itself in that reaction.

epistemology: The study of the nature and limitations of human knowledge.

eugenics: The field of biology that is concerned with the improvement of the human gene pool.

evolution: See *organic evolution.*

exergonic reaction: Any chemical reaction in which energy is given off as a product of the reaction. Whole series of reactions may be classified as endergonic if the net result is that energy is released or given off in the system. For example, the complete respiration of a molecule of glucose involving numerous specific reactions may be classified as an exergonic reaction.

fermentation: The production of lactic acid or ethyl alcohol from a carbohydrate substrate under anaerobic conditions. Within cells, this process occurs whenever the pyruvic acid resulting from glycolysis cannot proceed through the Krebs cycle and the cytochrome oxidase system.

fungi: A group of nonphotosynthetic organisms, most of which are relatively simple in structure—for example, molds and mushrooms. Classically, the fungi have been considered "lower" plants. However, within recent years, many biologists have come to regard them as members of the kingdom Protista, which includes those organisms that do not fit readily into the animal or plant kingdoms. Most protistans (hence, most fungi, including bacteria) are microorganisms.

gene: In classical terms, a unit of material, usually chromosomal, that acts as a hereditary determiner. In modern terms, the gene is defined as a certain number of nucleotide pairs that constitute a portion of a DNA molecule, and that dictate (by way of messenger RNA) the formation of a specific polypeptide (protein) chain.

genetics: The field of biology that is concerned with the basis for the similiarities and differences among organisms. The major concern of genetics is determining the role of heredity in bringing about these similarities and differences.

genotype: The formal, or symbolic, representation of a genetic trait, for example, *AA, Aa,* or *aa.*

glycolysis: That phase of cellular respiration wherein a carbohydrate substrate (for example, glucose) is degraded to two molecules of pyruvic acid and four atoms of hydrogen, accompanied by a net synthesis of two molecules of ATP for each monosaccharide molecule that enters the process; the anaerobic phase of cellular respiration. In overall significance, glycolysis "prepares" the substrate molecule for entrance into the Krebs cycle.

haploidy: The condition of a cell or organism possessing only a single "set," or genome, of chromosomes.

heterotrophic nutrition: A mode of nutrition wherein a cell or organism obtains its energy-rich organic molecules in micromolecular form from a source that is independent of its own synthetic processes.

hypothesis: A tentative explanation for a phenomenon under consideration; an "educated guess."

idealism: The viewpoint that holds ultimate reality to be mental, spiritual, or in some fashion mind-dependent. The opposing viewpoint to idealism is *materialism.*

induction: A process of reasoning whereby theories are generated from knowledge gained by observation and/or experimentation; a process of formulating generalizations from specific events.

laissez-faire: A French idiom whose literal meaning is "let do." As an expression, it represents a philosophy of economic individualism. Its proponents maintain that a government does best when it interferes least with natural "laws" of supply and demand.

Lamarckianism: A genetic–evolutionary viewpoint whose major tenets are (1) that organisms possess an inherent tendency toward progression, and (2) that reproductive cells are influenced genetically by ordinary body cells or by environmental factors. *Darwinism* rejects the first of these points, but tacitly accepts the second. Ironically, Lamarckianism is usually identified only with the second of these tenets, whereas it was on the first tenet that Darwin disagreed totally with Lamarck.

materialism: The viewpoint that holds ultimate reality to be matter, or (to accommodate energetic phenomena) "matter in motion." The opposing viewpoint is *idealism.*

mechanism: A theory of life that holds that living organisms, or all phenomena related to the term "life," can be exhaustively explained by the laws of chemistry and physics. The opposing view is *vitalism.*

meiosis: A process of nuclear division whereby the chromosome number is reduced. Ordinarily, the process involves two successive divisions, beginning with a diploid cell and ending with four haploid cells (gametes or spores). Meiosis is always associated in some fashion with sexual reproduction, making possible subsequent *recombination* of chromosomes and their genes in fertilization.

metabolism: The sum total of all the chemical changes or reactions that occur in a living organism.

metaphysics: The study of the ultimate nature of reality; the attempt to understand the nature and meaning of the whole of reality; the basic principles of being. The two most common metaphysical views are *materialism* and *idealism.*

mitosis: A process of nuclear division whereby the chromosome number remains constant. Thus, mitosis is a conservative factor in cellular reproduction, maintaining the genetic *status quo.*

morphology: The field of biology that is concerned with the study of gross, or overall, structure.

mutation: A change in a gene. More specifically, and in modern terminology, an alteration in nucleotide sequence on one strand of a DNA molecule, such that the replicative and translational properties of the gene involved are changed.

natural history: The descriptive aspect of science, with a view toward studying natural entities (for example, organisms) in as nearly an undisturbed state as possible. In contrast, experimental science involves the manipulation of natural entities to suit the needs of the experimenter.

natural selection: (1) Darwinian: the struggle of organisms in nature for existence and the concomitant survival of the fittest. (2) Modern: the differential reproduction of genetic types.

organic evolution: The process of genetic change in populations of organisms throughout time.

phagotrophic nutrition: A mode of nutrition wherein a cell or organism obtains its energy-rich organic molecules in the form of macromolecular complexes (*phagos,* to eat).

phenomenon: Any product, aspect, or process of sense experience.

phenotype: The observable or otherwise detectable expression of a stated genotype; an adjective that describes some particular trait of an organism.

philosophy: The field of study one aspect of which is the comprehensive, or overall, view of life and the universe with an attempt to discover meaning. Philosophy is also dedicated to a critical analysis of basic concepts, beliefs, propositions, and attitudes through logical methods.

physiology: The field of biology that is concerned with the study of function.

protozoa: A group of unicellular organisms characterized by phagotrophic nutrition. Classically, they have been considered the one-celled animals. However, within recent years, many biologists have come to regard them as members of the kingdom Protista, which includes those organisms that do not fit readily into the animal or plant kingdoms.

radioisotope: An isotope of an element, the atoms of which possess unstable nuclei that emit ionizing radiations.

rationalism: The view that holds reason to be the most important source of human knowledge. In its most extreme form, it holds reason to be the only *reliable* source of human knowledge. Historically, rationalism stands In contrast to *empiricism.* See also footnote on page 50.

recombination: Any process whereby new combinations of genes find expression in an organism. Recombination may occur by means of (1) genetic exchange (crossing over) between chromosomes during meiosis, and (2) by the combination of two differing genomes during fertilization.

reductionism: The view that all phenomena can ultimately be defined according to physical principles of matter and energy. As applied to biology, it holds that biology is merely a special case of physics, and that the life phenomenon at all levels is definable only in physicochemical terms.

religion: The appreciation of the relation in which men believe they and the whole world stand to something above and beyond nature, a relation transcending those in the sciences (Lewis White Beck); religion is concerned about experiences which are regarded as of supreme value; devotion toward a power or powers believed to originate, increase, and conserve these values; and some suitable expression of this concern and devotion, whether through symbolic rites or through other individual and social conduct (Edgar Sheffield Brightman).

respiration: The oxidative breakdown of organic molecules within a cell under such conditions that gaseous oxygen serves as the ultimate hydrogen acceptor, and free energy is made available to the cell.

Scholasticism: The authoritarian philosophy of the medieval universities. It was especially marked by a worship of the past, a distrust of new information, and total dependence on revelation as opposed to reason, observation, and experimentation.

self-perpetuation: The capacity of a living system (for example, a cell) to replace or repair its molecules and organelles, add to its total quantity, or reproduce itself, utilizing raw materials received from its environment.

species: A group of organisms that are either actually or potentially capable of interbreeding freely in nature with the production of fully fertile offspring.

taxonomy: The field of biology that is concerned with the study of classification of organisms.

technology: The application of accepted scientific principles toward practical ends. Although a clear-cut distinction between science and technology is difficult, it is generally recognized that the major activity of science is the formulation and use of theories, whereas the major activity of technology is "cut-and-try" experimentation to achieve an immediate, practical goal.

teleology: The view that explanations based on purposiveness have a legitimate place in science. More specifically for biology, the view that development, whether in an organism or in evolution, is purposeful and goal-seeking.

theology: The study of the existence and attributes of God and of His relation to man.

theory: A scientific generalization, derived by observation and experimentation from a hypothesis or conceptual scheme, that is valuable in explanation and predictability.

thermodynamics: The field of physics that is concerned with energy transformations.

vitalism: A theory of life that holds that living organisms, or phenomena related to the term "life," cannot be exhaustively explained by the laws of chemistry and physics, that life processes and phenomena are the result of forces that exist in addition to those forces that are physical and chemical in nature. The opposing view is *mechanism.*

Tables

Table 4.1 *The elements most commonly found in living systems**

Name	Symbol	Weight percentage
Bulk elements		
Oxygen	O	65
Carbon	C	18
Hydrogen	H	10
Nitrogen	N	3
Calcium	Ca	2
Phosphorus	P	1
Total		99
Lesser elements		
Potassium	K	—
Sulfur	S	—
Sodium	Na	—
Chlorine	Cl	—
Magnesium	Mg	—
Iron	Fe	—
Copper	Cu	—
Manganese	Mn	—
Cobalt	Co	—
Zinc	Zn	—
Total		Less than 1

*Approximate relative abundance.

Table 4.2 *Constituents of protoplasm*

Substance	Percentage
Water	75 – 90
Electrolytes and other inorganic compounds	1 – 1.5
Proteins and nucleic acids	7 – 10
Lipids	1 – 2
Carbohydrates	1 – 1.5
Other organic compounds	Less than 1

Index

372   Index

Teleology (*cont.*)
   relation to evolution, 250
Thales, 6, 8
Theophrastus, 14, 57
Thermodynamics:
   first law, 76, 78
   second law, 76–78
      relation to diffusion, 150
      relation to direction of reactions, 87
      relation to ecosystems, 262, 266
Tracers, radioisotopic, 166, 249
Transcription, 214
Translation, 216
Trisaccharides, 96–98
Truth, 9

Universities:
   medieval, 27–30
   modern, 311, 343

Values:
   in Hobbes's philosophy, 51
   inability of science to deal with, 340
   in Kant's philosophy, 54
   rejected by Greek materialists, 11

Vesalius, A., 39, 44
Virchow, R., 127
Viruses, 130–132
   as biological "pesticides," 294
   relation to biogenesis, 119
Vitalism:
   contrasted with mechanism, 333–336
   equation of "life" with "God," 119
   evaluation as a philosophy of biology, 65, 184

Wallace, A. R., 235
Warfare, nuclear, 280
Watson, J. D., 108–110, 210
Watson-Crick model, 108–110, 210–213
Waxes, 100
White, A. D., 312
Whitehead, A. N., 310, 328
Wicks, R., 338–339
Wilkins, M. H. F., 108–110

XYY syndrome, 326–327

Zygote, 170